Glencoe

Algebra 2

Integration
Applications
Connections

Study Guide Masters

GLENCOE
McGraw-Hill

New York, New York   Columbus, Ohio   Woodland Hills, California   Peoria, Illinois

Glencoe/McGraw-Hill

A Division of The McGraw-Hill Companies

Send all inquiries to:
Glencoe/McGraw-Hill
936 Eastwind Drive
Westerville, OH 43081

ISBN: 0-02-825150-4

Algebra 2
Study Guide Masters

4 5 6 7 8 9 10 024 03 02 01 00 99 98

Contents

iv

1-1

Study Guide

Expressions and Formulas

To find the value of a numerical expression, you must follow the established order of operations. Always remember to do operations within grouping symbols first. Study the chart below.

Evaluate $8 - 4 \div 2 + 3 \cdot 2^3$	Order of Operations
$\begin{aligned} 8 - 4 \div 2 + 3 \cdot 2^3 &= 8 - 4 \div 2 + 3 \cdot 8 \\ &= 8 - 2 + 24 \\ &= 6 + 24 \\ &= 30 \end{aligned}$ The value is 30.	1. Evaluate all powers. 2. Do all multiplications and divisions from left to right. 3. Do all additions and subtractions from left to right.

Find the value of each expression.

1. $7 + 6 - 4$

2. $9(3^2 + 6)$

3. $11 - (3 + 2)^2$

4. $14 + (6 \div 2)$

5. $[18 - (6 + 4)] \div 2$

6. $(7 - 2)(3 + 8)$

7. $7 + 2^3 - 18 \div 3$

8. $6 \cdot 7 + 4 \div 4 - 5$

9. $2 + (4 - 2)^3 - 6$

Evaluate each expression if $a = 12$, $b = 4$, $c = 5$, $x = \frac{1}{2}$, and $y = 3$.

10. $y - a \div b$

11. $cb \div xb$

12. $8y + b^2\,(ay)$

13. $\dfrac{(abc \div x) - (6b^2 - 4)}{0.5}$

14. $\dfrac{1}{3}(y - x)^2$

15. $x \div \dfrac{a + b}{b^2}$

Algebra 2

Study Guide

Expressions and Formulas

To find the value of a numerical expression, you must follow the
established order of operations. Always remember to do operations
within grouping symbols first. Study the chart below.

Evaluate $8 - 4 \div 2 + 3 \cdot 2^3$	Order of Operations
$\begin{aligned} 8 - 4 \div 2 + 3 \cdot 2^3 &= 8 - 4 \div 2 + 3 \cdot 8 \\ &= 8 - 2 + 24 \\ &= 6 + 24 \\ &= 30 \end{aligned}$ The value is 30.	1. Evaluate all powers. 2. Do all multiplications and divisions from left to right. 3. Do all additions and subtractions from left to right.

Find the value of each expression.

1. $7 + 6 - 4$ **9**

2. $9(3^2 + 6)$ **135**

3. $11 - (3 + 2)^2$ **−14**

4. $14 + (6 \div 2)$ **17**

5. $[18 - (6 + 4)] \div 2$ **4**

6. $(7 - 2)(3 + 8)$ **55**

7. $7 + 2^3 - 18 \div 3$ **9**

8. $6 \cdot 7 + 4 \div 4 - 5$ **38**

9. $2 + (4 - 2)^3 - 6$ **4**

Evaluate each expression if $a = 12$, $b = 4$, $c = 5$, $x = \frac{1}{2}$, and $y = 3$.

10. $y - a \div b$
 0

11. $cb \div xb$
 160

12. $8y + b^2 (ay)$
 600

13. $\dfrac{(abc \div x) - (6b^2 - 4)}{0.5}$
 776

14. $\frac{1}{3}(y - x)^2$ **$\dfrac{25}{12}$**

15. $x \div \dfrac{a + b}{b^2}$ **$\dfrac{1}{2}$**

Study Guide

Properties of Real Numbers

You should be familiar with the following sets of numbers.

natural numbers: $N = \{1, 2, 3, 4, 5, 6, 7, 8, 9, 10, \cdots\}$

whole numbers: $W = \{0, 1, 2, 3, 4, 5, 6, 7, 8, 9, 10, \cdots\}$

integers: $Z = \{\cdots, -4, -3, -2, -1, 0, 1, 2, 3, 4, \cdots\}$

rational numbers: $Q = \{$all numbers that can be expressed in the form $\frac{m}{n}$, where m and n are integers and n is not zero$\}$

irrational numbers: $I = \{$all nonterminating, nonrepeating decimals$\}$

real numbers: $R = \{$all rationals and irrationals$\}$

You should also be familiar with the basic properties that hold for addition and multiplication of real numbers.

Property	For any real numbers *a*, *b*, and *c*	
	Addition	*Multiplication*
Commutative	$a + b = b + a$	$a \cdot b = b \cdot a$
Associative	$(a + b) + c = a + (b + c)$	$(a \cdot b) \cdot c = a \cdot (b \cdot c)$
Identity	$a + 0 = a = 0 + a$	$a \cdot 1 = a = 1 \cdot a$
Inverse	$a + (-a) = 0 = (-a) + a$	If a is *not* zero, then $a \cdot \frac{1}{a} = 1 = \frac{1}{a} \cdot a$
Distributive	Addition and Multiplication $a(b + c) = ab + ac$ and $(b + c)a = ba + ca$	

Name the sets of numbers to which each number belongs.

1. $-\dfrac{11}{3}$

2. $-\sqrt{81}$

3. -12

4. 0

5. 7.22

6. $\sqrt{15}$

7. $\sqrt{25}$

8. π

9. $-4.\overline{17}$

10. 20

11. $5.\overline{44}$

12. $\dfrac{3}{5}$

State the property illustrated in each equation.

13. $7 + (2.4 + 9) = (7 + 2.4) + 9$

14. $4(1 + 7) = 4(1) + 4(7)$

15. $9(3 - 5) = (3 - 5)9$

16. $(19a + 11b) + 0 = 19a + 11b$

17. $1 = 11^2 \cdot \dfrac{1}{11^2}$

18. $(8 + (-8)) - 9 = 0 - 9$

Simplify each expression.

19. $9x + 3y + 12y - 0.9x$

20. $2a + 7b + 8a - 3b + 4a$

21. $10(6g + 3h) + 4(5g - h)$

22. $9(7e - 4f) - 0.6(e + 5f)$

23. $2(15 + 45c) + \dfrac{5}{6}(12 + 18c)$

24. $4(20 - 4p) - \dfrac{3}{4}(4 - 16p)$

2

Study Guide

Properties of Real Numbers

You should be familiar with the following sets of numbers.

natural numbers: $N = \{1, 2, 3, 4, 5, 6, 7, 8, 9, 10, \cdots\}$

whole numbers: $W = \{0, 1, 2, 3, 4, 5, 6, 7, 8, 9, 10, \cdots\}$

integers: $Z = \{\cdots, -4, -3, -2, -1, 0, 1, 2, 3, 4, \cdots\}$

rational numbers: $Q = \{$all numbers that can be expressed in the form $\frac{m}{n}$, where m and n are integers and n is not zero$\}$

irrational numbers: $I = \{$all nonterminating, nonrepeating decimals$\}$

real numbers: $R = \{$all rationals and irrationals$\}$

You should also be familiar with the basic properties that hold for addition and multiplication of real numbers.

Property	For any real numbers a, b, and c	
	Addition	Multiplication
Commutative	$a + b = b + a$	$a \cdot b = b \cdot a$
Associative	$(a + b) + c = a + (b + c)$	$(a \cdot b) \cdot c = a \cdot (b \cdot c)$
Identity	$a + 0 = a = 0 + a$	$a \cdot 1 = a = 1 \cdot a$
Inverse	$a + (-a) = 0 = (-a) + a$	If a is *not* zero, then $a \cdot \frac{1}{a} = 1 = \frac{1}{a} \cdot a$
Distributive	Addition and Multiplication $a(b + c) = ab + ac$ and $(b + c)a = ba + ca$	

Name the sets of numbers to which each number belongs.

1. $-\frac{11}{3}$ **Q, R**

2. $-\sqrt{81}$ **Z, Q, R**

3. -12 **Z, Q, R**

4. 0 **W, Z, Q, R**

5. 7.22 **Q, R**

6. $\sqrt{15}$ **I, R**

7. $\sqrt{25}$ **N, W, Z, Q, R**

8. π **I, R**

9. $-4.\overline{17}$ **Q, R**

10. 20 **N, W, Z, Q, R**

11. $5.\overline{44}$ **Q, R**

12. $\frac{3}{5}$ **Q, R**

State the property illustrated in each equation.

13. $7 + (2.4 + 9) = (7 + 2.4) + 9$ **associative +**

14. $4(1 + 7) = 4(1) + 4(7)$ **distributive**

15. $9(3 - 5) = (3 - 5)9$ **commutative ×**

16. $(19a + 11b) + 0 = 19a + 11b$ **identity +**

17. $1 = 11^2 \cdot \frac{1}{11^2}$ **inverse ×**

18. $(8 + (-8)) - 9 = 0 - 9$ **inverse +**

Simplify each expression.

19. $9x + 3y + 12y - 0.9x$ **8.1x + 15y**

20. $2a + 7b + 8a - 3b + 4a$ **14a + 4b**

21. $10(6g + 3h) + 4(5g - h)$ **80g + 26h**

22. $9(7e - 4f) - 0.6(e + 5f)$ **62.4e − 39f**

23. $2(15 + 45c) + \frac{5}{6}(12 + 18c)$ **40 + 105c**

24. $4(20 - 4p) - \frac{3}{4}(4 - 16p)$ **77 − 4p**

Integration: Statistics
Graphs and Measures of Central Tendency

Two ways to display data are a **stem-and-leaf plot** and a **line plot.**

Example: Display the following scores from an algebra quiz using a line plot and a stem-and-leaf plot.
82, 95, 74, 82, 95, 73, 88, 76, 90, 82

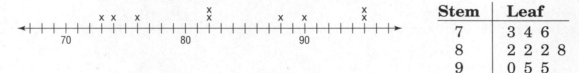

Stem	Leaf
7	3 4 6
8	2 2 2 8
9	0 5 5

The most commonly used averages are the **median, mode,** and **mean.** These terms are described in the chart below.

Term	Definition	Example for 10, 11, 12, 12, 13, 13, 15
Median	The **median** of a set of data is the middle value. If there are two middle values, it is the number halfway between them.	The median is 12.
Mode	The **mode** of a set data is the most frequent value. Some sets of data have multiple modes and others have no mode.	There are two modes, 12 and 13.
Mean	The **mean** of a set of data is the sum of all the values divided by the number of values.	mean $= \dfrac{10 + 11 + 12 + 12 + 13 + 13 + 15}{7}$ The mean is approximately 12.3.

Each number below is the number of games won by a member team of the National Basketball League prior to the All Star Break.

39	37	34	30	25	19	16	39	29	25
19	17	18	37	33	31	20	17	17	15
44	40	35	29	24	17	15			

1. Make a line plot of the wins of National Basketball League teams.

2. Make a stem-and-leaf plot of the wins of the National Basketball League teams.

Find the median, mode, and mean for each set of data.

3. {1, 4, 8, 3, 4, 5, 2, 2, 2, 5}

4. {95, 67, 22, 36, 67}

5. {299, 302, 500, 115, 89, 432}

6. {23, 30, 23, 68, 91, 81, 12, 75}

Study Guide

Integration: Statistics
Graphs and Measures of Central Tendency

Two ways to display data are a **stem-and-leaf plot** and a **line plot**.

Example: Display the following scores from an algebra quiz using a
line plot and a stem-and-leaf plot.
82, 95, 74, 82, 95, 73, 88, 76, 90, 82

Stem	Leaf
7	3 4 6
8	2 2 2 8
9	0 5 5

The most commonly used averages are the **median, mode,** and
mean. These terms are described in the chart below.

Term	Definition	Example for 10, 11, 12, 12, 13, 13, 15
Median	The **median** of a set of data is the middle value. If there are two middle values, it is the number halfway between them.	The median is 12.
Mode	The **mode** of a set data is the most frequent value. Some sets of data have multiple modes and others have no mode.	There are two modes, 12 and 13.
Mean	The **mean** of a set of data is the sum of all the values divided by the number of values.	mean $= \dfrac{10 + 11 + 12 + 12 + 13 + 13 + 15}{7}$ The mean is approximately 12.3.

*Each number below is the number of games won by a member
team of the National Basketball League prior to the All Star Break.*

39	37	34	30	25	19	16	39	29	25
19	17	18	37	33	31	20	17	17	15
44	40	35	29	24	17	15			

1. Make a line plot of the wins of National Basketball League
   teams.

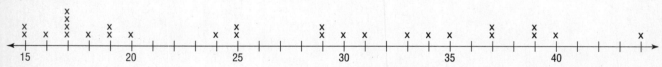

2. Make a stem-and-leaf plot of the wins
   of the National Basketball League
   teams.

Stem	Leaf
1	5 5 6 7 7 7 7 8 9 9
2	0 4 5 5 9 9
3	0 1 3 4 5 7 7 9 9
4	0 4

Find the median, mode, and mean for each set of data.

3. {1, 4, 8, 3, 4, 5, 2, 2, 2, 5}
   3.5, 2, 3.6

4. {95, 67, 22, 36, 67}
   67, 67, 57.4

5. {299, 302, 500, 115, 89, 432}
   300.5, no mode, 289.5

6. {23, 30, 23, 68, 91, 81, 12, 75}
   49, 23, 50.375

Study Guide

Solving Equations

Many equations can be solved by using addition, subtraction, multiplication, or division.

Addition and Subtraction Properties of Equality	For any real numbers a, b, and c, if $a = b$, then $a + c = b + c$ and $a - c = b - c$.
Multiplication and Division Properties of Equality	For any real numbers a, b, and c, if $a = b$, then $a \cdot c = b \cdot c$ and, if c is not zero, $\dfrac{a}{c} = \dfrac{b}{c}$

Example: Solve $8x - 13 = 43$.

$$8x - 13 = 43$$
$$8x - 13 + 13 = 43 + 13$$
$$8x = 56$$
$$x = 7$$

Solve each equation.

1. $3s = 45$

2. $17 = 9 - a$

3. $5t - 1 = 6t - 5$

4. $\dfrac{2}{3}m = \dfrac{1}{2}$

5. $7 - \dfrac{1}{2}x = 3$

6. $-8 = -2(z + 7)$

Define a variable, write an equation, and solve the problem.

7. A number decreased by 11 is 46. Find the number.

8. The sum of three times a number and 6 is 39. Find the number.

9. Mrs. Chin bought some $0.20 stamps and an equal number of $0.32 stamps. She paid a total of $5.20 for all the stamps. How many of each type of stamp did Mrs. Chin buy?

10. Enrique Romero bought a refrigerator for $50 more than half its original price. He paid $525 for the refrigerator. What was the original price of the refrigerator?

NAME_____ DATE _____

Study Guide

Solving Equations

Many equations can be solved by using addition, subtraction, multiplication, or division.

Addition and Subtraction Properties of Equality	For any real numbers a, b, and c, if $a = b$, then $a + c = b + c$ and $a - c = b - c$.
Multiplication and Division Properties of Equality	For any real numbers a, b, and c, if $a = b$, then $a \cdot c = b \cdot c$ and, if c is not zero, $\dfrac{a}{c} = \dfrac{b}{c}$.

Example: Solve $8x - 13 = 43$.

$$8x - 13 = 43$$
$$8x - 13 + 13 = 43 + 13$$
$$8x = 56$$
$$x = 7$$

Solve each equation.

1. $3s = 45$ **15**

2. $17 = 9 - a$ **−8**

3. $5t - 1 = 6t - 5$ **4**

4. $\frac{2}{3}m = \frac{1}{2}$ **3/4**

5. $7 - \frac{1}{2}x = 3$ **8**

6. $-8 = -2(z + 7)$ **−3**

Define a variable, write an equation, and solve the problem.

7. A number decreased by 11 is 46. Find the number.
   57

8. The sum of three times a number and 6 is 39. Find the number.
   11

9. Mrs. Chin bought some $0.20 stamps and an equal number of $0.32 stamps. She paid a total of $5.20 for all the stamps. How many of each type of stamp did Mrs. Chin buy?
   10 stamps

10. Enrique Romero bought a refrigerator for $50 more than half its original price. He paid $525 for the refrigerator. What was the original price of the refrigerator?
    $950

1-5

Study Guide

Solving Absolute Value Equations

The absolute value of a number is the number of units it is from 0 on the number line. Absolute value can also be defined as shown in the box to the right.

Definition of Absolute Value
For any real number a: If $a \geq 0$, then $|a| = a$. If $a < 0$, then $|a| = -a$.

The definition of absolute value is used in solving absolute value equations.

Example: Solve $|x - 5| = 10$. Check each solution.

$$|x - 5| = 10$$

If $x - 5$ is positive or zero, then $|x - 5| = x - 5$.		If $x - 5$ is negative, then $|x - 5| = -(x - 5)$.

$$x - 5 = 10 \qquad \text{or} \qquad -(x - 5) = 10$$
$$x = 15 \qquad\qquad\qquad x - 5 = -10$$
$$x = -5$$

Check: $|x - 5| = 10$ or $|-5 - 5| \stackrel{?}{=} 10$

$$|15 - 5| \stackrel{?}{=} 10 \qquad\qquad |-10| \stackrel{?}{=} 10$$
$$|10| \stackrel{?}{=} 10 \qquad\qquad\quad 10 = 10 ✔$$
$$10 = 10 ✔$$

The solutions are -5 and 15.

Solve each equation.

1. $|x + 15| = 37$

2. $|t - 4| - 5 = 0$

3. $|m + 3| = 12 - 2m$

4. $|x - 5| = 45$

5. $|5x + 9| = 16$

6. $|8 + 5a| = 14 - a$

7. $2\left|x - \dfrac{6}{3}\right| = 8$

8. $\left|x - \dfrac{4}{3}\right| = 8$

9. $\left|\dfrac{1}{3}x + 3\right| = 0$

Algebra 2

NAME_____ DATE _____

Study Guide

Solving Absolute Value Equations

The absolute value of a number is the number of units it is from 0 on the number line. Absolute value can also be defined as shown in the box to the right.

Definition of Absolute Value
For any real number a:
If $a \geq 0$, then $\lvert a \rvert = a$.
If $a < 0$, then $\lvert a \rvert = -a$.

The definition of absolute value is used in solving absolute value equations.

Example: Solve $\lvert x - 5 \rvert = 10$. Check each solution.

$$\lvert x - 5 \rvert = 10$$

If $x - 5$ is positive or zero, then $\lvert x - 5 \rvert = x - 5$.

If $x - 5$ is negative, then $\lvert x - 5 \rvert = -(x - 5)$.

$$x - 5 = 10 \qquad\text{or}\qquad -(x - 5) = 10$$
$$x = 15 \qquad\qquad\qquad x - 5 = -10$$
$$x = -5$$

Check: $\lvert x - 5 \rvert = 10 \quad$ or $\quad \lvert -5 - 5 \rvert \overset{?}{=} 10$

$$\lvert 15 - 5 \rvert \overset{?}{=} 10 \qquad\qquad \lvert -10 \rvert \overset{?}{=} 10$$
$$\lvert 10 \rvert \overset{?}{=} 10 \qquad\qquad 10 = 10 \checkmark$$
$$10 = 10 \checkmark$$

The solutions are -5 and 15.

Solve each equation.

1. $\lvert x + 15 \rvert = 37$ **−52, 22**   2. $\lvert t - 4 \rvert - 5 = 0$ **−1, 9**   3. $\lvert m + 3 \rvert = 12 - 2m$ **3**

4. $\lvert x - 5 \rvert = 45$ **−40, 50**   5. $\lvert 5x + 9 \rvert = 16$ **$-5, \dfrac{7}{5}$**   6. $\lvert 8 + 5a \rvert = 14 - a$ **1**

7. $2\left\lvert x - \dfrac{6}{3} \right\rvert = 8$ **−2, 6**   8. $\left\lvert x - \dfrac{4}{3} \right\rvert = 8$ **$-\dfrac{20}{3}, \dfrac{28}{3}$**   9. $\left\lvert \dfrac{1}{3}x + 3 \right\rvert = 0$ **−9**

         Algebra 2

NAME_____ DATE _____

Study Guide

Solving Inequalities

The following properties can be used to solve inequalities.

Addition and Subtraction Properties for Inequalities
For any real numbers a, b, and c:
1. If $a > b$, then $a + c > b + c$ and $a - c > b - c$.
2. If $a < b$, then $a + c < b + c$ and $a - c < b - c$.

Multiplication and Division Properties for Inequalities
For any real numbers a, b, and c:
1. If c is positive and $a < b$, then $ac < bc$ and $\dfrac{a}{c} < \dfrac{b}{c}$.
2. If c is positive, and $a > b$, then $ac > bc$ and $\dfrac{a}{c} > \dfrac{b}{c}$.
3. If c is negative and $a < b$, then $ac > bc$ and $\dfrac{a}{c} > \dfrac{b}{c}$.
4. If c is negative and $a > b$, then $ac < bc$ and $\dfrac{a}{c} < \dfrac{b}{c}$.

Solve each inequality.

1. $3a - 15 > 6$

2. $2x + 4 > 36$

3. $7(7a - 9) \leq 84$

4. $17 - 3w \geq 35$

5. $2 + 3(n + 5) \geq 4(n + 3)$

6. $4s - 12 < 20$

7. $4(b - 7) + 6 \geq 22$

8. $3(9z + 4) > 35z - 4$

9. $4(m - 5) > 5 - m$

10. $4p + 7 > 5p + 1(16 - 2p)$

11. $32 + 11r^2 < 17(r + r^2) - 6r^2$

12. $4x - 2 > -7(4x - 2)$

NAME_____ DATE _____

Study Guide

Solving Inequalities

The following properties can be used to solve inequalities.

Addition and Subtraction Properties for Inequalities
For any real numbers a, b, and c:
1. If $a > b$, then $a + c > b + c$ and $a - c > b - c$.
2. If $a < b$, then $a + c < b + c$ and $a - c < b - c$.

Multiplication and Division Properties for Inequalities
For any real numbers a, b, and c:
1. If c is positive and $a < b$, then $ac < bc$ and $\dfrac{a}{c} < \dfrac{b}{c}$.
2. If c is positive, and $a > b$, then $ac > bc$ and $\dfrac{a}{c} > \dfrac{b}{c}$.
3. If c is negative and $a < b$, then $ac > bc$ and $\dfrac{a}{c} > \dfrac{b}{c}$.
4. If c is negative and $a > b$, then $ac < bc$ and $\dfrac{a}{c} < \dfrac{b}{c}$.

Solve each inequality.

1. $3a - 15 > 6$
   $\{a \mid a > 7\}$

2. $2x + 4 > 36$
   $\{x \mid x > 16\}$

3. $7(7a - 9) \le 84$
   $\{a \mid a \le 3\}$

4. $17 - 3w \ge 35$
   $\{w \mid w \le -6\}$

5. $2 + 3(n + 5) \ge 4(n + 3)$
   $\{n \mid n \le 5\}$

6. $4s - 12 < 20$
   $\{s \mid s < 8\}$

7. $4(b - 7) + 6 \ge 22$
   $\{b \mid b \ge 11\}$

8. $3(9z + 4) > 35z - 4$
   $\{z \mid z < 2\}$

9. $4(m - 5) > 5 - m$
   $\{m \mid m > 5\}$

10. $4p + 7 > 5p + 1(16 - 2p)$
    $\{p \mid p > 9\}$

11. $32 + 11r^2 < 17(r + r^2) - 6r^2$
    $\left\{r \mid r > \dfrac{32}{17}\right\}$

12. $4x - 2 > -7(4x - 2)$
    $\left\{x \mid x > \dfrac{1}{2}\right\}$

1-7

Study Guide

Solving Absolute Value Inequalities

The absolute value of a number represents its distance from zero on the number line. You can often use this idea to solve absolute value inequalities.

Example: Solve $|x - 3| \leq 2$. Graph the solution set.

$|x - 3| \leq 2$ means that $x - 3$ is no more than 2 units from 0 on the number line.

$$x - 3 \geq -2 \quad \text{and} \quad x - 3 \leq 2$$
$$x \geq 1 \quad \text{and} \quad x \leq 5$$

The solution set is $\{x | 1 \leq x \leq 5\}$.

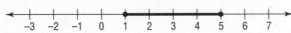

Solve each inequality.

1. $3y - 2 < -6$ or $2y + 4 \geq 6$

2. $p + 7 > -2$ or $p - 4 < 8$

3. $1 < z - 4 < 9$

4. $6a \leq 8 + 2a$ or $10 - 2a > 4$

Solve each inequality. Graph each solution set.

5. $|x + 2| > 4$

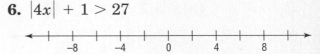

6. $|4x| + 1 > 27$

7. $|x + 9| \geq 30$

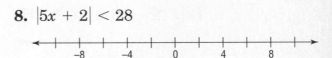

8. $|5x + 2| < 28$

Solve.

9. The Vikings play 36 games this year. At midseason, they had won 16 games. How many of the remaining games must they win in order to win at least 80% of *all* their games?

10. The city parking lot charges $2.50 for the first hour and $0.25 for each additional hour. If the most you can pay is $6.50, how long can you park your car?

Study Guide

Solving Absolute Value Inequalities

The absolute value of a number represents its distance from zero on the number line. You can often use this idea to solve absolute value inequalities.

Example: Solve $|x - 3| \leq 2$. Graph the solution set.

$|x - 3| \leq 2$ means that $x - 3$ is no more than 2 units from 0 on the number line.

$$x - 3 \geq -2 \quad \text{and} \quad x - 3 \leq 2$$
$$x \geq 1 \quad \text{and} \quad x \leq 5$$

The solution set is $\{x \mid 1 \leq x \leq 5\}$.

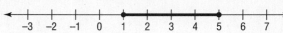

Solve each inequality.

1. $3y - 2 < -6$ or $2y + 4 \geq 6$

$$\left\{ y \mid y < -\frac{4}{3} \text{ or } y \geq 1 \right\}$$

2. $p + 7 > -2$ or $p - 4 < 8$

all reals

3. $1 < z - 4 < 9$
$\{z \mid 5 < z < 13\}$

4. $6a \leq 8 + 2a$ or $10 - 2a > 4$
$\{a \mid a < 3\}$

Solve each inequality. Graph each solution set.

5. $|x + 2| > 4$ $\{x \mid x > 2 \text{ or } x < -6\}$

6. $|4x| + 1 > 27$ $\left\{ x \mid x < -\frac{13}{2} \text{ or } x > \frac{13}{2} \right\}$

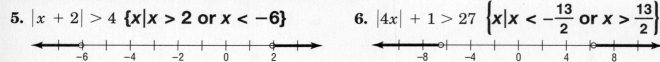

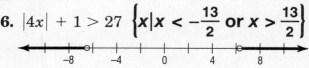

7. $|x + 9| \geq 30$ $\{x \mid x \leq -39 \text{ or } x \geq 21\}$

8. $|5x + 2| < 28$ $\left\{ x \mid -6 < x < \frac{26}{5} \right\}$

Solve.

9. The Vikings play 36 games this year. At midseason, they had won 16 games. How many of the remaining games must they win in order to win at least 80% of *all* their games?
at least 13 games

10. The city parking lot charges $2.50 for the first hour and $0.25 for each additional hour. If the most you can pay is $6.50, how long can you park your car?
at most 17 hours

Study Guide

Relations and Functions

Points in a plane can be named using ordered pairs of real numbers. The first coordinate indicates how far left or right of the y-axis the point is. The second coordinate indicates how far above or below the x-axis it is.

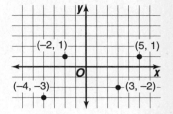

Example: Graph the set of ordered pairs $\{(1, 5), (3, -2), (-2, 1),$ $(-4, -3), (5, 1)\}$.

Definition of Relation, Domain, and Range	A relation is a set of ordered pairs. The domain is the set of all first coordinates of the ordered pairs. The range is the set of all second coordinates of the ordered pairs.
Definition of Function	A function is a relation in which each element of the domain is paired with exactly one element of the range.

If a function is described by an equation, you can find the y-value of the function for a given x-value by substituting the given value for x in the equation.

Example: Find $f(20)$ if $f(x) = 150 - 4x^2$.
Substitute 20 for x. $f(20) = 150 - 4(20)^2$
$$= 150 - 4(400)$$
$$= -1450$$
Therefore, $f(20) = -1450$.

State the domain and range of each relation. Then graph and identify whether it is a function or not. For each function, state whether it is discrete or continuous.

1. $\{(-5, 5), (-5, -5), (0, 3), (0, -3), (5, 0)\}$ **2.** $\{(-4, 2), (-3, -3), (-2, 0), (4, 2), (2, 4)\}$

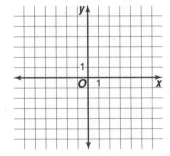   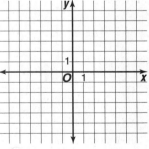

Find each value if $f(x) = \dfrac{6}{x-3}$.

3. $f(12)$ **4.** $f(6)$ **5.** $f(2b)$

Find each value if $g(x) = \dfrac{x^2+1}{4+x}$.

6. $g(5)$ **7.** $g(-2)$ **8.** $g(7c)$

Study Guide

Relations and Functions

Points in a plane can be named using ordered pairs of real numbers. The first coordinate indicates how far left or right of the y-axis the point is. The second coordinate indicates how far above or below the x-axis it is.

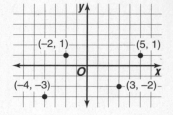

Example: Graph the set of ordered pairs $\{(1, 5), (3, -2), (-2, 1), (-4, -3), (5, 1)\}$.

Definition of Relation, Domain, and Range	A relation is a set of ordered pairs. The domain is the set of all first coordinates of the ordered pairs. The range is the set of all second coordinates of the ordered pairs.
Definition of Function	A function is a relation in which each element of the domain is paired with exactly one element of the range.

If a function is described by an equation, you can find the y-value of the function for a given x-value by substituting the given value for x in the equation.

Example: Find $f(20)$ if $f(x) = 150 - 4x^2$.
Substitute 20 for x.
$$f(20) = 150 - 4(20)^2$$
$$= 150 - 4(400)$$
$$= -1450$$
Therefore, $f(20) = -1450$.

State the domain and range of each relation. Then graph and identify whether it is a function or not. For each function, state whether it is discrete or continuous.

1. $\{(-5, 5), (-5, -5), (0, 3), (0, -3), (5, 0)\}$ **2.** $\{(-4, 2), (-3, -3), (-2, 0), (4, 2), (2, 4)\}$

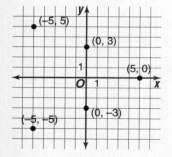
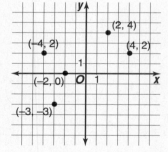

$D = \{-5, 0, 5\}, R =$
$\{-5, -3, 0, 3, 5\}$, **not a function**

$D = \{-4, -3, -2, 2, 4\}, R =$
$\{-3, 0, 2, 4\}$, **function, discrete**

Find each value if $f(x) = \dfrac{6}{x - 3}$.

3. $f(12)$ $\dfrac{2}{3}$ **4.** $f(6)$ **2**   **5.** $f(2b)$ $\dfrac{6}{2b - 3}$

Find each value if $g(x) = \dfrac{x^2 + 1}{4 + x}$.

6. $g(5)$ $\dfrac{26}{g}$ **7.** $g(-2)$ $\dfrac{5}{2}$ **8.** $g(7c)$ $\dfrac{49c^2 + 1}{7c + 4}$

Study Guide

Linear Equations

An equation whose graph is a straight line is called a **linear equation.** Any linear equation can be written in **standard form.**

> The standard form of a linear equation is
> $$Ax + By = C,$$
> where A, B, and C are real numbers, and A and B are not both zero.

To graph a linear equation, it is helpful to make a table of ordered pairs that satisfy the equation. These ordered pairs can then be graphed and connected with a straight line.

Example: Write the equation $x = \frac{1}{4}y - 9$ in standard form.

$$x = \frac{1}{4}y - 9$$

$4x = y - 9$ Multiply each side by 4 to eliminate the fraction.

$4x - y = -9$ Add $-y$ to each side.

Write each equation in standard form.

1. $x = \frac{2}{7} + y$

2. $y = \frac{7}{12}x + 1$

3. $y = 3x - 5$

4. $x = 10$

5. $y = 5x$

6. $5x = 5 + 2x + y$

7. $y - 6 = 0$

8. $y = -7x + 2$

9. $4s + 3r = 12$

Complete the table. Then graph the equation.

10. $y = 6x + 2$

x	−2	−1	0	1	2
y					

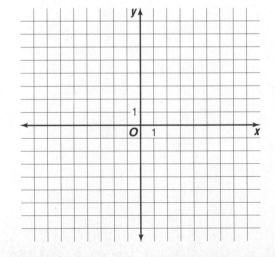

11. $x - y = -7$

x	−4	−2	0	1	2
y					

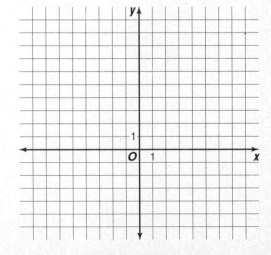

NAME_____ DATE _____

Study Guide

Linear Equations

An equation whose graph is a straight line is called a **linear equation.** Any linear equation can be written in **standard form.**

> The standard form of a linear equation is
> $$Ax + By = C,$$
> where A, B, and C are real numbers, and A and B are not both zero.

To graph a linear equation, it is helpful to make a table of ordered pairs that satisfy the equation. These ordered pairs can then be graphed and connected with a straight line.

Example: Write the equation $x = \frac{1}{4}y - 9$ in standard form.

$$x = \frac{1}{4}y - 9$$

$$4x = y - 9 \quad \text{Multiply each side by 4 to eliminate the fraction.}$$
$$4x - y = -9 \quad \text{Add } -y \text{ to each side.}$$

Write each equation in standard form.

1. $x = \frac{2}{7} + y$
   $$x - y = \frac{2}{7}$$

2. $y = \frac{7}{12}x + 1$
   $$-7x + 12y = 12$$

3. $y = 3x - 5$
   $$3x - y = 5$$

4. $x = 10$
   $$x + 0y = 10$$

5. $y = 5x$
   $$-5x + y = 0$$

6. $5x = 5 + 2x + y$
   $$3x - y = 5$$

7. $y - 6 = 0$
   $$0x + y = 6$$

8. $y = -7x + 2$
   $$7x + y = 2$$

9. $4s + 3r = 12$
   in standard form

Complete the table. Then graph the equation.

10. $y = 6x + 2$

x	−2	−1	0	1	2
y	−10	−4	2	8	14

11. $x - y = -7$

x	−4	−2	0	1	2
y	3	5	7	8	9

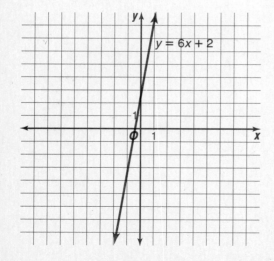

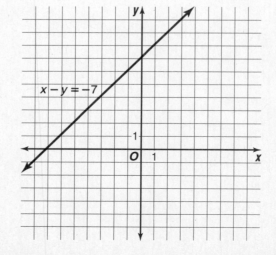

NAME_____ DATE _____

Study Guide

Slope

The slope of a line indicates whether the line is horizontal or whether it rises or falls from left to right.

Definition of Slope	The slope m of a line passing through points (x_1, y_1) and (x_2, y_2) is given by $$m = \frac{y_2 - y_1}{x_2 - x_1}.$$

Example: Determine the slope of the line that passes through $(0, -3)$, and $(2, 1)$. Then graph the line.
Let $(x_1, y_1) = (0, -3)$ and $(x_2, y_2) = (2, 1)$.

$$m = \frac{y_2 - y_1}{x_2 - x_1}$$

$$= \frac{1 - (-3)}{2 - 0}$$

$$= \frac{4}{2} \text{ or } 2$$

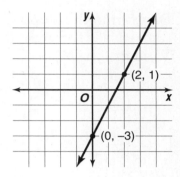

Graph the two ordered pairs and draw the line.

Determine the slope of each line.

1.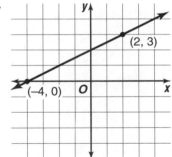

2.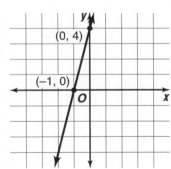

3.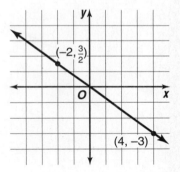

Find the slope of the line that passes through each pair of points.

4. $(-3, -1), (5, 7)$

5. $(6, 4), (3, 4)$

6. $(5, 1), (7, -3)$

7. $(6, 2), (-3, -8)$

8. $(6, 1), (-6, -1)$

9. $(3, 18), (5, 20)$

Determine whether the graph of each equation rises to the right, falls to the right, is horizontal, or is vertical.

10. $x + y = 10$

11. $4x - y = 3$

12. $x = 6$

Slope

The slope of a line indicates whether the line is horizontal or whether it rises or falls from left to right.

Definition of Slope	The slope m of a line passing through points (x_1, y_1) and (x_2, y_2) is given by $m = \dfrac{y_2 - y_1}{x_2 - x_1}.$

Example: Determine the slope of the line that passes through $(0, -3)$, and $(2, 1)$. Then graph the line.
Let $(x_1, y_1) = (0, -3)$ and $(x_2, y_2) = (2, 1)$.

$$m = \frac{y_2 - y_1}{x_2 - x_1}$$

$$= \frac{1 - (-3)}{2 - 0}$$

$$= \frac{4}{2} \text{ or } 2$$

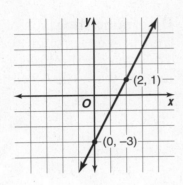

Graph the two ordered pairs and draw the line.

Determine the slope of each line.

1.

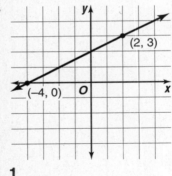

$\dfrac{1}{2}$

2.

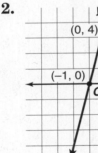

4

3.

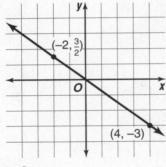

$-\dfrac{3}{4}$

Find the slope of the line that passes through each pair of points.

4. $(-3, -1), (5, 7)$ **1**

5. $(6, 4), (3, 4)$ **0**

6. $(5, 1), (7, -3)$ **−2**

7. $(6, 2), (-3, -8)$ $\dfrac{10}{9}$

8. $(6, 1), (-6, -1)$ $\dfrac{1}{6}$

9. $(3, 18), (5, 20)$ **1**

Determine whether the graph of each equation rises to the right, falls to the right, is horizontal, or is vertical.

10. $x + y = 10$ **falls**

11. $4x - y = 3$ **rises**

12. $x = 6$ **vertical**

Study Guide

Writing Linear Equations

Given the slope and y-intercept of a line, you can find an equation of the line by substituting these values into the *slope-intercept form* of the equation. The slope-intercept form of the equation of the line is $y = mx + b$, where m is the slope and b is the y-intercept.

Example: Find the slope-intercept form of the equation of the line that has a slope of $\frac{1}{2}$ and that passes through $(3, 6)$.

First, substitute the slope and coordinates of the point into the slope-intercept form and solve for b.

$$y = mx + b$$

$$6 = \frac{1}{2}(3) + b \qquad \text{Substitute 6 for } y, \frac{1}{2} \text{ for } m, \text{ and 3 for } x.$$

$$6 = \frac{3}{2} + b$$

$$4\frac{1}{2} = b$$

Write the equation in slope-intercept form.

$$y = \frac{1}{2}x + 4\frac{1}{2} \qquad \text{Substitute } \frac{1}{2} \text{ for } m, \text{ and } 4\frac{1}{2} \text{ for } b.$$

State the slope and y-intercept of the graph of each equation.

1. $y = 7x - 14$
2. $4y = 2x - 10$
3. $-y = \frac{2}{3}x + 3$

Write an equation in slope-intercept form that satisfies each condition.

4. slope $= -2$, passes through $(-4, 6)$
5. slope $= -\frac{13}{5}$, passes through $(5, -7)$

6. slope $= 1$, passes through $(2, 5)$
7. no x-intercept, y-intercept $= -4$

8. passes through $(-2, -2)$ and $(3, 3)$
9. x-intercept $= -3$, and y-intercept $= 2$

10. slope $= -\frac{3}{2}$, passes through $(3, -2)$
11. slope $= -\frac{5}{2}$, passes through $(8, -4)$

Study Guide

Writing Linear Equations

Given the slope and y-intercept of a line, you can find an equation of the line by substituting these values into the *slope-intercept form* of the equation. The slope-intercept form of the equation of the line is $y = mx + b$, where m is the slope and b is the y-intercept.

Example: Find the slope-intercept form of the equation of the line that has a slope of $\frac{1}{2}$ and that passes through $(3, 6)$.

First, substitute the slope and coordinates of the point into the slope-intercept form and solve for b.

$y = mx + b$

$6 = \frac{1}{2}(3) + b$ **Substitute 6 for *y*, $\frac{1}{2}$ for *m*, and 3 for *x*.**

$6 = \frac{3}{2} + b$

$4\frac{1}{2} = b$

Write the equation in slope-intercept form.

$y = \frac{1}{2}x + 4\frac{1}{2}$ **Substitute $\frac{1}{2}$ for *m*, and $4\frac{1}{2}$ for *b*.**

State the slope and y-intercept of the graph of each equation.

1. $y = 7x - 14$

$m = 7,$
$y\text{-intercept} = -14$

2. $4y = 2x - 10$

$m = \frac{1}{2},$
$y\text{-intercept} = -\frac{5}{2}$

3. $-y = \frac{2}{3}x + 3$

$m = -\frac{2}{3},$
$y\text{-intercept} = -3$

Write an equation in slope-intercept form that satisfies each condition.

4. slope $= -2$, passes through $(-4, 6)$

$y = -2x - 2$

5. slope $= -\frac{13}{5}$, passes through $(5, -7)$

$y = -\frac{13}{5}x + 6$

6. slope $= 1$, passes through $(2, 5)$
$y = x + 3$

7. no x-intercept, y-intercept $= -4$
$y = 0x - 4$

8. passes through $(-2, -2)$ and $(3, 3)$
$x - y = 0$

9. x-intercept $= -3$, and y-intercept $= 2$
$-2x + 3y = 6$

10. slope $= -\frac{3}{2}$, passes through $(3, -2)$
$3x + 2y = 5$

11. slope $= -\frac{5}{2}$, passes through $(8, -4)$
$5x + 2y = 32$

Integration: Statistics
Modeling Real-World Data Using Scatter Plots

One method for analyzing data is the **scatter plot.** A scatter plot visually shows the nature of a relationship, both its shape and dispersion. A line may be drawn to show the approximate relationship formed by the plotted points. By choosing several points on the lines, you can find the equation of the line. This equation is called the **prediction equation** of the relationship.

1. According to a certain prediction equation, the cost of 200 square feet of storage space is $60. The cost of 325 square feet of storage space is $160. Let x stand for the amount of storage space in square feet and y stand for the cost in dollars.

   a. What is the independent variable?

   b. What is the dependent variable?

   c. Find the prediction equation.

   d. Find the slope of the prediction equation.

   e. Predict the number of square feet for storage space costing $44.

2. The table below shows the years of experience for eight technicians at Lewis Techomatic and the hourly rate of pay each technician earns.

Experience (years)	9	4	3	1	10	6	12	8
Hourly Rate of Pay	$17	$10	$10	$7	$19	$12	$20	$15

   a. Draw a scatter plot to show how experience and hourly rate of pay are related. Draw a line along which the points seem to cluster.

   b. Write a prediction equation to show how hourly rate of pay (y) and years of experience (x) are related.

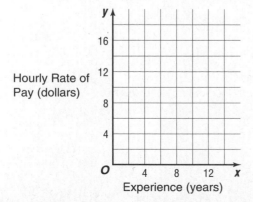

   c. Predict the hourly rate of pay for a person who has 7 years of experience.

   d. Predict the years of experience for a technician who makes $16 an hour.

Study Guide

Integration: Statistics
Modeling Real-World Data Using Scatter Plots

One method for analyzing data is the **scatter plot.** A scatter plot visually shows the nature of a relationship, both its shape and dispersion. A line may be drawn to show the approximate relationship formed by the plotted points. By choosing several points on the lines, you can find the equation of the line. This equation is called the **prediction equation** of the relationship.

1. According to a certain prediction equation, the cost of 200 square feet of storage space is $60. The cost of 325 square feet of storage space is $160. Let x stand for the amount of storage space in square feet and y stand for the cost in dollars.

   a. What is the independent variable?
   x, the amount of storage space
   b. What is the dependent variable?
   y, the cost in dollars
   c. Find the prediction equation.
   $y = 0.8x - 100$
   d. Find the slope of the prediction equation.
   0.8
   e. Predict the number of square feet for storage space costing $44.
   180 square feet

2. The table below shows the years of experience for eight technicians at Lewis Techomatic and the hourly rate of pay each technician earns.

Experience (years)	9	4	3	1	10	6	12	8
Hourly Rate of Pay	$17	$10	$10	$7	$19	$12	$20	$15

   a. Draw a scatter plot to show how experience and hourly rate of pay are related. Draw a line along which the points seem to cluster.

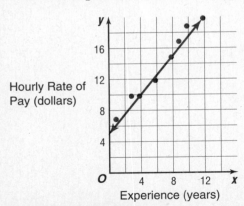

Hourly Rate of Pay (dollars)

Experience (years)

   Lines may vary.

   b. Write a prediction equation to show how hourly rate of pay (y) and years of experience (x) are related.
   Equations may vary.
   Possible equation:
   $y = 5.5 + 1.2x$

   c. Predict the hourly rate of pay for a person who has 7 years of experience.
   Answers may vary.
   Possible answer: $13.90

   d. Predict the years of experience for a technician who makes $16 an hour.
   about 8.75 years

2-6

Study Guide

Special Functions

Some linear functions have special names and special graphs.

Function	Written as	Graph
constant	$y = b$ or $f(x) = b$	horizontal line
direct variation	$y = mx$ or $f(x) = mx$ where $m \neq 0$	passes through origin
absolute value	$y = |x|$ or $f(x) = |x|$	mirror image
greatest integer	$f(x) = [x]$	one-unit horizontal segments (right endpoints missing) arranged like steps

Identify each function as constant, direct variation, absolute value, or greatest integer function. Then graph each function.

1. $f(x) = 2[x]$

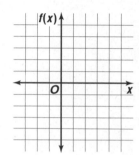

2. $f(x) = 2$

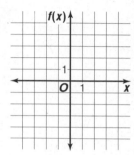

3. $f(x) = |2x + 1|$

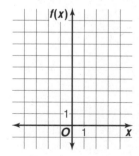

4. $f(x) = x$

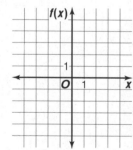

5. $r(x) = |2x|$

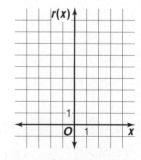

6. $f(x) = \left[x - \dfrac{1}{2} \right]$

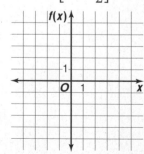

Algebra 2

NAME_____ DATE _____

Study Guide

Special Functions

Some linear functions have special names and special graphs.

Function	Written as	Graph
constant	$y = b$ or $f(x) = b$	horizontal line
direct variation	$y = mx$ or $f(x) = mx$ where $m \neq 0$	passes through origin
absolute value	$y = |x|$ or $f(x) = |x|$	mirror image
greatest integer	$f(x) = [x]$	one-unit horizontal segments (right endpoints missing) arranged like steps

Identify each function as constant, direct variation, absolute value, or greatest integer function. Then graph each function.

1. $f(x) = 2[x]$

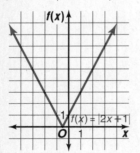

greatest integer function

2. $f(x) = 2$

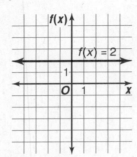

constant

3. $f(x) = |2x + 1|$

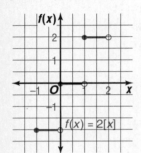

absolute value

4. $f(x) = x$

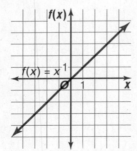

direct variation

5. $r(x) = |2x|$

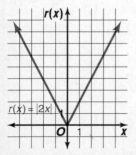

absolute value

6. $f(x) = \left[x - \dfrac{1}{2}\right]$

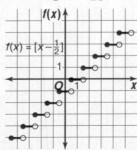

greatest integer

Algebra 2

NAME _____ DATE _____

Study Guide

Linear Inequalities

The graph of $y = \frac{1}{4}x + \frac{3}{4}$ is a line that separates the coordinate plane into two regions. It is called the *boundary* of each region. If the boundary is part of a graph, it is drawn as a solid line. If the boundary is *not* part of a graph, it is drawn as a dashed line.

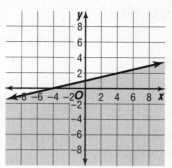

The graph of $y \leq \frac{1}{4}x + \frac{3}{4}$ is the line and the region *below* the line.

Graph each inequality.

1. $y < 3x + 1$

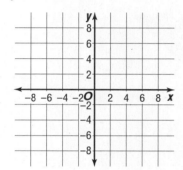

2. $y \geq |x| + 1$

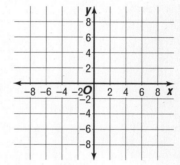

3. $3x \geq 4y$

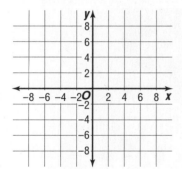

4. $y \geq x - 5$

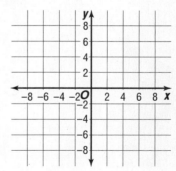

5. $|x| + y \geq 4$

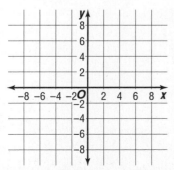

6. $3x - y < 6$

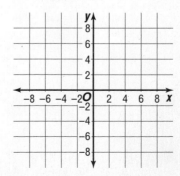

Algebra 2

Study Guide

Linear Inequalities

The graph of $y = \frac{1}{4}x + \frac{3}{4}$ is a line that
separates the coordinate plane into two
regions. It is called the *boundary* of each
region. If the boundary is part of a
graph, it is drawn as a solid line. If the
boundary is *not* part of a graph, it is
drawn as a dashed line.

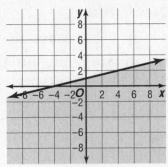

The graph of $y \leq \frac{1}{4}x + \frac{3}{4}$ is the line and
the region *below* the line.

Graph each inequality.

1. $y < 3x + 1$

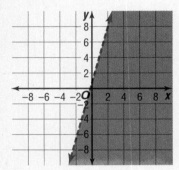

2. $y \geq |x| + 1$

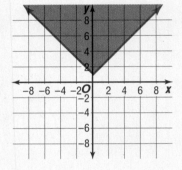

3. $3x \geq 4y$

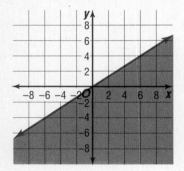

4. $y \geq x - 5$

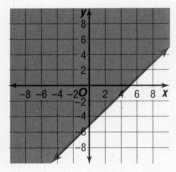

5. $|x| + y \geq 4$

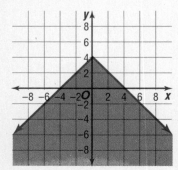

6. $3x - y < 6$

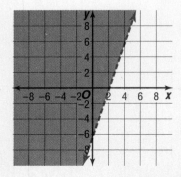

Algebra 2

Study Guide

Graphing Systems of Equations

You can solve a system of equations (two equations) by graphing the slope-intercept form of an equation. The *solution* is the intersection point of the two graphs.

Example: Graph this system of equations and state its solution.

$$x + y = 6$$
$$3x + 4y = 12$$

The slope-intercept form of $x + y = 6$ is $y = -x + 6$.

The slope-intercept form of $3x + 4y = 12$ is $y = -\frac{3}{4}x + 3$.

Since the two lines have different slopes, the graphs of the equations are intersecting lines. They intersect at $(12, -6)$. The solution of the system is $(12, -6)$.

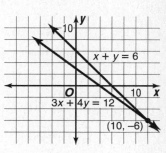

The following chart summarizes the possibilities for the graphs of two linear equations in two variables.

Graphs of Equations	Slopes of Lines	Name of System of Equations	Number of Solutions
lines intersect	different slopes	consistent and independent	one
lines coincide	same slope, same intercepts	consistent and dependent	infinite
lines parallel	same slope, different intercepts	inconsistent	none

Graph each system of equations and state its solution. Also, state whether the system is consistent and independent, consistent and dependent, or inconsistent.

1. $3x - y = 0$
$x - y = -2$

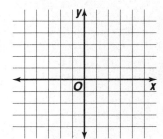

2. $3x + y = -2$
$6x + 2y = 10$

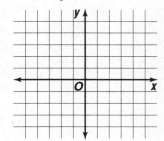

3. $4x + 2y = 8$
$12x + 6y = 24$

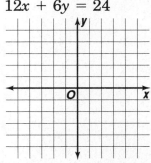

4. $x + 2y = 5$
$3x - 15 = -6y$

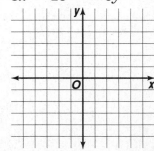

NAME_____ DATE _____

Study Guide

Graphing Systems of Equations

You can solve a system of equations (two equations) by graphing the slope-intercept form of an equation. The *solution* is the intersection point of the two graphs.

Example: Graph this system of equations and state its solution.

$$x + y = 6$$
$$3x + 4y = 12$$

The slope-intercept form of $x + y = 6$ is $y = -x + 6$.

The slope-intercept form of $3x + 4y = 12$ is $y = -\frac{3}{4}x + 3$.

Since the two lines have different slopes, the graphs of the equations are intersecting lines. They intersect at $(12, -6)$. The solution of the system is $(12, -6)$.

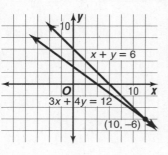

The following chart summarizes the possibilities for the graphs of two linear equations in two variables.

Graphs of Equations	Slopes of Lines	Name of System of Equations	Number of Solutions
lines intersect	different slopes	consistent and independent	one
lines coincide	same slope, same intercepts	consistent and dependent	infinite
lines parallel	same slope, different intercepts	inconsistent	none

Graph each system of equations and state its solution. Also, state whether the system is consistent and independent, consistent and dependent, or inconsistent.

1. $3x - y = 0$ **consistent,**
$x - y = -2$ **independent, (1, 3)**

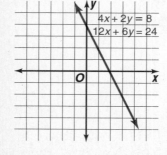

2. $3x + y = -2$ **inconsistent,**
$6x + 2y = 10$ **∅**

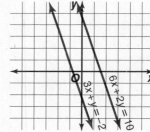

3. $4x + 2y = 8$ **consistent,**
$12x + 6y = 24$ **dependent,**
{(x, y)|
4x + 2y = 8}

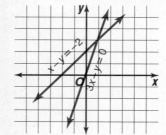

4. $x + 2y = 5$ **consistent,**
$3x - 15 = -6y$ **dependent,**
{(x, y)|
x + 2y = 4}

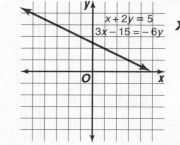

Algebra 2

Study Guide

Student Edition
Pages 133–140

Solving Systems of Equations Algebraically

Usually a system of equations is easier to solve by algebraic methods than by graphing. Two algebraic methods are the **substitution method** and the **elimination method.**

Example: $4x - y = 11$
$2x + 2y = 18$

Substitution Method
1. Solve the first equation for y: $y = 4x - 11$.
2. Substitute $4x - 11$ for y in the second equation.
3. Solve for x: $x = 4$.
4. Find y by substituting 4 for x in $4x - y = 11$. The solution is (4, 5).

Example: $5x + 3y = -1$
$4x - 3y = -17$

Elimination Method
1. Add the two equations: $9x = -18$
2. Solve for x: $x = -2$
3. Find y by substituting -2 for x in $4x - 3y = -17$. The solution is $(-2, 3)$.

Solve each system of equations by using substitution.

1. $x = 4$
$2x - 3y = -19$

2. $3x + y = 7$
$4x + 2y = 16$

3. $2x + y = 5$
$3x - 3y = 3$

4. $2x + 2y = 4$
$x - 2y = 0$

Solve each system of equations by using elimination.

5. $-4x + y = -12$
$4x + 2y = 6$

6. $5x + 2y = 12$
$-6x - 2y = -14$

7. $5x + 4y = 12$
$7x - 6y = 40$

8. $5m + 2n = -8$
$4m + 3n = 2$

3-2

Study Guide

Solving Systems of Equations Algebraically

Usually a system of equations is easier to solve by algebraic methods than by graphing. Two algebraic methods are the **substitution method** and the **elimination method.**

Example: $4x - y = 11$
$2x + 2y = 18$

Substitution Method
1. Solve the first equation for y: $y = 4x - 11$.
2. Substitute $4x - 11$ for y in the second equation.
3. Solve for x: $x = 4$.
4. Find y by substituting 4 for x in $4x - y = 11$. The solution is (4, 5).

Example: $5x + 3y = -1$
$4x - 3y = -17$

Elimination Method
1. Add the two equations: $9x = -18$
2. Solve for x: $x = -2$
3. Find y by substituting -2 for x in $4x - 3y = -17$. The solution is $(-2, 3)$.

Solve each system of equations by using substitution.

1. $x = 4$
$2x - 3y = -19$
(4, 9)

2. $3x + y = 7$
$4x + 2y = 16$
(−1, 10)

3. $2x + y = 5$
$3x - 3y = 3$
(2, 1)

4. $2x + 2y = 4$
$x - 2y = 0$
$\left(\dfrac{4}{3}, \dfrac{2}{3}\right)$

Solve each system of equations by using elimination.

5. $-4x + y = -12$
$4x + 2y = 6$
$\left(\dfrac{5}{2}, -2\right)$

6. $5x + 2y = 12$
$-6x - 2y = -14$
(2, 1)

7. $5x + 4y = 12$
$7x - 6y = 40$
(4, −2)

8. $5m + 2n = -8$
$4m + 3n = 2$
(−4, 6)

Algebra 2

Study Guide

Cramer's Rule

A **determinant** is a square arrangement of numbers or variables enclosed between vertical lines.

To find the value of the determinant use the following:

$$\begin{vmatrix} a & b \\ c & d \end{vmatrix} = ad - bc$$

The solution to a system of two linear equations in two variables can be found using determinants. This method is known as **Cramer's Rule:**

If $\begin{vmatrix} a & b \\ d & e \end{vmatrix} \neq 0$, then the solution of $\begin{cases} ax + by = c \\ dx + ey = f \end{cases}$ is $x = \dfrac{\begin{vmatrix} c & b \\ f & e \end{vmatrix}}{\begin{vmatrix} a & b \\ d & e \end{vmatrix}}, y = \dfrac{\begin{vmatrix} a & c \\ d & f \end{vmatrix}}{\begin{vmatrix} a & b \\ d & e \end{vmatrix}}.$

Use Cramer's Rule to solve each system of equations.

1. $7x - 2y = 4$
$3x + y = -6$

2. $2x - 5y = 18$
$-x + 3y = -10$

3. $3x - 2y = 15$
$4x + y = 9$

4. $5x + 4y = -4$
$2x - y = 10$

5. $-7x + 5y = 1$
$x - 2y = 9$

6. $6x - 4y = 1$
$-3x + 3y = 2$

7. $\dfrac{1}{2}x - \dfrac{7}{5}y = 8$
$\dfrac{1}{3}x - y = 1$

8. $5x + 6y = 7$
$4x + 5y = -9$

Algebra 2

3-3

Study Guide

Cramer's Rule

A **determinant** is a square arrangement of numbers or variables enclosed between vertical lines.

To find the value of the determinant use the following:

$$\begin{vmatrix} a & b \\ c & d \end{vmatrix} = ad - bc$$

The solution to a system of two linear equations in two variables can be found using determinants. This method is known as **Cramer's Rule:**

If $\begin{vmatrix} a & b \\ d & e \end{vmatrix} \neq 0$, then the solution of $\begin{cases} ax + by = c \\ dx + ey = f \end{cases}$ is $x = \dfrac{\begin{vmatrix} c & b \\ f & e \end{vmatrix}}{\begin{vmatrix} a & b \\ d & e \end{vmatrix}}$, $y = \dfrac{\begin{vmatrix} a & c \\ d & f \end{vmatrix}}{\begin{vmatrix} a & b \\ d & e \end{vmatrix}}$.

Use Cramer's Rule to solve each system of equations.

1. $7x - 2y = 4$
$3x + y = -6$ $\left(-\dfrac{8}{13}, -\dfrac{54}{13}\right)$

2. $2x - 5y = 18$
$-x + 3y = -10$ **(4, −2)**

3. $3x - 2y = 15$
$4x + y = 9$ **(3, −3)**

4. $5x + 4y = -4$
$2x - y = 10$ **(3, −4)**

5. $-7x + 5y = 1$
$x - 2y = 9$ $\left(-\dfrac{47}{9}, -\dfrac{64}{9}\right)$

6. $6x - 4y = 1$
$-3x + 3y = 2$ $\left(\dfrac{11}{6}, \dfrac{5}{2}\right)$

7. $\dfrac{1}{2}x - \dfrac{7}{5}y = 8$

$\dfrac{1}{3}x - y = 1$ **(198, 65)**

8. $5x + 6y = 7$
$4x + 5y = -9$ **(89, −73)**

Study Guide

Graphing Systems of Inequalities

To solve a system of inequalities, we need to find the ordered pairs that satisfy all the inequalities involved. One way to do this is to graph the inequalities on the same coordinate plane. The solution set is then represented by the intersection, or overlap, of the graphs.

Example 1: Solve the system of inequalities by graphing.

$$x - y \geq -1$$
$$x + y \leq 2$$

$x - y \geq -1$ represents regions 2 and 3.
$x + y \leq 2$ represents regions 1 and 2.

The intersection of these regions is region 2, which is the solution of the system of inequalities.

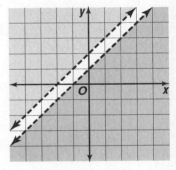

It is possible that two regions *do not* intersect. In such cases, we say the solution is the empty set, ∅, and no solution exists.

Example 2: Solve the system of inequalities by graphing.

$$y < x + 1$$
$$y > x + 2$$

The two solutions have no points in common. The solution set is ∅.

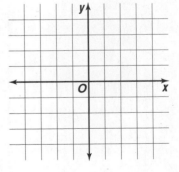

Solve each system of inequalities by graphing.

1. $x < 3$
   $y \geq -1$

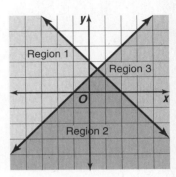

2. $x - y \leq 2$
   $x + 2y \geq 1$

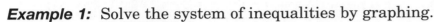

3. $|y| \leq 1$
   $x > 2$

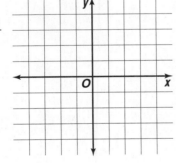

4. $3x - 2y \leq -1$
   $x + 4y \geq -12$

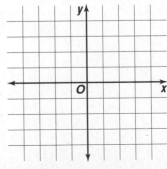

3-4

Study Guide

Graphing Systems of Inequalities

To solve a system of inequalities, we need to find the ordered pairs that satisfy all the inequalities involved. One way to do this is to graph the inequalities on the same coordinate plane. The solution set is then represented by the intersection, or overlap, of the graphs.

Example 1: Solve the system of inequalities by graphing.
$$x - y \geq -1$$
$$x + y \leq 2$$

$x - y \geq -1$ represents regions 2 and 3.
$x + y \leq 2$ represents regions 1 and 2.

The intersection of these regions is region 2, which is the solution of the system of inequalities.

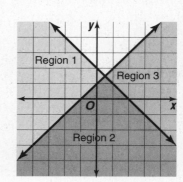

It is possible that two regions *do not* intersect. In such cases, we say the solution is the empty set, ∅, and no solution exists.

Example 2: Solve the system of inequalities by graphing.
$$y < x + 1$$
$$y > x + 2$$

The two solutions have no points in common. The solution set is ∅.

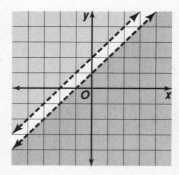

Solve each system of inequalities by graphing.

1. $x < 3$
  $y \geq -1$

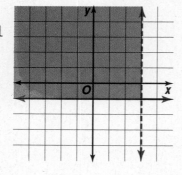

2. $x - y \leq 2$
  $x + 2y \geq 1$

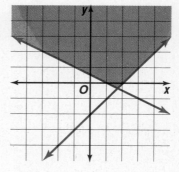

3. $|y| \leq 1$
  $x > 2$

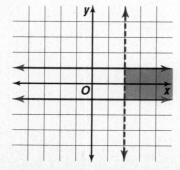

4. $3x - 2y \leq -1$
  $x + 4y \geq -12$

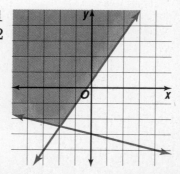

Algebra 2

NAME _____ DATE _____

Study Guide

Linear Programming

Practical problems can be solved by **linear programming.**
Linear programming is a procedure for finding the maximum or
minimum value of a function in two variables, subject to given
conditions on the variables called **constraints.**

Example: Find the maximum or minimum value
for the function $f(x, y) = 6x - 2y$.

The values of x and y have the
following constraints.

$x \geq 0 \quad 0 \leq y \leq 4 \quad x + y < 5 \quad 2y \geq x - 2$

Graph each inequality.

The maximum and the minimum occur at
vertices of the region for the solution set. The
minimum value of $f(x, y)$ is $f(0, 4) = -8$.
The maximum is $f(4, 1) = 22$.

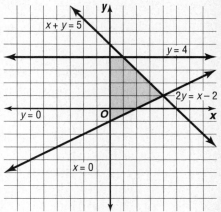

**Graph each system of inequalities. Name the coordinates of
the vertices of the feasible region. Find the maximum and
minimum values of the given function for this region.**

1. $y \geq 2$
  $1 \leq x \leq 5$
  $y \leq x + 3$
  $f(x, y) = 3x - 2y$

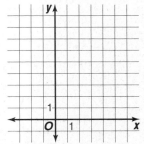

2. $x + y \geq 2$
  $4y \leq x + 8$
  $y \geq 2x - 5$
  $f(x, y) = 4x + 3y$

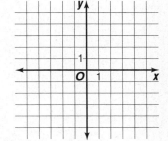

3. $x + y \geq 2$
  $4y \leq x + 8$
  $2y \geq 3x - 6$
  $f(x, y) = 3y + x$

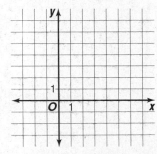

4. $y \leq x + 5$
  $y \geq x$
  $x \geq -3$
  $y + 2x \leq 5$
  $f(x, y) = x - 2y$

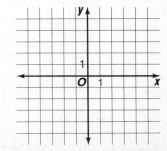

19 *Algebra 2*

Study Guide

Linear Programming

Practical problems can be solved by **linear programming.**
Linear programming is a procedure for finding the maximum or
minimum value of a function in two variables, subject to given
conditions on the variables called **constraints.**

Example: Find the maximum or minimum value
for the function $f(x, y) = 6x - 2y$.

The values of x and y have the
following constraints.

$x \geq 0 \quad 0 \leq y \leq 4 \quad x + y < 5 \quad 2y \geq x - 2$

Graph each inequality.

The maximum and the minimum occur at
vertices of the region for the solution set. The
minimum value of $f(x, y)$ is $f(0, 4) = -8$.
The maximum is $f(4, 1) = 22$.

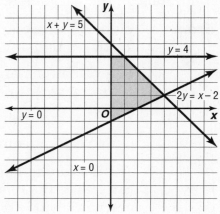

**Graph each system of inequalities. Name the coordinates of
the vertices of the feasible region. Find the maximum and
minimum values of the given function for this region.**

1. $y \geq 2$
   $1 \leq x \leq 5$
   $y \leq x + 3$
   $f(x, y) = 3x - 2y$

   vertices: (1, 2),
   (1, 4), (5, 8), (5, 2);
   max: 11; min: −5

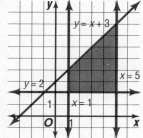

2. $x + y \geq 2$
   $4y \leq x + 8$
   $y \geq 2x - 5$
   $f(x, y) = 4x + 3y$

   vertices: (0, 2),
   (4, 3), $\left(\frac{7}{3}, -\frac{1}{3}\right)$;
   max: 25; min: 6

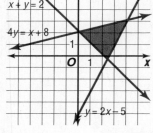

3. $x + y \geq 2$
   $4y \leq x + 8$
   $2y \geq 3x - 6$
   $f(x, y) = 3y + x$

   vertices: (0, 2),
   (4, 3), (2, 0);
   max: 13; min: 2

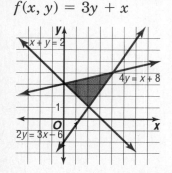

4. $y \leq x + 5$
   $y \geq x$
   $x \geq -3$
   $y + 2x \leq 5$
   $f(x, y) = x - 2y$

   vertices: (−3, −3),
   (−3, 2), (0, 5),
   $\left(\frac{5}{3}, \frac{5}{3}\right)$;
   max: 3; min: −10

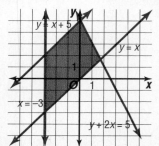

Algebra 2

NAME_____ DATE _____

Study Guide

Applications of Linear Programming

When solving linear programming problems, use the following procedure.

Linear Programming Procedure
1. Define variables.
2. Write a system of inequalities.
3. Graph the system of inequalities.
4. Find the coordinates of the vertices of the feasible region.
5. Write an expression to be maximized or minimized.
6. Substitute values for the vertices in the expression.
7. Select the greatest or least result. Answer the problem.

Solve.

1. A painter has exactly 32 units of yellow dye and 54 units of green dye. He plans to mix as many gallons as possible of color A and color B. Each gallon of color A requires 4 units of yellow dye and 1 unit of green dye. Each gallon of color B requires 1 unit of yellow dye and 6 units of green dye.

   a. Let x be the number of gallons of color A and let y be the number of gallons of color B. Write the inequalities.

   b. Graph the system of inequalities and name the vertices of the polygon formed.

   c. Find the maximum number of gallons, $x + y$, possible.

2. A delicatessen has 10 pounds of garlic-flavored sausage and 10 pounds of plain sausage. The deli wants to make as many pounds of bratwurst as possible. Each pound of bratwurst requires $\frac{1}{2}$ pound of plain sausage and $\frac{1}{2}$ pound of garlic-flavored sausage. Find the maximum number of pounds of bratwurst, $x + y$, that can be made.

3. Machine A can produce 30 steering wheels per hour at a cost of $16 per hour. Machine B can produce 40 steering wheels per hour at a cost of $22 per hour. At least 360 steering wheels must be made in each 8-hour shift. What is the least cost involved in making 360 steering wheels, if maintenance of the machines limits their use to no more than 8 consecutive hours?

20

Applications of Linear Programming

When solving linear programming problems, use the following procedure.

Linear Programming Procedure
1. Define variables.
2. Write a system of inequalities.
3. Graph the system of inequalities.
4. Find the coordinates of the vertices of the feasible region.
5. Write an expression to be maximized or minimized.
6. Substitute values for the vertices in the expression.
7. Select the greatest or least result. Answer the problem.

Solve.

1. A painter has exactly 32 units of yellow dye and 54 units of green dye. He plans to mix as many gallons as possible of color A and color B. Each gallon of color A requires 4 units of yellow dye and 1 unit of green dye. Each gallon of color B requires 1 unit of yellow dye and 6 units of green dye.

   a. Let x be the number of gallons of color A and let y be the number of gallons of color B. Write the inequalities.
   $x \geq 0, y \geq 0, 4x + y \leq 32, x + 6y \leq 54$

   b. Graph the system of inequalities and name the vertices of the polygon formed.
   (0, 9), (8, 0), (6, 8), (0, 0)

   c. Find the maximum number of gallons, $x + y$, possible.
   14 gallons (6A, 8B)

2. A delicatessen has 10 pounds of garlic-flavored sausage and 10 pounds of plain sausage. The deli wants to make as many pounds of bratwurst as possible. Each pound of bratwurst requires $\frac{1}{2}$ pound of plain sausage and $\frac{1}{2}$ pound of garlic-flavored sausage. Find the maximum number of pounds of bratwurst, $x + y$, that can be made.
20 pounds

3. Machine A can produce 30 steering wheels per hour at a cost of $16 per hour. Machine B can produce 40 steering wheels per hour at a cost of $22 per hour. At least 360 steering wheels must be made in each 8-hour shift. What is the least cost involved in making 360 steering wheels, if maintenance of the machines limits their use to no more than 8 consecutive hours? **$194**

Study Guide

Solving Systems of Equations in Three Variables

Systems of equations in three variables are solved using the same methods as those for equations in two variables.

Example: Solve this system of equations.

$$x + y + 3z = 7$$
$$2x - z = 6$$
$$z = 4$$

The third equation is already solved.

$$z = 4$$

Substitute 4 for z in the second equation, $2x - z = 6$, to find x.

$$2x - 4 = 6$$
$$2x = 10$$
$$x = 5$$

Substitute 4 for z and 5 for x in the first equation, $x + y + 3z = 7$, to find y.

$$5 + y + 3(4) = 7$$
$$5 + y + 12 = 7$$
$$y = -10$$

The solution is $(5, -10, 4)$.

Check: First equation: $5 - 10 + 12 = 7$

Second equation: $10 - 4 = 6$

Third equation: $4 = 4$ ✔

Solve each system of equations.

1. $x + 2z = 5$
$-4x + 6y = 0$
$x - 2z = 9$

2. $4x + 6y + 4z = 5$
$2x - 9y + 8z = 0$
$6x + 15y - 4z = 5$

3. The Laredo Sports Shop sold 10 balls, 3 bats, and 2 bases for $99 on Monday; 4 balls, 8 bats, and 2 bases for $78 on Tuesday; and 2 balls, 3 bats, and 1 base for $33.60 on Wednesday. What are the prices of 1 ball, 1 bat, and 1 base?

4. The sum of three numbers is 110. The second number is twice the first. The third number is equal to three times the first minus one-half the first. Find the numbers.

Study Guide

Solving Systems of Equations in Three Variables

Systems of equations in three variables are solved using the same methods as those for equations in two variables.

Example: Solve this system of equations.

$$x + y + 3z = 7$$
$$2x - z = 6$$
$$z = 4$$

The third equation is already solved.

$$z = 4$$

Substitute 4 for z in the second equation, $2x - z = 6$, to find x.

$$2x - 4 = 6$$
$$2x = 10$$
$$x = 5$$

Substitute 4 for z and 5 for x in the first equation, $x + y + 3z = 7$, to find y.

$$5 + y + 3(4) = 7$$
$$5 + y + 12 = 7$$
$$y = -10$$

The solution is $(5, -10, 4)$.

Check: First equation: $5 - 10 + 12 = 7$

Second equation: $10 - 4 = 6$

Third equation: $4 = 4$ ✔

Solve each system of equations.

1. $x + 2z = 5$
$-4x + 6y = 0$
$x - 2z = 9$
$\left(7, \dfrac{14}{3}, -1\right)$

2. $4x + 6y + 4z = 5$
$2x - 9y + 8z = 0$
$6x + 15y - 4z = 5$
$\left(0, \dfrac{10}{21}, \dfrac{15}{28}\right)$

3. The Laredo Sports Shop sold 10 balls, 3 bats, and 2 bases for $99 on Monday; 4 balls, 8 bats, and 2 bases for $78 on Tuesday; and 2 balls, 3 bats, and 1 base for $33.60 on Wednesday. What are the prices of 1 ball, 1 bat, and 1 base?
ball = $8.00; bat = $5.40; base = $1.40

4. The sum of three numbers is 110. The second number is twice the first. The third number is equal to three times the first minus one-half the first. Find the numbers.
$x = 20; y = 40; z = 50$

NAME_____ DATE _____

Study Guide

Student Edition
Pages 186–193

An Introduction to Matrices

A **matrix** is a system of rows and columns that is often used as a problem-solving tool. Each value in the matrix is called an **element**.

Matrices are usually named by an uppercase letter. Matrices can also be named by using the matrix **dimensions** with the letter name. The dimensions tell how many rows and columns, in that order, are in the matrix. The matrix at the right would be named $A_{2 \times 3}$ since it has 2 rows and 3 columns.

$$A = \begin{bmatrix} 2 & 1 & 3 \\ 0 & 5 & 6 \end{bmatrix} \rbrace \text{2 rows}$$

3 columns

The element 6 is in row 2, column 3.

Matrices have special algebraic rules. For example, you can multiply any matrix by a constant. This is called **scalar multiplication.**

Scalar Multiplication of a Matrix	$k\begin{bmatrix} a & b & c \\ d & e & f \end{bmatrix} = \begin{bmatrix} ka & kb & kc \\ kd & ke & kf \end{bmatrix}$

Two matrices are considered equal if they have the same dimensions and each element of one matrix is equal to the corresponding element of the other.

Example: Solve $\begin{bmatrix} 5x \\ 5x + 4y \end{bmatrix} = \begin{bmatrix} y \\ 10 \end{bmatrix}$ for x and y.

Since the matrices are equal, the corresponding elements are equal.
$$5x = y$$
$$5x + 4y = 10$$

The first equation gives a value for y that can be substituted into the second equation to find a value for x.

$5x + 4y = 10$	
$5x + 4(5x) = 10$	**Substitute 5x for y.**
$5x + 20x = 10$	**Simplify.**
$25x = 10$	**Combine like terms.**
$x = \dfrac{2}{5}$	**Divide each side by 25 and simplify.**

To find a value for y, substitute $\dfrac{2}{5}$ into either equation.

$5x = y$	
$5\left(\dfrac{2}{5}\right) = y$	**Substitute $\dfrac{2}{5}$ for x.**
$2 = y$	

The solution is $\left(\dfrac{2}{5}, 2\right)$.

Perform the indicated operation.

1. $-3[6 \quad 8 \quad 10]$

2. $5\begin{bmatrix} 0 & -6 & 4 \\ 1 & -8 & 7 \end{bmatrix}$

Solve for the variables.

3. $[6x \quad 2y] = [3 \quad 2]$

4. $\begin{bmatrix} 2x \\ y \end{bmatrix} = \begin{bmatrix} 40 + 2y \\ 5 - 4x \end{bmatrix}$

5. $\begin{bmatrix} 3x \\ y \end{bmatrix} = \begin{bmatrix} 28 + 4y \\ -3x - 2 \end{bmatrix}$

Algebra 2

Study Guide

An Introduction to Matrices

A **matrix** is a system of rows and columns that is often used as a problem-solving tool. Each value in the matrix is called an **element**.

Matrices are usually named by an uppercase letter. Matrices can also be named by using the matrix **dimensions** with the letter name. The dimensions tell how many rows and columns, in that order, are in the matrix. The matrix at the right would be named $A_{2 \times 3}$ since it has 2 rows and 3 columns.

$$A = \begin{bmatrix} 2 & 1 & 3 \\ 0 & 5 & 6 \end{bmatrix} \quad 2 \text{ rows}$$

3 columns

The element 6 is in row 2, column 3.

Matrices have special algebraic rules. For example, you can multiply any matrix by a constant. This is called **scalar multiplication**.

Scalar Multiplication of a Matrix	$k\begin{bmatrix} a & b & c \\ d & e & f \end{bmatrix} = \begin{bmatrix} ka & kb & kc \\ kd & ke & kf \end{bmatrix}$

Two matrices are considered equal if they have the same dimensions and each element of one matrix is equal to the corresponding element of the other.

Example: Solve $\begin{bmatrix} 5x \\ 5x + 4y \end{bmatrix} = \begin{bmatrix} y \\ 10 \end{bmatrix}$ for x and y.

Since the matrices are equal, the corresponding elements are equal.
$5x = y$
$5x + 4y = 10$

The first equation gives a value for y that can be substituted into the second equation to find a value for x.

$5x + 4y = 10$	
$5x + 4(5x) = 10$	**Substitute 5x for y.**
$5x + 20x = 10$	**Simplify.**
$25x = 10$	**Combine like terms.**
$x = \dfrac{2}{5}$	**Divide each side by 25 and simplify.**

To find a value for y, substitute $\dfrac{2}{5}$ into either equation.

$5x = y$	
$5\left(\dfrac{2}{5}\right) = y$	**Substitute $\dfrac{2}{5}$ for x.**
$2 = y$	

The solution is $\left(\dfrac{2}{5}, 2\right)$.

Perform the indicated operation.

1. $-3[6 \quad 8 \quad 10]$ **[−18 −24 −30]**

2. $5\begin{bmatrix} 0 & -6 & 4 \\ 1 & -8 & 7 \end{bmatrix}$ $\begin{bmatrix} \mathbf{0} & \mathbf{-30} & \mathbf{20} \\ \mathbf{5} & \mathbf{-40} & \mathbf{35} \end{bmatrix}$

Solve for the variables.

3. $[6x \quad 2y] = [3 \quad 2]$
$x = \dfrac{1}{2}; y = 1$

4. $\begin{bmatrix} 2x \\ y \end{bmatrix} = \begin{bmatrix} 40 + 2y \\ 5 - 4x \end{bmatrix}$
$x = 5; y = -15$

5. $\begin{bmatrix} 3x \\ y \end{bmatrix} = \begin{bmatrix} 28 + 4y \\ -3x - 2 \end{bmatrix}$
$x = 1\dfrac{1}{3}; y = -6$

Algebra 2

NAME_____ DATE _____

Study Guide

Student Edition
Pages 194–198

Adding and Subtracting Matrices

In order to add or subtract matrices, the matrices must have the same dimensions.

Addition of Matrices	If A and B are two $m \times n$ matrices, then $A + B$ is an $m \times n$ matrix where each element is the sum of the corresponding elements of A and B. $$\begin{bmatrix} a & b \\ c & d \end{bmatrix} + \begin{bmatrix} e & f \\ g & h \end{bmatrix} = \begin{bmatrix} a + e & b + f \\ c + g & d + h \end{bmatrix}$$
Subtraction of Matrices	If A and B are two $m \times n$ matrices, then $A - B$ is an $m \times n$ matrix where each element is the difference of the corresponding elements of A and B. $$\begin{bmatrix} a & b \\ c & d \end{bmatrix} - \begin{bmatrix} e & f \\ g & h \end{bmatrix} = \begin{bmatrix} a - e & b - f \\ c - g & d - h \end{bmatrix}$$

Examples: Perform the indicated operations.

1 $\begin{bmatrix} 8 & -2 \\ 7 & 3 \end{bmatrix} + \begin{bmatrix} 4 & 1 \\ 6 & 5 \end{bmatrix} = \begin{bmatrix} 12 & -1 \\ 13 & 8 \end{bmatrix}$

2 $\begin{bmatrix} 15 & 0 \\ 12 & -9 \end{bmatrix} - \begin{bmatrix} -3 & 2 \\ 6 & -4 \end{bmatrix} = \begin{bmatrix} 18 & -2 \\ 6 & -5 \end{bmatrix}$

Perform the indicated operations.

1. $\begin{bmatrix} 10 & -3 \\ 5 & 8 \end{bmatrix} + \begin{bmatrix} -2 & -12 \\ 20 & 22 \end{bmatrix}$

2. $\begin{bmatrix} 3 & -2 \\ 1 & 2 \end{bmatrix} - \begin{bmatrix} 1 & 1 \\ -5 & -6 \end{bmatrix}$

3. $\begin{bmatrix} 5 & -4 & 35 \\ 2 & -2 & 16 \end{bmatrix} - \begin{bmatrix} 1 & 4 & -35 \\ -2 & 2 & 0 \end{bmatrix}$

4. $3\begin{bmatrix} 1 & 3 \\ -2 & 1 \end{bmatrix} - 2\begin{bmatrix} 1 & 1 \\ -5 & -6 \end{bmatrix}$

5. $\dfrac{1}{4}\left(\begin{bmatrix} 9 & 1 \\ -7 & 0 \end{bmatrix} + \begin{bmatrix} 3 & -5 \\ 1 & 7 \end{bmatrix} \right)$

Study Guide

Adding and Subtracting Matrices

In order to add or subtract matrices, the matrices must have the same dimensions.

Addition of Matrices	If A and B are two $m \times n$ matrices, then $A + B$ is an $m \times n$ matrix where each element is the sum of the corresponding elements of A and B. $$\begin{bmatrix} a & b \\ c & d \end{bmatrix} + \begin{bmatrix} e & f \\ g & h \end{bmatrix} = \begin{bmatrix} a+e & b+f \\ c+g & d+h \end{bmatrix}$$
Subtraction of Matrices	If A and B are two $m \times n$ matrices, then $A - B$ is an $m \times n$ matrix where each element is the difference of the corresponding elements of A and B. $$\begin{bmatrix} a & b \\ c & d \end{bmatrix} - \begin{bmatrix} e & f \\ g & h \end{bmatrix} = \begin{bmatrix} a-e & b-f \\ c-g & d-h \end{bmatrix}$$

Examples: Perform the indicated operations.

1 $\begin{bmatrix} 8 & -2 \\ 7 & 3 \end{bmatrix} + \begin{bmatrix} 4 & 1 \\ 6 & 5 \end{bmatrix} = \begin{bmatrix} 12 & -1 \\ 13 & 8 \end{bmatrix}$

2 $\begin{bmatrix} 15 & 0 \\ 12 & -9 \end{bmatrix} - \begin{bmatrix} -3 & 2 \\ 6 & -4 \end{bmatrix} = \begin{bmatrix} 18 & -2 \\ 6 & -5 \end{bmatrix}$

Perform the indicated operations.

1. $\begin{bmatrix} 10 & -3 \\ 5 & 8 \end{bmatrix} + \begin{bmatrix} -2 & -12 \\ 20 & 22 \end{bmatrix}$
$\begin{bmatrix} \mathbf{8} & \mathbf{-15} \\ \mathbf{25} & \mathbf{30} \end{bmatrix}$

2. $\begin{bmatrix} 3 & -2 \\ 1 & 2 \end{bmatrix} - \begin{bmatrix} 1 & 1 \\ -5 & -6 \end{bmatrix}$
$\begin{bmatrix} \mathbf{2} & \mathbf{-3} \\ \mathbf{6} & \mathbf{8} \end{bmatrix}$

3. $\begin{bmatrix} 5 & -4 & 35 \\ 2 & -2 & 16 \end{bmatrix} - \begin{bmatrix} 1 & 4 & -35 \\ -2 & 2 & 0 \end{bmatrix}$ $\begin{bmatrix} \mathbf{4} & \mathbf{-8} & \mathbf{70} \\ \mathbf{4} & \mathbf{-4} & \mathbf{16} \end{bmatrix}$

4. $3\begin{bmatrix} 1 & 3 \\ -2 & 1 \end{bmatrix} - 2\begin{bmatrix} 1 & 1 \\ -5 & -6 \end{bmatrix}$ $\begin{bmatrix} \mathbf{-2} & \mathbf{5} \\ \mathbf{-3} & \mathbf{-1} \end{bmatrix}$

5. $\frac{1}{4}\left(\begin{bmatrix} 9 & 1 \\ -7 & 0 \end{bmatrix} + \begin{bmatrix} 3 & -5 \\ 1 & 7 \end{bmatrix} \right)$ $\begin{bmatrix} \mathbf{3} & \mathbf{-1} \\ \mathbf{-\dfrac{3}{2}} & \mathbf{\dfrac{3}{4}} \end{bmatrix}$

NAME_____ DATE _____

Study Guide

Multiplying Matrices

The product AB of two matrices is defined if and only if the number of columns in A equals the number of rows in B. For the product AB, the element in row i column j is found as follows: Use the ith row of A and the jth row of B. Multiply the corresponding elements and add the products.

Example:

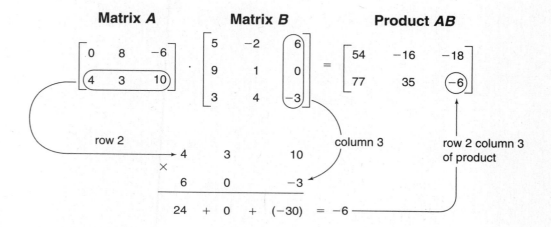

Perform the indicated operations, if possible.

1. $\begin{bmatrix} 4 & 1 \\ -2 & 3 \end{bmatrix} \cdot \begin{bmatrix} 3 & 0 \\ 0 & 3 \end{bmatrix}$

2. $\begin{bmatrix} -1 & 0 \\ 3 & 7 \end{bmatrix} \cdot \begin{bmatrix} 3 & -1 \\ 2 & 4 \end{bmatrix}$

3. $\begin{bmatrix} 3 & -1 \\ 2 & 4 \end{bmatrix} \cdot \begin{bmatrix} 3 & -1 \\ 2 & 4 \end{bmatrix}$

Use the matrices A, B, C, and D to evaluate each expression.

$A = \begin{bmatrix} 3 & 4 \\ 5 & 6 \end{bmatrix}$ 　　 $B = \begin{bmatrix} -3 & -4 & -5 \\ -1 & -2 & -3 \end{bmatrix}$ 　　 $C = \begin{bmatrix} 6 & 8 & 10 \\ 10 & 4 & 2 \\ -3 & 0 & -5 \end{bmatrix}$ 　　 $D = \begin{bmatrix} 3 & 6 \\ 9 & 12 \end{bmatrix}$

4. AD

5. DB

6. BD

7. DA

8. BC

9. AB

Algebra 2

NAME_____ DATE _____

Study Guide

Multiplying Matrices

The product AB of two matrices is defined if and only if the number of columns in A equals the number of rows in B. For the product AB, the element in row i column j is found as follows: Use the ith row of A and the jth row of B. Multiply the corresponding elements and add the products.

Example:

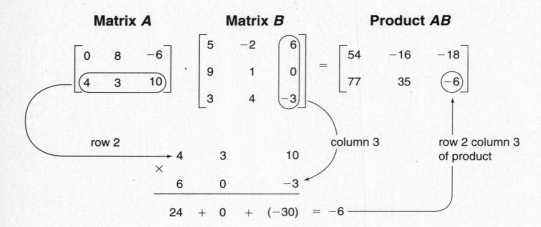

Perform the indicated operations, if possible.

1. $\begin{bmatrix} 4 & 1 \\ -2 & 3 \end{bmatrix} \cdot \begin{bmatrix} 3 & 0 \\ 0 & 3 \end{bmatrix}$

$\begin{bmatrix} \mathbf{12} & \mathbf{3} \\ \mathbf{-6} & \mathbf{9} \end{bmatrix}$

2. $\begin{bmatrix} -1 & 0 \\ 3 & 7 \end{bmatrix} \cdot \begin{bmatrix} 3 & -1 \\ 2 & 4 \end{bmatrix}$

$\begin{bmatrix} \mathbf{-3} & \mathbf{1} \\ \mathbf{23} & \mathbf{25} \end{bmatrix}$

3. $\begin{bmatrix} 3 & -1 \\ 2 & 4 \end{bmatrix} \cdot \begin{bmatrix} 3 & -1 \\ 2 & 4 \end{bmatrix}$

$\begin{bmatrix} \mathbf{7} & \mathbf{-7} \\ \mathbf{14} & \mathbf{14} \end{bmatrix}$

Use the matrices A, B, C, and D to evaluate each expression.

$A = \begin{bmatrix} 3 & 4 \\ 5 & 6 \end{bmatrix} \qquad B = \begin{bmatrix} -3 & -4 & -5 \\ -1 & -2 & -3 \end{bmatrix} \qquad C = \begin{bmatrix} 6 & 8 & 10 \\ 10 & 4 & 2 \\ -3 & 0 & -5 \end{bmatrix} \qquad D = \begin{bmatrix} 3 & 6 \\ 9 & 12 \end{bmatrix}$

4. AD

$\begin{bmatrix} \mathbf{45} & \mathbf{66} \\ \mathbf{69} & \mathbf{102} \end{bmatrix}$

5. DB

$\begin{bmatrix} \mathbf{-15} & \mathbf{-24} & \mathbf{-33} \\ \mathbf{-39} & \mathbf{-60} & \mathbf{-81} \end{bmatrix}$

6. BD
not defined

7. DA

$\begin{bmatrix} \mathbf{39} & \mathbf{48} \\ \mathbf{87} & \mathbf{108} \end{bmatrix}$

8. BC

$\begin{bmatrix} \mathbf{-43} & \mathbf{-40} & \mathbf{-13} \\ \mathbf{-17} & \mathbf{-16} & \mathbf{1} \end{bmatrix}$

9. AB

$\begin{bmatrix} \mathbf{-13} & \mathbf{-20} & \mathbf{-27} \\ \mathbf{-21} & \mathbf{-32} & \mathbf{-43} \end{bmatrix}$

NAME_____ DATE _____

Study Guide

Matrices and Determinants

Every square matrix has a determinant. The determinant of a 2×2 matrix is called a second-order determinant.

Rule for Second-Order Determinants	$\begin{vmatrix} a & b \\ c & d \end{vmatrix} = ad - bc$

A method called **expansion by minors** can be used to evaluate a third-order determinant.

Expansion of a Third-Order Determinant	$\begin{vmatrix} a & b & c \\ d & e & f \\ g & h & i \end{vmatrix} = a\begin{vmatrix} e & f \\ h & i \end{vmatrix} - b\begin{vmatrix} d & f \\ g & i \end{vmatrix} + c\begin{vmatrix} d & e \\ g & h \end{vmatrix}$

Another method for evaluating a third-order determinant is to use diagonals.

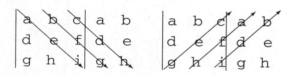

First, write the first two columns on the right of the determinant. Next, add the products of the numbers on the diagonals from upper left to lower right:

$$aei + bfg + cdh$$

Then subtract the products of the numbers on the diagonals from lower left to upper right:

$$aei + bfg + cdh - gec - hfa - idb$$

Evaluate each determinant using expansion by minors.

1. $\begin{bmatrix} 1 & 3 & -2 \\ 2 & -1 & 1 \\ -2 & 2 & 3 \end{bmatrix}$

2. $\begin{bmatrix} -4 & 1 & 3 \\ 2 & 0 & 1 \\ 4 & -5 & 0 \end{bmatrix}$

3. $\begin{bmatrix} 2 & -1 & 3 \\ 3 & 2 & 1 \\ 1 & 3 & -2 \end{bmatrix}$

Evaluate each determinant using diagonals.

4. $\begin{bmatrix} 1 & -1 & 1 \\ 4 & 3 & 1 \\ 0 & 5 & 2 \end{bmatrix}$

5. $\begin{bmatrix} 3 & -1 & 2 \\ 0 & 4 & 1 \\ 5 & -2 & -3 \end{bmatrix}$

6. $\begin{bmatrix} 40 & 20 & -25 \\ 10 & 15 & 55 \\ -5 & -10 & -30 \end{bmatrix}$

Algebra 2

NAME _____ DATE _____

Study Guide

Matrices and Determinants

Every square matrix has a determinant. The determinant of a 2×2 matrix is called a second-order determinant.

Rule for Second-Order Determinants	$\begin{vmatrix} a & b \\ c & d \end{vmatrix} = ad - bc$

A method called **expansion by minors** can be used to evaluate a third-order determinant.

Expansion of a Third-Order Determinant	$\begin{vmatrix} a & b & c \\ d & e & f \\ g & h & i \end{vmatrix} = a\begin{vmatrix} e & f \\ h & i \end{vmatrix} - b\begin{vmatrix} d & f \\ g & i \end{vmatrix} + c\begin{vmatrix} d & e \\ g & h \end{vmatrix}$

Another method for evaluating a third-order determinant is to use diagonals.

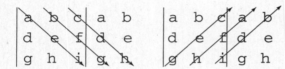

First, write the first two columns on the right of the determinant. Next, add the products of the numbers on the diagonals from upper left to lower right:

$$aei + bfg + cdh$$

Then subtract the products of the numbers on the diagonals from lower left to upper right:

$$aei + bfg + cdh - gec - hfa - idb$$

Evaluate each determinant using expansion by minors.

1. $\begin{bmatrix} 1 & 3 & -2 \\ 2 & -1 & 1 \\ -2 & 2 & 3 \end{bmatrix}$
−33

2. $\begin{bmatrix} -4 & 1 & 3 \\ 2 & 0 & 1 \\ 4 & -5 & 0 \end{bmatrix}$
−46

3. $\begin{bmatrix} 2 & -1 & 3 \\ 3 & 2 & 1 \\ 1 & 3 & -2 \end{bmatrix}$
0

Evaluate each determinant using diagonals.

4. $\begin{bmatrix} 1 & -1 & 1 \\ 4 & 3 & 1 \\ 0 & 5 & 2 \end{bmatrix}$
29

5. $\begin{bmatrix} 3 & -1 & 2 \\ 0 & 4 & 1 \\ 5 & -2 & -3 \end{bmatrix}$
−75

6. $\begin{bmatrix} 40 & 20 & -25 \\ 10 & 15 & 55 \\ -5 & -10 & -30 \end{bmatrix}$
5125

Study Guide

Identity and Inverse Matrices

Apply the following definitions for identities and inverses of matrices.

Identity Matrix for Multiplication	
Definition	**Example**
The identity matrix for multiplication, I, is a square matrix with 1 for every element of the principal diagonal and 0 for all other positions. The principal diagonal extends from upper left to lower right.	For 2×2 matrices, $\begin{bmatrix} 1 & 0 \\ 0 & 1 \end{bmatrix}$ is the identity matrix because $\begin{bmatrix} a & b \\ c & d \end{bmatrix}\begin{bmatrix} 1 & 0 \\ 0 & 1 \end{bmatrix} = \begin{bmatrix} a & b \\ c & d \end{bmatrix}$ and $\begin{bmatrix} 1 & 0 \\ 0 & 1 \end{bmatrix}\begin{bmatrix} a & b \\ c & d \end{bmatrix} = \begin{bmatrix} a & b \\ c & d \end{bmatrix}$.

Inverse of a 2 × 2 Matrix	
Definition	**Example**
Any matrix $M = \begin{bmatrix} a & b \\ c & d \end{bmatrix}$ will have an inverse M^{-1} if and only if $\begin{vmatrix} a & b \\ c & d \end{vmatrix} \neq 0$. Then $M^{-1} = \dfrac{1}{ad - bc}\begin{bmatrix} d & -b \\ -c & a \end{bmatrix}$.	Find the inverse of $A = \begin{bmatrix} 4 & 3 \\ -2 & 8 \end{bmatrix}$, if it exists. 1. Compute the value of the determinant to make sure that the inverse exists. $\begin{vmatrix} 4 & 3 \\ -2 & 8 \end{vmatrix} = 32 - (-6) = 38$ 2. Since the determinant does not equal 0, A^{-1} exists and $A^{-1} = \dfrac{1}{38}\begin{bmatrix} 8 & -3 \\ 2 & 4 \end{bmatrix}$.

Find the inverse of each matrix, if it exists.

1. $\begin{bmatrix} 24 & 12 \\ 8 & 4 \end{bmatrix}$

2. $\begin{bmatrix} 26 & -8 \\ 4 & -9 \end{bmatrix}$

3. $\begin{bmatrix} 40 & -10 \\ -20 & 30 \end{bmatrix}$

4. $\begin{bmatrix} -5 & -4 \\ 0 & 3 \end{bmatrix}$

5. $\begin{bmatrix} 18 & 9 \\ 3 & 6 \end{bmatrix}$

6. $\begin{bmatrix} 3 & 6 \\ 4 & 8 \end{bmatrix}$

7. $\begin{bmatrix} 1 & 0 \\ 0 & 1 \end{bmatrix}$

8. $\begin{bmatrix} -2 & 0 \\ 0 & -2 \end{bmatrix}$

9. $\begin{bmatrix} 1 & 1 \\ 0 & 1 \end{bmatrix}$

Study Guide

Identity and Inverse Matrices

Apply the following definitions for identities and inverses of matrices.

Identity Matrix for Multiplication	
Definition	**Example**
The identity matrix for multiplication, I, is a square matrix with 1 for every element of the principal diagonal and 0 for all other positions. The principal diagonal extends from upper left to lower right.	For 2×2 matrices, $\begin{bmatrix} 1 & 0 \\ 0 & 1 \end{bmatrix}$ is the identity matrix because $\begin{bmatrix} a & b \\ c & d \end{bmatrix}\begin{bmatrix} 1 & 0 \\ 0 & 1 \end{bmatrix} = \begin{bmatrix} a & b \\ c & d \end{bmatrix}$ and $\begin{bmatrix} 1 & 0 \\ 0 & 1 \end{bmatrix}\begin{bmatrix} a & b \\ c & d \end{bmatrix} = \begin{bmatrix} a & b \\ c & d \end{bmatrix}$.

Inverse of a 2 × 2 Matrix	
Definition	**Example**
Any matrix $M = \begin{bmatrix} a & b \\ c & d \end{bmatrix}$ will have an inverse M^{-1} if and only if $\begin{vmatrix} a & b \\ c & d \end{vmatrix} \neq 0$. Then $M^{-1} = \dfrac{1}{ad - bc}\begin{bmatrix} d & -b \\ -c & a \end{bmatrix}$.	Find the inverse of $A = \begin{bmatrix} 4 & 3 \\ -2 & 8 \end{bmatrix}$, if it exists. 1. Compute the value of the determinant to make sure that the inverse exists. $\begin{vmatrix} 4 & 3 \\ -2 & 8 \end{vmatrix} = 32 - (-6) = 38$ 2. Since the determinant does not equal 0, A^{-1} exists and $A^{-1} = \dfrac{1}{38}\begin{bmatrix} 8 & -3 \\ 2 & 4 \end{bmatrix}$.

Find the inverse of each matrix, if it exists.

1. $\begin{bmatrix} 24 & 12 \\ 8 & 4 \end{bmatrix}$

   no inverse exists

2. $\begin{bmatrix} 26 & -8 \\ 4 & -9 \end{bmatrix}$

   $\dfrac{1}{202}\begin{bmatrix} -9 & 8 \\ -4 & 26 \end{bmatrix}$

3. $\begin{bmatrix} 40 & -10 \\ -20 & 30 \end{bmatrix}$

   $\dfrac{1}{1000}\begin{bmatrix} 30 & 10 \\ 20 & 40 \end{bmatrix}$

4. $\begin{bmatrix} -5 & -4 \\ 0 & 3 \end{bmatrix}$

   $-\dfrac{1}{15}\begin{bmatrix} 3 & 4 \\ 0 & -5 \end{bmatrix}$

5. $\begin{bmatrix} 18 & 9 \\ 3 & 6 \end{bmatrix}$

   $\dfrac{1}{81}\begin{bmatrix} 6 & -9 \\ -3 & 18 \end{bmatrix}$

6. $\begin{bmatrix} 3 & 6 \\ 4 & 8 \end{bmatrix}$

   no inverse exists

7. $\begin{bmatrix} 1 & 0 \\ 0 & 1 \end{bmatrix}\begin{bmatrix} 1 & 0 \\ 0 & 1 \end{bmatrix}$

8. $\begin{bmatrix} -2 & 0 \\ 0 & -2 \end{bmatrix}\begin{bmatrix} -\dfrac{1}{2} & 0 \\ 0 & -\dfrac{1}{2} \end{bmatrix}$

9. $\begin{bmatrix} 1 & 1 \\ 0 & 1 \end{bmatrix}\begin{bmatrix} 1 & -1 \\ 0 & 1 \end{bmatrix}$

Algebra 2

NAME_____ DATE _____

Study Guide

Using Matrices to Solve Systems of Equations

You can use matrix equations to solve systems of equations. To solve matrix equations change the coefficient matrix into the appropriate identity matrix by multiplying each side of the matrix equation by the inverse of the coefficient matrix.

Example: Solve $\begin{cases} 3x - 2y + z = 0 \\ 2x + 3y = 12 \\ y + 4z = -18 \end{cases}$ if the inverse of the coefficient matrix is $\dfrac{1}{54}\begin{bmatrix} 12 & 9 & -3 \\ -8 & 12 & 2 \\ 2 & -3 & 13 \end{bmatrix}$.

$$\begin{bmatrix} 3 & -2 & 1 \\ 2 & 3 & 0 \\ 0 & 1 & 4 \end{bmatrix}\begin{bmatrix} x \\ y \\ z \end{bmatrix} = \begin{bmatrix} 0 \\ 12 \\ -18 \end{bmatrix}$$

$$\frac{1}{54}\begin{bmatrix} 12 & 9 & -3 \\ -8 & 12 & 2 \\ 2 & -3 & 13 \end{bmatrix}\begin{bmatrix} 3 & -2 & 1 \\ 2 & 3 & 0 \\ 0 & 1 & 4 \end{bmatrix}\begin{bmatrix} x \\ y \\ z \end{bmatrix} = \frac{1}{54}\begin{bmatrix} 12 & 9 & -3 \\ -8 & 12 & 2 \\ 2 & -3 & 13 \end{bmatrix}\begin{bmatrix} 0 \\ 12 \\ -18 \end{bmatrix}$$

$$\begin{bmatrix} 1 & 0 & 0 \\ 0 & 1 & 0 \\ 0 & 0 & 1 \end{bmatrix}\begin{bmatrix} x \\ y \\ z \end{bmatrix} = \frac{1}{54}\begin{bmatrix} 162 \\ 108 \\ -270 \end{bmatrix}$$

$$\begin{bmatrix} x \\ y \\ z \end{bmatrix} = \begin{bmatrix} 3 \\ 2 \\ -5 \end{bmatrix}$$ The solution is $(3, 2, -5)$.

Write the system of linear equations represented by each matrix equation.

1. $\begin{bmatrix} 4 & 6 \\ 5 & 8 \end{bmatrix}\begin{bmatrix} x \\ y \end{bmatrix} = \begin{bmatrix} 24 \\ 40 \end{bmatrix}$

2. $\begin{bmatrix} 5 & 4 & 6 \\ 1 & 2 & 3 \\ -7 & 9 & 8 \end{bmatrix}\begin{bmatrix} x \\ y \\ z \end{bmatrix} = \begin{bmatrix} 40 \\ 6 \\ -72 \end{bmatrix}$

Solve each matrix equation or system of equations by using inverse matrices.

3. $\begin{bmatrix} 1 & 2 \\ 3 & -1 \end{bmatrix}\begin{bmatrix} x \\ y \end{bmatrix} = \begin{bmatrix} 3 \\ -6 \end{bmatrix}$

4. $\begin{bmatrix} -4 & -8 \\ 6 & 12 \end{bmatrix}\begin{bmatrix} x \\ y \end{bmatrix} = \begin{bmatrix} 16 \\ 12 \end{bmatrix}$

5. $4x - 2y = 22$
$6x + 4y = -2$

6. $5x + 4y = 5$
$9x - 8y = 0$

Algebra 2

Study Guide

Using Matrices to Solve Systems of Equations

You can use matrix equations to solve systems of equations. To solve matrix equations change the coefficient matrix into the appropriate identity matrix by multiplying each side of the matrix equation by the inverse of the coefficient matrix.

Example: Solve $\begin{cases} 3x - 2y + z = 0 \\ 2x + 3y = 12 \\ y + 4z = -18 \end{cases}$ if the inverse of the coefficient matrix is $\dfrac{1}{54}\begin{bmatrix} 12 & 9 & -3 \\ -8 & 12 & 2 \\ 2 & -3 & 13 \end{bmatrix}$.

$$\begin{bmatrix} 3 & -2 & 1 \\ 2 & 3 & 0 \\ 0 & 1 & 4 \end{bmatrix}\begin{bmatrix} x \\ y \\ z \end{bmatrix} = \begin{bmatrix} 0 \\ 12 \\ -18 \end{bmatrix}$$

$$\frac{1}{54}\begin{bmatrix} 12 & 9 & -3 \\ -8 & 12 & 2 \\ 2 & -3 & 13 \end{bmatrix}\begin{bmatrix} 3 & -2 & 1 \\ 2 & 3 & 0 \\ 0 & 1 & 4 \end{bmatrix}\begin{bmatrix} x \\ y \\ z \end{bmatrix} = \frac{1}{54}\begin{bmatrix} 12 & 9 & -3 \\ -8 & 12 & 2 \\ 2 & -3 & 13 \end{bmatrix}\begin{bmatrix} 0 \\ 12 \\ -18 \end{bmatrix}$$

$$\begin{bmatrix} 1 & 0 & 0 \\ 0 & 1 & 0 \\ 0 & 0 & 1 \end{bmatrix}\begin{bmatrix} x \\ y \\ z \end{bmatrix} = \frac{1}{54}\begin{bmatrix} 162 \\ 108 \\ -270 \end{bmatrix}$$

$$\begin{bmatrix} x \\ y \\ z \end{bmatrix} = \begin{bmatrix} 3 \\ 2 \\ -5 \end{bmatrix}$$ The solution is $(3, 2, -5)$.

Write the system of linear equations represented by each matrix equation.

1. $\begin{bmatrix} 4 & 6 \\ 5 & 8 \end{bmatrix}\begin{bmatrix} x \\ y \end{bmatrix} = \begin{bmatrix} 24 \\ 40 \end{bmatrix}$

4x + 6y = 24,
5x + 8y = 40

2. $\begin{bmatrix} 5 & 4 & 6 \\ 1 & 2 & 3 \\ -7 & 9 & 8 \end{bmatrix}\begin{bmatrix} x \\ y \\ z \end{bmatrix} = \begin{bmatrix} 40 \\ 6 \\ -72 \end{bmatrix}$

5x + 4y + 6z = 40,
x + 2y + 3z = 6,
−7x + 9y + 8z = −72

Solve each matrix equation or system of equations by using inverse matrices.

3. $\begin{bmatrix} 1 & 2 \\ 3 & -1 \end{bmatrix}\begin{bmatrix} x \\ y \end{bmatrix} = \begin{bmatrix} 3 \\ -6 \end{bmatrix}$

$\left(-\dfrac{9}{7}, \dfrac{15}{7}\right)$

4. $\begin{bmatrix} -4 & -8 \\ 6 & 12 \end{bmatrix}\begin{bmatrix} x \\ y \end{bmatrix} = \begin{bmatrix} 16 \\ 12 \end{bmatrix}$

no solution

5. $4x - 2y = 22$
$\quad 6x + 4y = -2$
(3, −5)

6. $5x + 4y = 5$
$\quad 9x - 8y = 0$
$\left(\dfrac{10}{19}, \dfrac{45}{76}\right)$

Using Augmented Matrices

A system of three equations may be represented by a matrix called an **augmented matrix.** The system of equations can be solved by using the augmented matrix rather than the equations themselves. This matrix can be modified by transforming rows since each row represents an equation.

You may also use row operations on an augmented matrix. The resulting matrix yields the same solution as the original matrix.

System of Equations

$$3x + 4y - 2z = 5$$
$$2x + y - z = 1$$
$$-x - y - 2z = -9$$

Augmented Matrix

$$\begin{bmatrix} 3 & 4 & -2 & 5 \\ 2 & 1 & -1 & 1 \\ -1 & -1 & -2 & -9 \end{bmatrix}$$

Row Operations on Matrices
1. Interchange any two rows.
2. Replace any row with a nonzero multiple of that row.
3. Replace any row with the sum of that row and a multiple of another row.

Write an augmented matrix for each system of equations. Then solve each system.

1. $3x - 5y = 25$
  $2x + 4y = 24$

2. $-3x - 2y = 6$
  $9x + 7y = 36$

3. $2m + 4n = 3$
  $5m - 3n = 6$

4. $12x - y + 12z = 6$
  $2x + y - 2z = -4$
  $9x + 2y + 3z = 3$

4-7

Study Guide

Using Augmented Matrices

A system of three equations may be represented by a matrix called an **augmented matrix.** The system of equations can be solved by using the augmented matrix rather than the equations themselves. This matrix can be modified by transforming rows since each row represents an equation.

You may also use row operations on an augmented matrix. The resulting matrix yields the same solution as the original matrix.

System of Equations

$$3x + 4y - 2z = 5$$
$$2x + y - z = 1$$
$$-x - y - 2z = -9$$

Augmented Matrix

$$\begin{bmatrix} 3 & 4 & -2 & 5 \\ 2 & 1 & -1 & 1 \\ -1 & -1 & -2 & -9 \end{bmatrix}$$

Row Operations on Matrices
1. Interchange any two rows.
2. Replace any row with a nonzero multiple of that row.
3. Replace any row with the sum of that row and a multiple of another row.

Write an augmented matrix for each system of equations. Then solve each system.

1. $3x - 5y = 25$
$2x + 4y = 24$
$$\begin{bmatrix} 3 & -5 & 25 \\ 2 & 4 & 24 \end{bmatrix}, (10, 1)$$

2. $-3x - 2y = 6$
$9x + 7y = 36$
$$\begin{bmatrix} -3 & -2 & 6 \\ 9 & 7 & 36 \end{bmatrix}, (-38, 54)$$

3. $2m + 4n = 3$
$5m - 3n = 6$
$$\begin{bmatrix} 2 & 4 & 3 \\ 5 & -3 & 6 \end{bmatrix}, \left(\frac{33}{26}, \frac{3}{26}\right)$$

4. $12x - y + 12z = 6$
$2x + y - 2z = -4$
$9x + 2y + 3z = 3$
$$\begin{bmatrix} 12 & -1 & 12 & 6 \\ 2 & 1 & -2 & -4 \\ 9 & 2 & 3 & 3 \end{bmatrix},$$
$(-2, 6, 3)$

Algebra 2

4-8

Study Guide

Student Edition
Pages 235–244

Integration: Statistics
Box-and-Whisker Plots

There are several ways to measure variation in a set of data.
The simplest is called the **range.**

Definition of Range	The range of a set of data is the difference between the greatest and least values in the set.

Another way to measure a set of data is to use **quartiles.**
Quartiles are the values in a set that separate the data into four
sections, each containing 25% of the data.

The lower extreme is the least value.	The lower quartile, Q_1, is the median of the lower half of the data	The median, Q_2, separates the data into two equal halves.	The upper quartile, Q_3, is the median of the upper half of the data	The upper extreme is the greatest value.
25% of the data	25% of the data	25% of the data	25% of the data	

←   The interquartile range is the difference   →
between Q_1 and Q_2.

Another way to organize and represent data
is to use a **box-and-whisker plot.** In a box-
and-whisker plot, the quartiles and the
extreme values of a set of data are displayed
using a number line. The extreme values are
referred to as **outliers.**

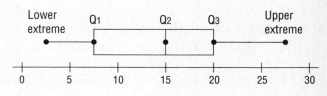

Definition of Outlier	An outlier is any value in the set of data that is at least 1.5 interquartile ranges beyond the upper or lower quartile.

1. Use the box-and-whisker plot at the right to answer each
    question.
    a. What is the range of the data?
    b. What are the upper and lower extremes?
    c. What is the median?
    d. What is the interquartile range?

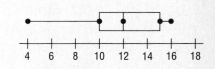

*Find the range, quartiles, interquartile range, and outliers for each
set of data. Then make a box-and-whisker plot for each set of data.*

2. {15, 16, 18, 10, 7, 30, 12}

3. {2, 0, 5, 8, 14, 20, 100, 50, 1}

4. {7, 2, 3, 5, 8, 6, 10}

Study Guide

Integration: Statistics
Box-and-Whisker Plots

There are several ways to measure variation in a set of data.
The simplest is called the **range**.

Definition of Range	The range of a set of data is the difference between the greatest and least values in the set.

Another way to measure a set of data is to use **quartiles**.
Quartiles are the values in a set that separate the data into four
sections, each containing 25% of the data.

The lower extreme is the least value.

The lower quartile, Q_1, is the median of the lower half of the data

The median, Q_2, separates the data into two equal halves.

The upper quartile, Q_3, is the median of the upper half of the data

The upper extreme is the greatest value.

| 25% of the data | 25% of the data | 25% of the data | 25% of the data |

← The interquartile range is the difference between Q_1 and Q_2. →

Another way to organize and represent data
is to use a **box-and-whisker plot.** In a box-
and-whisker plot, the quartiles and the
extreme values of a set of data are displayed
using a number line. The extreme values are
referred to as **outliers**.

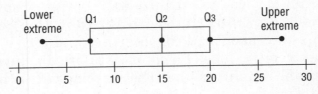

Definition of Outlier	An outlier is any value in the set of data that is at least 1.5 interquartile ranges beyond the upper or lower quartile.

1. Use the box-and-whisker plot at the right to answer each
   question.
   a. What is the range of the data? **12**
   b. What are the upper and lower extremes? **4; 16**
   c. What is the median? **12**
   d. What is the interquartile range? **5**

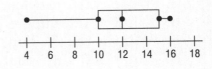

Find the range, quartiles, interquartile range, and outliers for each
set of data. Then make a box-and-whisker plot for each set of data.

2. {15, 16, 18, 10, 7, 30, 12} **range = 23; Q_1 = 10;**
   Q_3 = 18; interquartile range = 8; outliers = none

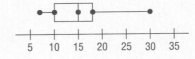

3. {2, 0, 5, 8, 14, 20, 100, 50, 1} **range = 100;**
   Q_1 = 1.5; Q_3 = 35; interquartile range = 33.5;
   outliers = 100

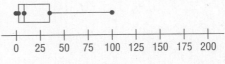

4. {7, 2, 3, 5, 8, 6, 10} **range = 8; Q_1 = 3; Q_3 = 8;**
   interquartile range = 5; outliers = none

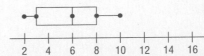

Algebra 2

NAME_____ DATE _____

Study Guide

Monomials

Refer to this table when simplifying monomials.

Property/Term	Definition	Example
Multiplying Powers	For any real number a and positive integers m and n, $a^m \cdot a^n = a^{m+n}$.	Simplify: $(x^3y^2)(x^2y^4)$ $(x^3y^2)(x^2y^4) = (xxxyy)(xxyyyy)$ $\quad = (xxxxx)(yyyyyy)$ $\quad = (x^5y^6)$
Raising a Power to a Power	For any real number a and positive integers m and n, $(a^m)^n = a^{mn}$.	Simplify: $(3^2)^3$ $(3^2)^3 = 3^2 \cdot 3^2 \cdot 3^2$ $\quad = 3^{2+2+2}$ Multiplying Powers $\quad = 3^6$
Finding a Power of a Product	For any real numbers a, b, and positive integer m, $(ab)^m = a^m b^m$.	Simplify: $(2ab)^3$ $(2ab)^3 = (2ab)(2ab)(2ab)$ $\quad = 2 \cdot 2 \cdot 2 \cdot a \cdot a \cdot a \cdot b \cdot b \cdot b$ $\quad = 8a^3b^3$
Dividing Powers	For any real number a and integers m and n, $\dfrac{a^m}{a^n} = a^{m-n}$ if $a \neq 0$.	Simplify: $\dfrac{x^7}{x^4}$ $\dfrac{x^7}{x^4} = x^{7-4}$ $\quad = x^3$
Negative Exponents	For any real number a, where $a \neq 0$, and for any integer n, $a^{-n} = \dfrac{1}{a^n}$ and $\dfrac{1}{a^{-n}} = a^n$.	Simplify: $\dfrac{x^4}{x^6}$ $\dfrac{x^4}{x^6} = \dfrac{x \cdot x \cdot x \cdot x}{x \cdot x \cdot x \cdot x \cdot x \cdot x}$ $\quad = \dfrac{1}{x \cdot x}$ or $\dfrac{1}{x^2}$ $\quad\quad \dfrac{x^4}{x^6} = x^{4-6}$ $\quad\quad = x^{-2}$

Simplify. Assume that no variable equals 0.

1. $18x^2 - 4y^2 - (-7x^2) - 6y^2$

2. $2x^3 + 3x^3 + (-6x^3)$

3. $(a^4)^5$

4. $\dfrac{1}{2}(2x^2)^3 + (5x^3)^2$

5. $\dfrac{1}{5}(-5a^2b^3)^2(abc)^2$

6. $m^7 \cdot m^8$

7. $\dfrac{8m^3n^2}{4mn^3}$

8. $\dfrac{2^3c^4t^2}{2^2c^4t^2}$

9. $\dfrac{m^{2a+3}}{m^{a-4}}$

10. $(r^2s^3)^{-4}$

11. $a^{-2}(a^4 + a^2 + a)$

12. $\dfrac{(x+7)^{-2}}{(x^2-49)^{-1}}$

Study Guide

Monomials

Refer to this table when simplifying monomials.

Property/Term	Definition	Example
Multiplying Powers	For any real number a and positive integers m and n, $a^m \cdot a^n = a^{m+n}$.	Simplify: $(x^3y^2)(x^2y^4)$ $(x^3y^2)(x^2y^4) = (xxxyy)(xxyyyy)$ $\qquad = (xxxxx)(yyyyyy)$ $\qquad = (x^5y^6)$
Raising a Power to a Power	For any real number a and positive integers m and n, $(a^m)^n = a^{mn}$.	Simplify: $(3^2)^3$ $(3^2)^3 = 3^2 \cdot 3^2 \cdot 3^2$ $\qquad = 3^{2+2+2}$ Multiplying Powers $\qquad = 3^6$
Finding a Power of a Product	For any real numbers a, b, and positive integer m, $(ab)^m = a^m b^m$.	Simplify: $(2ab)^3$ $(2ab)^3 = (2ab)(2ab)(2ab)$ $\qquad = 2 \cdot 2 \cdot 2 \cdot a \cdot a \cdot a \cdot b \cdot b \cdot b$ $\qquad = 8a^3b^3$
Dividing Powers	For any real number a and integers m and n, $\dfrac{a^m}{a^n} = a^{m-n}$ if $a \neq 0$.	Simplify: $\dfrac{x^7}{x^4}$ $\dfrac{x^7}{x^4} = x^{7-4}$ $\qquad = x^3$
Negative Exponents	For any real number a, where $a \neq 0$, and for any integer n, $a^{-n} = \dfrac{1}{a^n}$ and $\dfrac{1}{a^{-n}} = a^n$.	Simplify: $\dfrac{x^4}{x^6}$ $\dfrac{x^4}{x^6} = \dfrac{x \cdot x \cdot x \cdot x}{x \cdot x \cdot x \cdot x \cdot x \cdot x}$ $\qquad \dfrac{x^4}{x^6} = x^{4-6}$ $\qquad = \dfrac{1}{x \cdot x}$ or $\dfrac{1}{x^2}$ $\qquad = x^{-2}$

Simplify. Assume that no variable equals 0.

1. $18x^2 - 4y^2 - (-7x^2) - 6y^2$
   $25x^2 - 10y^2$

2. $2x^3 + 3x^3 + (-6x^3)$
   $-x^3$

3. $(a^4)^5$
   a^{20}

4. $\dfrac{1}{2}(2x^2)^3 + (5x^3)^2$
   $29x^6$

5. $\dfrac{1}{5}(-5a^2b^3)^2(abc)^2$
   $5a^6b^8c^2$

6. $m^7 \cdot m^8$
   m^{15}

7. $\dfrac{8m^3n^2}{4mn^3}$
   $\dfrac{2m^2}{n}$

8. $\dfrac{2^3c^4t^2}{2^2c^4t^2}$
   2

9. $\dfrac{m^{2a+3}}{m^{a-4}}$
   m^{a+7}

10. $(r^2s^3)^{-4}$
    $\dfrac{1}{r^8s^{12}}$

11. $a^{-2}(a^4 + a^2 + a)$
    $a^2 + 1 + \dfrac{1}{a}$

12. $\dfrac{(x+7)^{-2}}{(x^2-49)^{-1}}$
    $\dfrac{x-7}{x+7}$

Study Guide

Polynomials

A polynomial is either a monomial or the sum of monomials. Each monomial in the polynomial is called a **term** of the polynomial. The **degree of a polynomial** is the degree of the monomial of the greatest degree. You can simplify polynomials with like terms by using the **distributive property,** by **adding or subtracting like terms,** or by using the **FOIL method.**

Example: Simplify $3x^2y + 2xy^3 + 6y + 5xy^3 - 8x^2y$.
First, group like terms.
$$3x^2y + 2xy^3 + 6y + 5xy^3 - 8x^2y = (3x^2y - 8x^2y) + (2xy^3 + 5xy^3) + 6y$$
$$= -5x^2y + 7xy^3 + 6y$$

Example: Find $3x(4xy^3 - 7x^2y - 3y)$.
Use the distributive property.
$$3x(4xy^3 - 7x^2y - 3y) = 3x \cdot 4xy^3 - 3x \cdot 7x^2y - 3x \cdot 3y$$
$$= 12x^2y^3 - 21x^3y - 9xy$$

FOIL Method for Multiplying Binomials
The product of two binomials is the sum of the products of **F** the first terms **O** the outer terms **I** the inner terms **L** the last terms.

Example: Find $(2x + 3)(x - 5)$.

$$\begin{array}{ccccccc} & F & & O & & I & & L \\ (2x + 3)(x - 5) = & 2x \cdot x & + & 2x \cdot (-5) & + & 3 \cdot x & + & 3 \cdot (-5) \\ = & 2x^2 & - & 10x & + & 3x & - & 15 \\ = & 2x^2 & - & 7x & & & - & 15 \end{array}$$

Simplify.

1. $(-4m^2 - 6m) - (6m + 4m^2)$ **2.** $3(2a + 5c) - 2(4a - 6c)$ **3.** $5a(7a^2b + 6ac^2 - 8ac)$

4. $15x^2y^3 + 8x^4y + 7x^2y^3$ **5.** $2wy - 2w^2y - 2yw$ **6.** $2x(x + 5) - x^2(3 - x)$

7. $(3t^2 - 8)(t^2 + 5)$ **8.** $(2r + 7)^2$ **9.** $2(a - 6)(2a + 7)$

10. $(c + 7)(c - 3)$ **11.** $(5a + 7)(5a - 7)$ **12.** $(2n^2 - 3)(n^2 + 5n - 1)$

Polynomials

A polynomial is either a monomial or the sum of monomials. Each monomial in the polynomial is called a **term** of the polynomial. The **degree of a polynomial** is the degree of the monomial of the greatest degree. You can simplify polynomials with like terms by using the **distributive property,** by **adding or subtracting like terms,** or by using the **FOIL method.**

Example: Simplify $3x^2y + 2xy^3 + 6y + 5xy^3 - 8x^2y$.
First, group like terms.
$$3x^2y + 2xy^3 + 6y + 5xy^3 - 8x^2y = (3x^2y - 8x^2y) + (2xy^3 + 5xy^3) + 6y$$
$$= -5x^2y + 7xy^3 + 6y$$

Example: Find $3x(4xy^3 - 7x^2y - 3y)$.
Use the distributive property.
$$3x(4xy^3 - 7x^2y - 3y) = 3x \cdot 4xy^3 - 3x \cdot 7x^2y - 3x \cdot 3y$$
$$= 12x^2y^3 - 21x^3y - 9xy$$

FOIL Method for Multiplying Binomials
The product of two binomials is the sum of the products of
F the first terms
O the outer terms
I the inner terms
L the last terms.

Example: Find $(2x + 3)(x - 5)$.

$$\begin{array}{ccccc} & \textbf{F} & \textbf{O} & \textbf{I} & \textbf{L} \\ (2x + 3)(x - 5) = & 2x \cdot x + & 2x \cdot (-5) + & 3 \cdot x + & 3 \cdot (-5) \\ = & 2x^2 - & 10x + & 3x - & 15 \\ = & 2x^2 - & 7x & - & 15 \end{array}$$

Simplify.

1. $(-4m^2 - 6m) - (6m + 4m^2)$
   $-8m^2 - 12m$

2. $3(2a + 5c) - 2(4a - 6c)$
   $-2a + 27c$

3. $5a(7a^2b + 6ac^2 - 8ac)$
   $35a^3b + 30a^2c^2 - 40a^2c$

4. $15x^2y^3 + 8x^4y + 7x^2y^3$
   $22x^2y^3 + 8x^4y$

5. $2wy - 2w^2y - 2yw$
   $-2w^2y$

6. $2x(x + 5) - x^2(3 - x)$
   $x^3 - x^2 + 10x$

7. $(3t^2 - 8)(t^2 + 5)$
   $3t^4 + 7t^2 - 40$

8. $(2r + 7)^2$
   $4r^2 + 28r + 49$

9. $2(a - 6)(2a + 7)$
   $4a^2 - 10a - 84$

10. $(c + 7)(c - 3)$
   $c^2 + 4c - 21$

11. $(5a + 7)(5a - 7)$
   $25a^2 - 49$

12. $(2n^2 - 3)(n^2 + 5n - 1)$
   $2n^4 + 10n^3 - 5n^2 - 15n + 3$

5-3

Study Guide

Dividing Polynomials

Properties of exponents are used to divide a monomial by a monomial and a polynomial by a monomial.

Example: $\dfrac{24x^4y - 12x^2y^2}{12x^2y} = \dfrac{24x^4y}{12x^2y} - \dfrac{12x^2y^2}{12x^2y}$

$$= \dfrac{24}{12}x^{4-2}y^{1-1} - \dfrac{12}{12}x^{2-2}y^{2-1}$$

$$= 2x^2 - y$$

Dividing a polynomial by a polynomial is similar to long division.

Example: $(x^2 + 3x - 18) \div (x - 3) \rightarrow$

$$\begin{array}{r} x + 6 \\ x - 3 \overline{)x^2 + 3x - 18} \\ \underline{x^2 - 3x} \\ 6x - 18 \\ \underline{6x - 18} \\ 0 \end{array}$$

Simplify.

1. $(x^3 - 1)(x^2 - 1)^{-1}$

2. $(x^3 - 1) \div (x - 1)^{-1}$

3. $\dfrac{18a^3 + 30a^2}{3a}$

4. $\dfrac{12p^3t^2r - 21p^2qtr^4 - 9p^3tr}{3p^2tr}$

5. $\dfrac{c^2 + 4c - 21}{c + 7}$

6. $\dfrac{24mn^6 - 40m^2n^3}{4m^2n^3}$

7. $(2x^2 - 5x - 3) \div (x - 3)$

8. $(m^2 - 3m - 7) \div (m + 2)$

9. $(p^3 - 6) \div (p - 1)$

10. $(t^3 - 6t^2 + 1) \div (t + 2)$

11. $(x^5 - 1) \div (x - 1)$

12. $(p^3 - p^2 - p - 1) \div (p + 1)$

32

5-3

Study Guide

Dividing Polynomials

Properties of exponents are used to divide a monomial by a monomial and a polynomial by a monomial.

Example:
$$\frac{24x^4y - 12x^2y^2}{12x^2y} = \frac{24x^4y}{12x^2y} - \frac{12x^2y^2}{12x^2y}$$
$$= \frac{24}{12}x^{4-2}y^{1-1} - \frac{12}{12}x^{2-2}y^{2-1}$$
$$= 2x^2 - y$$

Dividing a polynomial by a polynomial is similar to long division.

Example: $(x^2 + 3x - 18) \div (x - 3) \rightarrow$
$$\begin{array}{r} x + 6 \\ x - 3 \overline{\smash{\big)}\ x^2 + 3x - 18} \\ \underline{x^2 - 3x} \\ 6x - 18 \\ \underline{6x - 18} \\ 0 \end{array}$$

Simplify.

1. $(x^3 - 1)(x^2 - 1)^{-1}$

$x + \dfrac{1}{x + 1}$

2. $(x^3 - 1) \div (x - 1)^{-1}$

$x^2 + x + 1$

3. $\dfrac{18a^3 + 30a^2}{3a}$

$2a(3a + 5)$

4. $\dfrac{12p^3t^2r - 21p^2qtr^4 - 9p^3tr}{3p^2tr}$

$4pt - 7qr^3 - 3p$

5. $\dfrac{c^2 + 4c - 21}{c + 7}$

$c - 3$

6. $\dfrac{24mn^6 - 40m^2n^3}{4m^2n^3}$

$\dfrac{6n^3}{m} - 10$

7. $(2x^2 - 5x - 3) \div (x - 3)$

$2x + 1$

8. $(m^2 - 3m - 7) \div (m + 2)$

$m - 5 + \dfrac{3}{m + 2}$

9. $(p^3 - 6) \div (p - 1)$

$p^2 + p + 1 - \dfrac{5}{p - 1}$

10. $(t^3 - 6t^2 + 1) \div (t + 2)$

$t^2 - 8t + 16 - \dfrac{31}{t + 2}$

11. $(x^5 - 1) \div (x - 1)$

$x^4 + x^3 + x^2 + x + 1$

12. $(p^3 - p^2 - p - 1) \div (p + 1)$

$p^2 - 2p + 1 - \dfrac{2}{p + 1}$

5-4

Study Guide

Factoring

When factoring polynomials, there are general guidelines to follow.

Guidelines for Factoring

1. Check for the greatest common factor (GCF).
2. Check for special products. Remember, for any numbers a and b:
   a. Difference of two squares: $a^2 - b^2 = (a - b)(a + b)$
   b. Sum of two cubes: $a^3 + b^3 = (a + b)(a^2 - ab + b^2)$
   c. Difference of two cubes: $a^3 - b^3 = (a - b)(a^2 + ab + b^2)$
   d. Perfect square trinomials: $a^2 + 2ab + b^2 = (a + b)^2$ and $a^2 - 2ab + b^2 = (a - b)^2$
   e. General Trinomials: $acx^2 + (ad + bc)x + bd = (ax + b)(cx + d)$ FOIL method
3. If there are four or more terms, try grouping.

Example of Greatest Common Factor

$16x^3 - 32x^2y + 8xy^2 = 8x(2x^2 - 4xy + y^2)$

Examples of Grouping Method

a. $xm + xn + ym + yn =$
   $x(m + n) + y(m + n) = (x + y)(m + n)$

b. $x^4 - 12x^3y + 24x^2y^2 - 8xy^3 =$
   $x(x - 2y)(x^2 - 10xy + 4y^2)$

Examples of Special Products

a. $2m^2 - 98 = 2(m^2 - 49) =$
   $2(m - 7)(m + 7)$

b. $125c^6 + 1 = (5c^2 + 1)(25c^4 - 5c^2 + 1)$

c. $m^{12}n^3 - 27 =$
   $(m^4n - 3)(m^8n^2 + 3m^4n + 9)$

d. $121 + 22m + m^2 = (11 + m)^2$

Example of FOIL Method

$x^2 - 7x + 10$

Factors of 10	Sum of Factors
1, 10	11
−1, −10	−11
2, 5	7
−2, −5	−7

The two numbers are −2 and −5.
$x^2 - 7x + 10 = (x - 5)(x - 2)$

Factor.

1. $x^4 - 1$

2. $35x^3y^4 - 60x^4y$

3. $2r^3 + 250$

4. $100m^8 - 9$

5. $3z^2 + 16z - 35$

6. $162x^6 - 98$

7. $4m^6 - 12m^3 + 9$

8. $x^3 - 343$

9. $ac^2 - a^5c$

10. $2m^5 - 12m^3 + 18m$

11. $c^4 + c^3 - c^2 - c$

12. $x^6 - 1$

NAME_____ DATE _____

Study Guide

Factoring

When factoring polynomials, there are general guidelines to follow.

Guidelines for Factoring
1. Check for the greatest common factor (GCF).
2. Check for special products. Remember, for any numbers a and b:
a. Difference of two squares: $a^2 - b^2 = (a - b)(a + b)$
b. Sum of two cubes: $a^3 + b^3 = (a + b)(a^2 - ab + b^2)$
c. Difference of two cubes: $a^3 - b^3 = (a - b)(a^2 + ab + b^2)$
d. Perfect square trinomials: $a^2 + 2ab + b^2 = (a + b)^2$ and $a^2 - 2ab + b^2 = (a - b)^2$
e. General Trinomials: $acx^2 + (ad + bc)x + bd = (ax + b)(cx + d)$ FOIL method
3. If there are four or more terms, try grouping.

Example of Greatest Common Factor

$16x^3 - 32x^2y + 8xy^2 = 8x(2x^2 - 4xy + y^2)$

Examples of Grouping Method

a. $xm + xn + ym + yn =$
$x(m + n) + y(m + n) = (x + y)(m + n)$

b. $x^4 - 12x^3y + 24x^2y^2 - 8xy^3 =$
$x(x - 2y)(x^2 - 10xy + 4y^2)$

Examples of Special Products

a. $2m^2 - 98 = 2(m^2 - 49) =$
$2(m - 7)(m + 7)$

b. $125c^6 + 1 = (5c^2 + 1)(25c^4 - 5c^2 + 1)$

c. $m^{12}n^3 - 27 =$
$(m^4n - 3)(m^8n^2 + 3m^4n + 9)$

d. $121 + 22m + m^2 = (11 + m)^2$

Example of FOIL Method

$x^2 - 7x + 10$

Factors of 10	Sum of Factors
1, 10	11
−1, −10	−11
2, 5	7
−2, −5	−7

The two numbers are −2 and −5.
$x^2 - 7x + 10 = (x - 5)(x - 2)$

Factor.

1. $x^4 - 1$
$(x^2 + 1)(x + 1)(x - 1)$

2. $35x^3y^4 - 60x^4y$
$5x^3y(7y^3 - 12x)$

3. $2r^3 + 250$
$2(r + 5)(r^2 - 5r + 25)$

4. $100m^8 - 9$
$(10m^4 - 3)(10m^4 + 3)$

5. $3z^2 + 16z - 35$
$(z + 7)(3z - 5)$

6. $162x^6 - 98$
$2(9x^3 + 7)(9x^3 - 7)$

7. $4m^6 - 12m^3 + 9$
$(2m^3 - 3)^2$

8. $x^3 - 343$
$(x - 7)(x^2 + 7x + 49)$

9. $ac^2 - a^5c$
$ac(c - a^4)$

10. $2m^5 - 12m^3 + 18m$
$2m(m^2 - 3)^2$

11. $c^4 + c^3 - c^2 - c$
$c(c + 1)^2(c - 1)$

12. $x^6 - 1$
$(x + 1)(x - 1)(x^2 - x + 1)$
$(x^2 + x + 1)$

NAME_____ DATE _____

Study Guide

Roots of Real Numbers

The inverse of raising a number to the nth power is finding the nth root of that number. The inverse of squaring is finding the square root.

Term	Definition	Examples
Square Root	For any real numbers a and b, if $a^2 = b$ then a is a square root of b.	Find $\sqrt{36}$ $6 \cdot 6 = 36$ 6 is a square root of 36. $(-6)(-6) = 36$ -6 is a square root of 36. $\sqrt{36} =$ principal square root of 36, or 6
nth Root	For any real numbers a and b and any positive integer n, if $a^n = b$, then a is an nth root of b.	Find $\sqrt{64b^2}$. $\sqrt{64b^2} = 8\lvert b \rvert$ Find $\sqrt[3]{27x^6}$. $\sqrt[3]{27x^6} = \sqrt[3]{(3x^2)^3} = 3x^2$
Property of nth root	For any real number a and any integer $n > 1$, **1.** if n is even, then $\sqrt[n]{a^n} = \lvert a \rvert$ and **2.** if n is odd, then $\sqrt[n]{a^n} = a$.	Find $\sqrt[6]{c^6}$. Since 6 is even, $\sqrt[6]{c^6}$ is $\lvert c \rvert$.

Simplify.

1. $\sqrt{169}$

2. $\sqrt{9x^{12}}$

3. $\sqrt[3]{27c^9y^{15}}$

4. $\sqrt[3]{-8x^2y}$

5. $\sqrt[6]{64c^6a^5}$

6. $\sqrt{460x^3y^4}$

7. $\sqrt{625x^6y^2}$

8. $\sqrt[3]{(3c + 2)^3}$

9. $\sqrt{(2a - 1)^2}$

Use a calculator to find each value to three places. Check your approximation by using the power key.

10. $\sqrt{122}$

11. $-\sqrt[3]{237}$

12. $\sqrt[4]{5.116}$

Study Guide

Roots of Real Numbers

The inverse of raising a number to the *n*th power is finding the *n*th root of that number. The inverse of squaring is finding the square root.

Term	Definition	Examples
Square Root	For any real numbers a and b, if $a^2 = b$ then a is a square root of b.	Find $\sqrt{36}$ $6 \cdot 6 = 36$ 6 is a square root of 36. $(-6)(-6) = 36$ -6 is a square root of 36. $\sqrt{36}$ = principal square root of 36, or 6
*n*th Root	For any real numbers a and b and any positive integer n, if $a^n = b$, then a is an *n*th root of b.	Find $\sqrt{64b^2}$. $\sqrt{64b^2} = 8\lvert b\rvert$ Find $\sqrt[3]{27x^6}$. $\sqrt[3]{27x^6} = \sqrt[3]{(3x^2)^3} = 3x^2$
Property of *n*th root	For any real number a and any integer $n > 1$, **1.** if n is even, then $\sqrt[n]{a^n} = \lvert a\rvert$ and **2.** if n is odd, then $\sqrt[n]{a^n} = a$.	Find $\sqrt[6]{c^6}$. Since 6 is even, $\sqrt[6]{c^6}$ is $\lvert c\rvert$.

Simplify.

1. $\sqrt{169}$
   13

2. $\sqrt{9x^{12}}$
   $3x^6$

3. $\sqrt[3]{27c^9y^{15}}$
   $3c^3y^5$

4. $\sqrt[3]{-8x^2y}$
   $-2\sqrt[3]{x^2y}$

5. $\sqrt[6]{64c^6a^5}$
   $2\lvert c\rvert\sqrt[6]{a^5}$

6. $\sqrt{460x^3y^4}$
   $2y^2\lvert x\rvert\sqrt{115x}$

7. $\sqrt{625x^6y^2}$
   $25\lvert x^3y\rvert$

8. $\sqrt[3]{(3c + 2)^3}$
   $3c + 2$

9. $\sqrt{(2a - 1)^2}$
   $\lvert 2a - 1\rvert$

Use a calculator to find each value to three places. Check your approximation by using the power key.

10. $\sqrt{122}$
   11.045

11. $-\sqrt[3]{237}$
   −6.188

12. $\sqrt[4]{5.116}$
   1.504

5-6

Study Guide

Radical Expressions

Radicals are added, subtracted, or multiplied the same way monomials are added, subtracted, or multiplied.

Use the following definitions and properties when multiplying and dividing radicals.

Term	Definition/Property	Example
Product Property of Radicals	For any real numbers a and b and any integer n, $n > 1$, **1.** if n is even, then $\sqrt[n]{ab} = \sqrt[n]{a} \cdot \sqrt[n]{b}$ when a and b are both nonnegative and **2.** if n is odd, then $\sqrt[n]{ab} = \sqrt[n]{a} \cdot \sqrt[n]{b}$.	Simplify $\sqrt{63}$. $\sqrt{63} = \sqrt{9 \cdot 7}$ $\phantom{\sqrt{63}} = \sqrt{9} \cdot \sqrt{7}$ $\phantom{\sqrt{63}} = 3\sqrt{7}$
Quotient Property of Radicals	For any real numbers a and b, $b \neq 0$, and any integer n, $n > 1$, $\sqrt[n]{\dfrac{a}{b}} = \dfrac{\sqrt[n]{a}}{\sqrt[n]{b}}$ if all roots are defined.	Simplify $\sqrt[3]{\dfrac{3}{8}}$. $\sqrt[3]{\dfrac{3}{8}} = \dfrac{\sqrt[3]{3}}{\sqrt[3]{8}}$ $\phantom{\sqrt[3]{\dfrac{3}{8}}} = \dfrac{\sqrt[3]{3}}{2}$

Example: Simplify $4\sqrt{3} + 5\sqrt{12} - 7\sqrt{27}$.

$$
\begin{aligned}
4\sqrt{3} + 5\sqrt{12} - 7\sqrt{27} &= 4\sqrt{3} + 5\sqrt{2^2 \cdot 3} \\
&\quad - 7\sqrt{3^2 \cdot 3} \\
&= 4\sqrt{3} + 5\sqrt{2^2}\sqrt{3} \\
&\quad - 7\sqrt{3^2}\sqrt{3} \\
&= 4\sqrt{3} + 5 \cdot 2\sqrt{3} \\
&\quad - 7 \cdot 3\sqrt{3} \\
&= 4\sqrt{3} + 10\sqrt{3} \\
&\quad - 21\sqrt{3} \\
&= -7\sqrt{3}
\end{aligned}
$$

Example: Simplify $\dfrac{1 - \sqrt{2}}{6 + 5\sqrt{2}}$.

$$
\begin{aligned}
\frac{1 - \sqrt{2}}{6 + 5\sqrt{2}} &= \frac{1 - \sqrt{2}}{6 + 5\sqrt{2}} \cdot \frac{6 - 5\sqrt{2}}{6 - 5\sqrt{2}} \\
&= \frac{6 - 5\sqrt{2} - 6\sqrt{2} + 5\sqrt{2^2}}{36 - (5\sqrt{2})^2} \\
&= \frac{6 - 5\sqrt{2} - 6\sqrt{2} + 10}{36 - 25(2)} \\
&= \frac{-16 + 11\sqrt{2}}{14}
\end{aligned}
$$

Simplify.

1. $5\sqrt{54}$

2. $\sqrt[3]{24}$

3. $3\sqrt{2} + \sqrt{50} - 4\sqrt{8}$

4. $\sqrt[3]{(-y)^5}$

5. $\sqrt[3]{-27x^2}$

6. $\sqrt[3]{2}(\sqrt[3]{4} + \sqrt[3]{12})$

7. $\dfrac{(5\sqrt{48} + \sqrt{75})}{5\sqrt{3}}$

8. $\sqrt[3]{81}\sqrt[3]{24}$

9. $(4\sqrt{2} - 3\sqrt{5})(2\sqrt{20} + 5)$

5-6

Study Guide

Radical Expressions

Radicals are added, subtracted, or multiplied the same way monomials are added, subtracted, or multiplied.

Use the following definitions and properties when multiplying and dividing radicals.

Term	Definition/Property	Example
Product Property of Radicals	For any real numbers a and b and any integer n, $n > 1$, 1. if n is even, then $\sqrt[n]{ab} = \sqrt[n]{a} \cdot \sqrt[n]{b}$ when a and b are both nonnegative and 2. if n is odd, then $\sqrt[n]{ab} = \sqrt[n]{a} \cdot \sqrt[n]{b}$.	Simplify $\sqrt{63}$. $\sqrt{63} = \sqrt{9 \cdot 7}$ $\quad\ = \sqrt{9} \cdot \sqrt{7}$ $\quad\ = 3\sqrt{7}$
Quotient Property of Radicals	For any real numbers a and b, $b \neq 0$, and any integer n, $n > 1$, $\sqrt[n]{\dfrac{a}{b}} = \dfrac{\sqrt[n]{a}}{\sqrt[n]{b}}$ if all roots are defined.	Simplify $\sqrt[3]{\dfrac{3}{8}}$. $\sqrt[3]{\dfrac{3}{8}} = \dfrac{\sqrt[3]{3}}{\sqrt[3]{8}}$ $\quad\ = \dfrac{\sqrt[3]{3}}{2}$

Example: Simplify $4\sqrt{3} + 5\sqrt{12} - 7\sqrt{27}$.

$$
\begin{aligned}
4\sqrt{3} + 5\sqrt{12} - 7\sqrt{27} &= 4\sqrt{3} + 5\sqrt{2^2 \cdot 3} \\
&\quad - 7\sqrt{3^2 \cdot 3} \\
&= 4\sqrt{3} + 5\sqrt{2^2}\sqrt{3} \\
&\quad - 7\sqrt{3^2}\sqrt{3} \\
&= 4\sqrt{3} + 5 \cdot 2\sqrt{3} \\
&\quad - 7 \cdot 3\sqrt{3} \\
&= 4\sqrt{3} + 10\sqrt{3} \\
&\quad - 21\sqrt{3} \\
&= -7\sqrt{3}
\end{aligned}
$$

Example: Simplify $\dfrac{1 - \sqrt{2}}{6 + 5\sqrt{2}}$.

$$
\begin{aligned}
\frac{1 - \sqrt{2}}{6 + 5\sqrt{2}} &= \frac{1 - \sqrt{2}}{6 + 5\sqrt{2}} \cdot \frac{6 - 5\sqrt{2}}{6 - 5\sqrt{2}} \\[2mm]
&= \frac{6 - 5\sqrt{2} - 6\sqrt{2} + 5\sqrt{2^2}}{36 - (5\sqrt{2})^2} \\[2mm]
&= \frac{6 - 5\sqrt{2} - 6\sqrt{2} + 10}{36 - 25(2)} \\[2mm]
&= \frac{-16 + 11\sqrt{2}}{14}
\end{aligned}
$$

Simplify.

1. $5\sqrt{54}$

   $15\sqrt{6}$

2. $\sqrt[3]{24}$

   $2\sqrt[3]{3}$

3. $3\sqrt{2} + \sqrt{50} - 4\sqrt{8}$

   0

4. $\sqrt[3]{(-y)^5}$

   $-y\sqrt[3]{y^2}$

5. $\sqrt[3]{-27x^2}$

   $-3\sqrt[3]{x^2}$

6. $\sqrt[3]{2}(\sqrt[3]{4} + \sqrt[3]{12})$

   $2 + 2\sqrt[3]{3}$

7. $\dfrac{(5\sqrt{48} + \sqrt{75})}{5\sqrt{3}}$

   5

8. $\sqrt[3]{81}\,\sqrt[3]{24}$

   $6\sqrt[3]{9}$

9. $(4\sqrt{2} - 3\sqrt{5})(2\sqrt{20} + 5)$

   $40\sqrt{2} - 30\sqrt{5}$

5-7

Study Guide

Rational Exponents

Definition of Rational Exponents	
Definition	**Example**
For any real number b and for any integer n, $n > 1$, $$b^{\frac{1}{n}} = \sqrt[n]{b}$$ except when $b < 0$ and n is even.	Evaluate $27^{\frac{1}{3}}$. $27^{\frac{1}{3}} = \sqrt[3]{27}$ or $27^{\frac{1}{3}} = (3^3)^{\frac{1}{3}}$ $\quad = \sqrt[3]{3^3} \qquad\qquad = 3^1$ $\quad = 3 \qquad\qquad\quad\ = 3$
For any nonzero real number b and any integers m and n, $n > 1$, $b^{\frac{m}{n}} = \sqrt[n]{b^m} = (\sqrt[n]{b})^m$ except when $b < 0$ and n is even.	Evaluate $8^{\frac{1}{3}} \cdot 8^{\frac{4}{3}}$. $8^{\frac{1}{3}} \cdot 8^{\frac{4}{3}} = 8^{\frac{5}{3}}$ $8^{\frac{5}{3}} = (\sqrt[3]{8})^5$ or $8^{\frac{5}{3}} = (2^3)^{\frac{5}{3}}$ $\quad = (2)^5 \qquad\qquad = 2^5$ $\quad = 32 \qquad\qquad\ = 32$

A rational expression that contains a fractional exponent in the denominator must also be rationalized. When you simplify an expression, be sure your answer meets all of the given conditions.

Conditions for a Simplified Expression
1. It has no negative exponents.   2. It has no fractional exponents in the denominator.   3. It is not a complex fraction.   4. The index of any remaining radical is as small as possible.

Evaluate.

1. $27^{\frac{2}{3}}$

2. $\dfrac{5^{-\frac{1}{2}}}{2\sqrt{5}}$

3. $(0.0004)^{\frac{1}{2}}$

Simplify.

4. $m^{\frac{3}{4}}n^{\frac{5}{4}}$

5. $a^{\frac{1}{3}}b^{\frac{1}{6}}c^{\frac{5}{12}}$

6. $\sqrt{2} \cdot \sqrt[3]{2^4}$

7. $(4x)^{\frac{3}{7}}y^{\frac{2}{7}}$

8. $8^{\frac{1}{2}}32^{\frac{1}{2}}2^{\frac{1}{2}}$

9. $6^{\frac{2}{5}}y^{\frac{8}{5}}$

10. $(ab^{-2})^{-\frac{1}{3}}$

11. $(8x^6y^{-9})^{-\frac{2}{3}}$

12. $(m^{-\frac{2}{3}}n^{-\frac{1}{2}})^{-\frac{6}{5}}$

13. $\left(\dfrac{2x^{-2}}{x^{-\frac{3}{2}}}\right)^{-2}$

14. $\dfrac{1}{m^{\frac{1}{2}} - 1}$

15. $\dfrac{c^{\frac{2}{3}} - c}{c^{-\frac{1}{2}}}$

Study Guide

Rational Exponents

Definition of Rational Exponents	
Definition	**Example**
For any real number b and for any integer n, $n > 1$, $$b^{\frac{1}{n}} = \sqrt[n]{b}$$ except when $b < 0$ and n is even.	Evaluate $27^{\frac{1}{3}}$. $27^{\frac{1}{3}} = \sqrt[3]{27}$ or $27^{\frac{1}{3}} = (3^3)^{\frac{1}{3}}$ $\quad\quad = \sqrt[3]{3^3} \quad\quad\quad = 3^1$ $\quad\quad = 3 \quad\quad\quad\quad\quad = 3$
For any nonzero real number b and any integers m and n, $n > 1$, $b^{\frac{m}{n}} = \sqrt[n]{b^m} = (\sqrt[n]{b})^m$ except when $b < 0$ and n is even.	Evaluate $8^{\frac{1}{3}} \cdot 8^{\frac{4}{3}}$. $8^{\frac{1}{3}} \cdot 8^{\frac{4}{3}} = 8^{\frac{5}{3}}$ $8^{\frac{5}{3}} = (\sqrt[3]{8})^5$ or $8^{\frac{5}{3}} = (2^3)^{\frac{5}{3}}$ $\quad\quad = (2)^5 \quad\quad\quad = 2^5$ $\quad\quad = 32 \quad\quad\quad\quad = 32$

A rational expression that contains a fractional exponent in the denominator must also be rationalized. When you simplify an expression, be sure your answer meets all of the given conditions.

Conditions for a Simplified Expression
1. It has no negative exponents.
2. It has no fractional exponents in the denominator.
3. It is not a complex fraction.
4. The index of any remaining radical is as small as possible.

Evaluate.

1. $27^{\frac{2}{3}}$

   9

2. $\dfrac{5^{-\frac{1}{2}}}{2\sqrt{5}}$

   $\dfrac{1}{10}$

3. $(0.0004)^{\frac{1}{2}}$

   0.02

Simplify.

4. $m^{\frac{3}{4}}n^{\frac{5}{4}}$

   $n\sqrt[4]{m^3 n}$

5. $a^{\frac{1}{3}}b^{\frac{1}{6}}c^{\frac{5}{12}}$

   $\sqrt[12]{a^4 b^2 c^5}$

6. $\sqrt{2} \cdot \sqrt[3]{2^4}$

   $2\sqrt[6]{32}$

7. $(4x)^{\frac{3}{7}}y^{\frac{2}{7}}$

   $\sqrt[7]{64x^3 y^2}$

8. $8^{\frac{1}{2}}32^{\frac{1}{2}}2^{\frac{1}{2}}$

   $16\sqrt{2}$

9. $6^{\frac{2}{5}}y^{\frac{8}{5}}$

   $y\sqrt[5]{36y^3}$

10. $(ab^{-2})^{-\frac{1}{3}}$

   $\dfrac{a^{\frac{2}{3}}b^{\frac{2}{3}}}{a}$

11. $(8x^6 y^{-9})^{-\frac{2}{3}}$

   $\dfrac{y^6}{4x^4}$

12. $(m^{-\frac{2}{3}}n^{-\frac{1}{2}})^{-\frac{6}{5}}$

   $m^{\frac{4}{5}}n^{\frac{3}{5}}$

13. $\left(\dfrac{2x^{-2}}{x^{-\frac{3}{2}}}\right)^{-2}$

   $\dfrac{x}{4}$

14. $\dfrac{1}{m^{\frac{1}{2}} - 1}$

   $\dfrac{m^{\frac{1}{2}} + 1}{m - 1}$

15. $\dfrac{c^{\frac{2}{3}} - c}{c^{-\frac{1}{2}}}$

   $c^{\frac{7}{6}} - c^{\frac{3}{2}}$

5-8

Study Guide

Solving Equations Containing Radicals

The properties of radicals can be used to solve equations. Equations that contain variables in the radicand of a radical are called **radical equations.** Squaring each side of the equation may produce results that do not satisfy the original equation. All possible solutions must be checked.

Examples:

Solve $7 + \sqrt{a - 3} = 1$.

$$7 + \sqrt{a - 3} = 1$$
$$\sqrt{a - 3} = -6 \qquad \textbf{Isolate the radical.}$$
$$(\sqrt{a - 3})^2 = (-6)^2 \qquad \textbf{Square each side.}$$
$$a - 3 = 36$$
$$a = 39$$

The equation has no solutions.

Check: $7 + \sqrt{a - 3} = 1$

$$7 + \sqrt{39 - 3} \stackrel{?}{=} 1$$
$$7 + \sqrt{36} \stackrel{?}{=} 1$$
$$13 \neq 1$$

The answer does not check.

Solve $\sqrt{2y - 3} - \sqrt{2y + 3} = -1$.

$$\sqrt{2y - 3} - \sqrt{2y + 3} = -1$$
$$\sqrt{2y - 3} = \sqrt{2y + 3} - 1$$
$$2y - 3 = 2y + 3 - 2\sqrt{2y + 3} + 1$$
$$-7 = -2\sqrt{2y + 3}$$
$$\frac{7}{2} = \sqrt{2y + 3}$$
$$\frac{49}{4} = 2y + 3$$
$$\frac{37}{4} = 2y$$
$$y = \frac{37}{8}$$

The solution is $\frac{37}{8}$ or $4\frac{5}{8}$.

Check: $\sqrt{2y - 3} - \sqrt{2y + 3} = -1$

$$\sqrt{2\left(\frac{37}{8}\right) - 3} - \sqrt{2\left(\frac{37}{8}\right) + 3} \stackrel{?}{=} -1$$
$$\sqrt{\frac{25}{4}} - \sqrt{\frac{49}{4}} \stackrel{?}{=} -1$$
$$\frac{5}{2} - \frac{7}{2} \stackrel{?}{=} -1$$
$$-1 = -1$$

Solve each equation.

1. $3 + 2x\sqrt{3} = 5$

2. $\sqrt{12 - x} = \sqrt{x + 6}$

3. $2\sqrt{3x + 4} + 1 = 15$

4. $8 + \sqrt{x + 1} = 2$

5. $\sqrt{5 - x} - 4 = 6$

6. $\sqrt{21} - \sqrt{5x - 4} = 0$

7. $\sqrt{2x} = \sqrt{\frac{x}{4}}$

8. $\sqrt{x^2 + 7x} = \sqrt{7x - 9}$

9. $\sqrt{x - 8} + \sqrt{x + 3} = 1$

37

Study Guide

Solving Equations Containing Radicals

The properties of radicals can be used to solve equations. Equations that contain variables in the radicand of a radical are called **radical equations.** Squaring each side of the equation may produce results that do not satisfy the original equation. All possible solutions must be checked.

Examples:

Solve $7 + \sqrt{a - 3} = 1$.

$$7 + \sqrt{a - 3} = 1$$
$$\sqrt{a - 3} = -6 \qquad \text{Isolate the radical.}$$
$$(\sqrt{a - 3})^2 = (-6)^2 \qquad \text{Square each side.}$$
$$a - 3 = 36$$
$$a = 39$$

The equation has no solutions.

Check: $7 + \sqrt{a - 3} = 1$
$$7 + \sqrt{39 - 3} \stackrel{?}{=} 1$$
$$7 + \sqrt{36} \stackrel{?}{=} 1$$
$$13 \neq 1$$

The answer does not check.

Solve $\sqrt{2y - 3} - \sqrt{2y + 3} = -1$.

$$\sqrt{2y - 3} - \sqrt{2y + 3} = -1$$
$$\sqrt{2y - 3} = \sqrt{2y + 3} - 1$$
$$2y - 3 = 2y + 3 - 2\sqrt{2y + 3} + 1$$
$$-7 = -2\sqrt{2y + 3}$$
$$\frac{7}{2} = \sqrt{2y + 3}$$
$$\frac{49}{4} = 2y + 3$$
$$\frac{37}{4} = 2y$$
$$y = \frac{37}{8}$$

The solution is $\frac{37}{8}$ or $4\frac{5}{8}$.

Check: $\sqrt{2y - 3} - \sqrt{2y + 3} = -1$
$$\sqrt{2\left(\frac{37}{8}\right) - 3} - \sqrt{2\left(\frac{37}{8}\right) + 3} \stackrel{?}{=} -1$$
$$\sqrt{\frac{25}{4}} - \sqrt{\frac{49}{4}} \stackrel{?}{=} -1$$
$$\frac{5}{2} - \frac{7}{2} \stackrel{?}{=} -1$$
$$-1 = -1$$

Solve each equation.

1. $\dfrac{3 \pm 2x\sqrt{3}}{\sqrt{3}} = 5$
$\dfrac{}{3}$

2. $\sqrt{12 - x} = \sqrt{x + 6}$
3

3. $2\sqrt{3x + 4} + 1 = 15$
15

4. $8 + \sqrt{x + 1} = 2$
no solution

5. $\sqrt{5 - x} - 4 = 6$
−95

6. $\sqrt{21} - \sqrt{5x - 4} = 0$
5

7. $\sqrt{2x} = \sqrt{\dfrac{x}{4}}$
0

8. $\sqrt{x^2 + 7x} = \sqrt{7x - 9}$
no solution

9. $\sqrt{x - 8} + \sqrt{x + 3} = 1$
no solution

Algebra 2

NAME_____ DATE _____

Study Guide

Complex Numbers

Pure Imaginary Numbers	
Definition	**Example**
For any positive real number b, $$\sqrt{-(b^2)} = \sqrt{b^2} \cdot \sqrt{-1} \text{ or } bi,$$ where i is the imaginary unit and bi is called a pure imaginary number.	Simplify $\sqrt{-24}$. $$\sqrt{-24} = \sqrt{24}\sqrt{-1}$$ $$= \sqrt{(4 \cdot 6)}i$$ $$= 2i\sqrt{6}$$

Numbers such as $6i$ and $13 + i$ are complex numbers. Use this chart as a guide to understanding addition, subtraction, and multiplication of complex numbers.

Definition or Process	Example
To add or subtract complex numbers, combine their real parts and combine their imaginary parts. $$(a + bi) + (c + di) = (a + c) + (b + d)i$$ $$(a + bi) - (c + di) = (a - c) + (b - d)i$$	$$(2 + 7i) + (5 - 4i) = (2 + 5) + (7 - 4)i$$ $$= 7 + 11i$$ $$(7 - 4i) - (4 - 2i) = (7 - 4) + [-4 - (-2)]i$$ $$= 3 + (-2)i$$ $$= 3 - 2i$$
To multiply complex numbers, use the FOIL method. $$(a + bi)(c + di) = (ac - bd) + (ad - bc)i$$	$$(2 + 4i)(5 - 3i) = 2 \cdot 5 + 2 \cdot (-3i) + (4i) \cdot 5 + (4i) \cdot (-3i)$$ $$= 10 - 6i + 20i - 12i^2$$ $$= (10 + 12) + (-6i + 20i)$$ $$= 22 + 14i$$

Simplify.

1. $\sqrt{-98}$

2. $\sqrt{\dfrac{-252}{4}}$

3. $\sqrt{-\dfrac{25}{121}}$

4. $(-3\sqrt{-5})^2$

5. $3i \cdot 6i^3$

6. $(2i \cdot 3i^2)^2$

7. $2i \cdot (4i^3)^2$

8. $\sqrt{-4} \cdot \sqrt{-9}$

9. $(-i)^3(i^2)^3$

10. $(7 + 5i) + (-4 - 6i)$

11. $(4 + 6i) - (2 - 7i)$

12. $(3 + 2i)^2$

13. $(5 - 3i)(5 + 3i)$

14. $i(5i) + i(7 - i)$

15. $2(3 + 2i) + 3(1 - i)$

Study Guide

Complex Numbers

Pure Imaginary Numbers	
Definition	**Example**
For any positive real number b, $\sqrt{-(b^2)} = \sqrt{b^2} \cdot \sqrt{-1}$ or bi, where i is the imaginary unit and bi is called a pure imaginary number.	Simplify $\sqrt{-24}$. $\sqrt{-24} = \sqrt{24}\sqrt{-1}$ $= \sqrt{(4 \cdot 6)}i$ $= 2i\sqrt{6}$

Numbers such as $6i$ and $13 + i$ are complex numbers. Use this chart as a guide to understanding addition, subtraction, and multiplication of complex numbers.

Definition or Process	Example
To add or subtract complex numbers, combine their real parts and combine their imaginary parts. $(a + bi) + (c + di) = (a + c) + (b + d)i$ $(a + bi) - (c + di) = (a - c) + (b - d)i$	$(2 + 7i) + (5 - 4i) = (2 + 5) + (7 - 4)i$ $= 7 + 11i$ $(7 - 4i) - (4 - 2i) = (7 - 4) + [-4 - (-2)]i$ $= 3 + (-2)i$ $= 3 - 2i$
To multiply complex numbers, use the FOIL method. $(a + bi)(c + di) = (ac - bd) + (ad - bc)i$	$(2 + 4i)(5 - 3i) = 2 \cdot 5 + 2 \cdot (-3i) + (4i) \cdot 5 + (4i) \cdot (-3i)$ $= 10 - 6i + 20i - 12i^2$ $= (10 + 12) + (-6i + 20i)$ $= 22 + 14i$

Simplify.

1. $\sqrt{-98}$
   $7i\sqrt{2}$

2. $\sqrt{\dfrac{-252}{4}}$
   $3i\sqrt{7}$

3. $\sqrt{-\dfrac{25}{121}}$
   $\dfrac{5i}{11}$

4. $(-3\sqrt{-5})^2$
   -45

5. $3i \cdot 6i^3$
   18

6. $(2i \cdot 3i^2)^2$
   -36

7. $2i \cdot (4i^3)^2$
   $-32i$

8. $\sqrt{-4} \cdot \sqrt{-9}$
   -6

9. $(-i)^3(i^2)^3$
   $-i$

10. $(7 + 5i) + (-4 - 6i)$
    $3 - i$

11. $(4 + 6i) - (2 - 7i)$
    $2 + 13i$

12. $(3 + 2i)^2$
    $5 + 12i$

13. $(5 - 3i)(5 + 3i)$
    34

14. $i(5i) + i(7 - i)$
    $-4 + 7i$

15. $2(3 + 2i) + 3(1 - i)$
    $9 + i$

NAME_____ DATE _____

Study Guide

Simplifying Expressions Containing Complex Numbers

Complex numbers of the form $a + bi$ and $a - bi$ are called **conjugates** of each other. Notice that the product of complex conjugates is always a real number. Study the example to the right.

Example: Find $(5 + 2i)(5 - 2i)$.

$$(5 + 2i)(5 - 2i) = 25 - 4i^2$$
$$= 25 - (-4)$$
$$= 29$$

Sometimes rational expressions contain complex numbers. Since i represents a radical, rational numbers are usually written without imaginary numbers in the denominator. As with radicals, the denominator should be rationalized. Study the example to the right.

Example: Simplify $\dfrac{2 + 9i}{3i}$

$$\frac{2 + 9i}{3i} = \frac{2 + 9i}{3i} \cdot \frac{i}{i}$$
$$= \frac{2i + 9i^2}{3i^2}$$
$$= \frac{-9 + 2i}{-3} \text{ or } \frac{9 - 2i}{3}$$

Find the conjugate of each complex number.

1. $4 - 2i$

2. $8 - 2i$

3. $6 + 3i$

Find the product of each complex number and its conjugate.

4. $4 - 2i$

5. $9 - 2i$

6. $5 - 4i$

Simplify.

7. $(5 - 7i)(5 + 7i)$

8. $5 \div (3 + i)$

9. $7 - 13i \div 2i$

10. $\dfrac{3 + i\sqrt{5}}{3 - i\sqrt{5}}$

11. $\dfrac{4 - i\sqrt{2}}{i\sqrt{2}}$

12. $\dfrac{\sqrt{6} + i\sqrt{3}}{\sqrt{2} - i}$

Simplifying Expressions Containing Complex Numbers

Complex numbers of the form $a + bi$ and $a - bi$ are called **conjugates** of each other. Notice that the product of complex conjugates is always a real number. Study the example to the right.

Example: Find $(5 + 2i)(5 - 2i)$.
$$(5 + 2i)(5 - 2i) = 25 - 4i^2$$
$$= 25 - (-4)$$
$$= 29$$

Sometimes rational expressions contain complex numbers. Since i represents a radical, rational numbers are usually written without imaginary numbers in the denominator. As with radicals, the denominator should be rationalized. Study the example to the right.

Example: Simplify $\dfrac{2 + 9i}{3i}$

$$\frac{2 + 9i}{3i} = \frac{2 + 9i}{3i} \cdot \frac{i}{i}$$
$$= \frac{2i + 9i^2}{3i^2}$$
$$= \frac{-9 + 2i}{-3} \text{ or } \frac{9 - 2i}{3}$$

Find the conjugate of each complex number.

1. $4 - 2i$
   $4 + 2i$

2. $8 - 2i$
   $8 + 2i$

3. $6 + 3i$
   $6 - 3i$

Find the product of each complex number and its conjugate.

4. $4 - 2i$
   20

5. $9 - 2i$
   85

6. $5 - 4i$
   41

Simplify.

7. $(5 - 7i)(5 + 7i)$
   74

8. $5 \div (3 + i)$
   $$\frac{3 - i}{2}$$

9. $7 - 13i \div 2i$
   $$\frac{1}{2}$$

10. $\dfrac{3 + i\sqrt{5}}{3 - i\sqrt{5}}$
   $$\frac{2 + 3i\sqrt{5}}{7}$$

11. $\dfrac{4 - i\sqrt{2}}{i\sqrt{2}}$
   $-1 - 2\sqrt{2i}$

12. $\dfrac{\sqrt{6} + i\sqrt{3}}{\sqrt{2} - i}$
   $$\frac{\sqrt{12} - \sqrt{3} + 2i\sqrt{6}}{3}$$

Study Guide

Solving Quadratic Equations by Graphing

Definition of a Quadratic Function	A quadratic function is a function described by an equation that can be written in the form $f(x) = ax^2 + bx + c$ where $a \neq 0$. In a quadratic function, ax^2 is called the **quadratic term**, bx is called the **linear term**, and c is called the **constant term**.

The graph of any quadratic function is a parabola. Parabolas have certain common characteristics. Study the chart below.

Common Characteristics of Parabolas	1. Axis of Symmetry: The line about which the parabola is symmetric. 2. Vertex: The point of the parabola where the parabola and the axis of symmetry intersect. 3. The graphs of all parabolas have the same general shape, a U shape. 4. A parabola whose equation is $y = (x - h)^2 + k$ has its vertex at (h, k) and axis of symmetry $x = h$.

Example: Write $f(x) = x^2 - 4x + 1$ in the form $f(x) = (x - h)^2 + k$. Name the vertex and axis of symmetry of the graph. Then draw the graph.

$$f(x) = x^2 - 4x + 1$$
$$= (x^2 - 4x + 4) + (1 - 4)$$
$$= (x - 2)^2 - 3$$

Vertex: $(2, -3)$
Axis of symmetry: $x = 2$

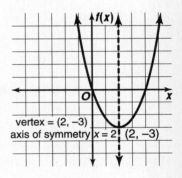

vertex = (2, –3)
axis of symmetry $x = 2$ (2, –3)

Identify the quadratic term, the linear term, and the constant term in each function.

1. $f(x) = 4x^2 - 8x + 4$

2. $m(p) = p^2 - 6p + 9$

3. $q(x) = -(x^2 - 5)^2 - x^4$

4. $f(x) = 5x^2 + (x - 4)^2$

Graph each function. Name the vertex and the axis of symmetry. Identify the solutions of the related equation.

5. $f(x) = x^2 - 10x + 215$

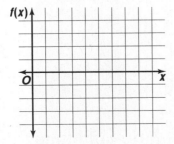

6. $f(x) = x^2 + 4x + 6$

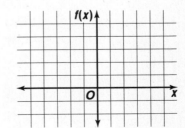

Algebra 2

NAME_____ DATE _____

Study Guide

Solving Quadratic Equations by Graphing

Definition of a Quadratic Function	A quadratic function is a function described by an equation that can be written in the form $f(x) = ax^2 + bx + c$ where $a \neq 0$. In a quadratic function, ax^2 is called the **quadratic term**, bx is called the **linear term**, and c is called the **constant term**.

The graph of any quadratic function is a parabola. Parabolas have certain common characteristics. Study the chart below.

Common Characteristics of Parabolas	1. Axis of Symmetry: The line about which the parabola is symmetric. 2. Vertex: The point of the parabola where the parabola and the axis of symmetry intersect. 3. The graphs of all parabolas have the same general shape, a U shape. 4. A parabola whose equation is $y = (x - h)^2 + k$ has its vertex at (h, k) and axis of symmetry $x = h$.

Example: Write $f(x) = x^2 - 4x + 1$ in the form $f(x) = (x - h)^2 + k$. Name the vertex and axis of symmetry of the graph. Then draw the graph.

$$f(x) = x^2 - 4x + 1$$
$$= (x^2 - 4x + 4) + (1 - 4)$$
$$= (x - 2)^2 - 3$$

Vertex: $(2, -3)$
Axis of symmetry: $x = 2$

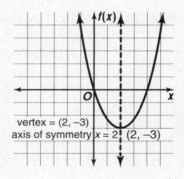

vertex = (2, –3)
axis of symmetry x = 2 (2, –3)

Identify the quadratic term, the linear term, and the constant term in each function.

1. $f(x) = 4x^2 - 8x + 4$
   $4x^2$; $-8x$; 4

2. $m(p) = p^2 - 6p + 9$
   p^2; $-6p$; 9

3. $q(x) = -(x^2 - 5)^2 - x^4$
   $-10x^2$; 0; 25

4. $f(x) = 5x^2 + (x - 4)^2$
   $6x^2$; $-8x$; 16

Graph each function. Name the vertex and the axis of symmetry. Identify the solutions of the related equation.

5. $f(x) = x^2 - 10x + 215$

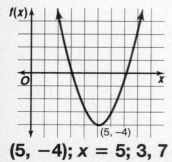

(5, –4)

(5, −4); x = 5; 3, 7

6. $f(x) = x^2 + 4x + 6$

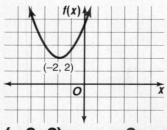

(–2, 2)

(−2, 2); x = −2; no solutions

Algebra 2

NAME_____ DATE _____

Study Guide

Solving Quadratic Equations by Factoring

The only way for the product of two numbers to equal 0 is for at least one of the factors to be 0. This fact is known as the **zero product property.** You use this property when you solve equations by factoring.

Zero Product Property	For any real numbers a and b, if $ab = 0$, then $a = 0$ or $b = 0$.

Example: Solve $x^2 - 4x = 12$ by factoring.

$$x^2 - 4x - 12 = 0$$ Rewrite the equation in standard form.

$$(x - 6)(x + 2) = 0$$ Factor.

$$x - 6 = 0 \qquad x + 2 = 0$$ Use the zero product property.
Set each factor equal to zero and solve.

$$x = 6 \qquad\qquad x = -2$$

Solve each equation by factoring.

1. $z^2 - 12z + 27 = 0$

2. $x^2 + 13x + 40 = 0$

3. $x^2 - 7x - 44 = 0$

4. $x^2 + 3x - 130 = 0$

5. $x^2 - 12x = -36$

6. $3s^2 - 13s = 10$

7. $16x^2 = 49$

8. $3s^2 - 13s = -10$

9. $4k^2 - 35k - 9 = 0$

10. $-2x^2 - 5x + 12 = 0$

41

Study Guide

Solving Quadratic Equations by Factoring

The only way for the product of two numbers to equal 0 is for at least one of the factors to be 0. This fact is known as the **zero product property.** You use this property when you solve equations by factoring.

Zero Product Property	For any real numbers a and b, if $ab = 0$, then $a = 0$ or $b = 0$.

Example: Solve $x^2 - 4x = 12$ by factoring.

$$x^2 - 4x - 12 = 0 \qquad \text{Rewrite the equation in standard form.}$$

$$(x - 6)(x + 2) = 0 \qquad \text{Factor.}$$

$$x - 6 = 0 \qquad x + 2 = 0 \qquad \text{Use the zero product property.}$$
Set each factor equal to zero and solve.

$$x = 6 \qquad x = -2$$

Solve each equation by factoring.

1. $z^2 - 12z + 27 = 0$
   9, 3

2. $x^2 + 13x + 40 = 0$
   −8, −5

3. $x^2 - 7x - 44 = 0$
   11, −4

4. $x^2 + 3x - 130 = 0$
   −13, 10

5. $x^2 - 12x = -36$
   6

6. $3s^2 - 13s = 10$
   $\dfrac{-2}{3}$**, 5**

7. $16x^2 = 49$
   $\dfrac{7}{4}, \dfrac{-7}{4}$

8. $3s^2 - 13s = -10$
   $\dfrac{10}{3}$**, 1**

9. $4k^2 - 35k - 9 = 0$
   9, $-\dfrac{1}{4}$

10. $-2x^2 - 5x + 12 = 0$
   $\dfrac{3}{2}$**, −4**

Study Guide

Completing the Square

Quadratic equations can be solved by taking the square root of each side. First the expression that contains the variable must be the square of a binomial. If this is not already the case, then you can make it so by using a process called **completing the square.** You find half the coefficient of the linear term, square it, and add the result to each side.

Example: Solve $x^2 - 6x + 4 = 0$ by completing the square.

$$x^2 - 6x + 4 = 0$$
$$x^2 - 6x = -4 \qquad \text{Isolate the terms with } x \text{ on the left.}$$
$$x^2 - 6x + 9 = -4 + 9 \qquad \text{Add } \left(\frac{-6}{2}\right)^2, \text{ or 9, to each side.}$$
$$(x - 3)^2 = 5 \qquad \text{Factor the left side (now a square).}$$
$$x - 3 = \pm\sqrt{5} \qquad \text{Take the square root of each side.}$$
$$x = 3 \pm\sqrt{5} \qquad \text{Add 3 to each side.}$$

The solutions are $3 + \sqrt{5}$ and $3 - \sqrt{5}$.

If the equation does not have 1 as the coefficient of x^2, divide each side by the coefficient of x^2 to get a coefficient of 1 for x^2. Do this *before* you complete the square.

Find the exact solution for each equation by completing the square.

1. $y^2 - 4y - 5 = 0$

2. $y^2 + 2y - 143 = 0$

3. $x^2 + 4x + 1 = 0$

4. $s^2 - 10s + 21 = 0$

5. $y^2 + 12y + 4 = 0$

6. $t^2 + 3t - 8 = 0$

7. $2x^2 - 3x + 1 = 0$

8. $-2x^2 + 13x + 7 = 0$

Completing the Square

Quadratic equations can be solved by taking the square root of each side. First the expression that contains the variable must be the square of a binomial. If this is not already the case, then you can make it so by using a process called **completing the square.** You find half the coefficient of the linear term, square it, and add the result to each side.

Example: Solve $x^2 - 6x + 4 = 0$ by completing the square.

$$x^2 - 6x + 4 = 0$$

$x^2 - 6x = -4$	Isolate the terms with x on the left.
$x^2 - 6x + 9 = -4 + 9$	Add $\left(\frac{-6}{2}\right)^2$, or 9, to each side.
$(x - 3)^2 = 5$	Factor the left side (now a square).
$x - 3 = \pm\sqrt{5}$	Take the square root of each side.
$x = 3 \pm\sqrt{5}$	Add 3 to each side.

The solutions are $3 + \sqrt{5}$ and $3 - \sqrt{5}$.

If the equation does not have 1 as the coefficient of x^2, divide each side by the coefficient of x^2 to get a coefficient of 1 for x^2. Do this *before* you complete the square.

Find the exact solution for each equation by completing the square.

1. $y^2 - 4y - 5 = 0$
   −1, 5

2. $y^2 + 2y - 143 = 0$
   −13, 11

3. $x^2 + 4x + 1 = 0$
   −2 ± $\sqrt{3}$

4. $s^2 - 10s + 21 = 0$
   3, 7

5. $y^2 + 12y + 4 = 0$
   −6 ± 4$\sqrt{2}$

6. $t^2 + 3t - 8 = 0$
   $\dfrac{-3 \pm \sqrt{41}}{2}$

7. $2x^2 - 3x + 1 = 0$
   1, $\dfrac{1}{2}$

8. $-2x^2 + 13x + 7 = 0$
   $-\dfrac{1}{2}$, 7

NAME _____ DATE _____

Study Guide

The Quadratic Formula and the Discriminant

The method of completing the square can be used to develop a general formula called the *quadratic formula* that can be used to solve any quadratic equation.

The Quadratic Formula
The roots of a quadratic equation of the form $ax^2 + bx + c = 0$, where $a \neq 0$, are given by: $x = \dfrac{-b \pm \sqrt{b^2 - 4ac}}{2a}$

In the quadratic formula, the expression $b^2 - 4ac$ is called the **discriminant.** The discriminant is used to determine how many real roots there are.

Nature of Roots of a Quadratic Equation	
Discriminant	**Nature of Roots**
$b^2 - 4ac > 0$	two distinct real roots
$b^2 - 4ac = 0$	one distinct real root
$b^2 - 4ac < 0$	no real roots

Find the value of the discriminant and describe the nature of the roots of each quadratic equation. Then solve the equation.

1. $3x^2 + 5x = 2$

2. $2y^2 + y - 15 = 0$

3. $r^2 - \dfrac{3r}{5} + \dfrac{2}{25} = 0$

4. $3t^2 - \dfrac{5}{4}t - \dfrac{1}{2} = 0$

5. $m^2 - 8m = -14$

6. $p^2 + 12p = -4$

7. $2x^2 - 7 = -3x$

8. $-2b^2 + b - 5 = 0$

Algebra 2

Study Guide

The Quadratic Formula and the Discriminant

The method of completing the square can be used to develop a general formula called the *quadratic formula* that can be used to solve any quadratic equation.

The Quadratic Formula
The roots of a quadratic equation of the form $ax^2 + bx + c = 0$, where $a \neq 0$, are given by: $$x = \frac{-b \pm \sqrt{b^2 - 4ac}}{2a}$$

In the quadratic formula, the expression $b^2 - 4ac$ is called the **discriminant.** The discriminant is used to determine how many real roots there are.

Nature of Roots of a Quadratic Equation	
Discriminant	**Nature of Roots**
$b^2 - 4ac > 0$	two distinct real roots
$b^2 - 4ac = 0$	one distinct real root
$b^2 - 4ac < 0$	no real roots

Find the value of the discriminant and describe the nature of the roots of each quadratic equation. Then solve the equation.

1. $3x^2 + 5x = 2$
   49; two real roots; $-2, \frac{1}{3}$

2. $2y^2 + y - 15 = 0$
   121; two real roots; $\frac{5}{2}, -3$

3. $r^2 - \frac{3r}{5} + \frac{2}{25} = 0$
   $\frac{1}{25}$; two real roots; $\frac{2}{5}, \frac{1}{5}$

4. $3t^2 - \frac{5}{4}t - \frac{1}{2} = 0$
   $\frac{121}{16}$; two real roots; $\frac{2}{3}, -\frac{1}{4}$

5. $m^2 - 8m = -14$
   8; two real roots;
   $4 + \sqrt{2}, 4 - \sqrt{2}$

6. $p^2 + 12p = -4$
   128; two real roots;
   $-6 + 4\sqrt{2}, -6 - 4\sqrt{2}$

7. $2x^2 - 7 = -3x$
   65; two real roots;
   $\frac{-3 + \sqrt{65}}{4}, \frac{-3 - \sqrt{65}}{4}$

8. $-2b^2 + b - 5 = 0$
   −36; no real roots;
   $\frac{-1 + i\sqrt{39}}{-4}, \frac{-1 - i\sqrt{39}}{-4}$

Study Guide

Sum and Product of Roots

The quadratic formula gives the roots of $ax^2 + bx + c = 0$, with $a \neq 0$, as

$$\frac{-b + \sqrt{b^2 - 4ac}}{2a} \quad \text{and} \quad \frac{-b - \sqrt{b^2 - 4ac}}{2a}.$$

You can add and simplify these expressions, then multiply and simplify to find expressions for the sum and the product of the roots.

Sum and Product of Roots
If the roots of $ax^2 + bx + c = 0$, with $a \neq 0$, are S_1 and S_2, then $S_1 + S_2 = -\dfrac{b}{a}$ and $S_1 S_2 = \dfrac{c}{a}$.

You can usually find the values of the expressions $-\dfrac{b}{a}$ and $\dfrac{c}{a}$ by merely glancing at the quadratic equation. Therefore, they give a quick check on the correctness of the solutions you obtain when you solve a quadratic equation.

Example: Tell what the sum and product of the roots of $9x^2 + 9x - 10 = 0$ will be and use the results to check whether $\dfrac{2}{3}$ and $\dfrac{5}{3}$ are correct solutions.

The sum of the roots will be $-\dfrac{9}{9}$ or -1. The product of the roots will be $-\dfrac{10}{9}$. Since $\dfrac{2}{3} + \dfrac{5}{3}$ does not equal -1 and $\dfrac{2}{3} \cdot \dfrac{5}{3}$ does not equal $-\dfrac{10}{9}$, the proposed solutions are *not* correct.

Without solving the equation, state the sum and the product of the roots of each quadratic equation.

1. $x^2 + 2x - 15 = 0$

2. $x^2 + 3x - 28 = 0$

3. $x^2 - x + 1 = 0$

4. $7x^2 + 14x - 3 = 0$

5. $-2x^2 - 5x = 6$

6. $16x^2 + 18x - 12 = 0$

Solve each equation. Then find the sum and the product of the roots to check your solutions.

7. $x^2 - 7x = 18$

8. $25x^2 = 36$

9. $7p^2 - 11p = 6$

10. $3c^2 + 7c - 2 = 0$

Sum and Product of Roots

The quadratic formula gives the roots of $ax^2 + bx + c = 0$, with $a \neq 0$, as

$$\frac{-b + \sqrt{b^2 - 4ac}}{2a} \quad \text{and} \quad \frac{-b - \sqrt{b^2 - 4ac}}{2a}.$$

You can add and simplify these expressions, then multiply and simplify to find expressions for the sum and the product of the roots.

Sum and Product of Roots
If the roots of $ax^2 + bx + c = 0$, with $a \neq 0$, are S_1 and S_2, then $S_1 + S_2 = -\dfrac{b}{a}$ and $S_1 S_2 = \dfrac{c}{a}$.

You can usually find the values of the expressions $-\dfrac{b}{a}$ and $\dfrac{c}{a}$ by merely glancing at the quadratic equation. Therefore, they give a quick check on the correctness of the solutions you obtain when you solve a quadratic equation.

Example: Tell what the sum and product of the roots of $9x^2 + 9x - 10 = 0$ will be and use the results to check whether $\dfrac{2}{3}$ and $\dfrac{5}{3}$ are correct solutions.

The sum of the roots will be $-\dfrac{9}{9}$ or -1. The product of the roots will be $-\dfrac{10}{9}$. Since $\dfrac{2}{3} + \dfrac{5}{3}$ does not equal -1 and $\dfrac{2}{3} \cdot \dfrac{5}{3}$ does not equal $-\dfrac{10}{9}$, the proposed solutions are *not* correct.

Without solving the equation, state the sum and the product of the roots of each quadratic equation.

1. $x^2 + 2x - 15 = 0$ **−2, −15**

2. $x^2 + 3x - 28 = 0$ **−3, −28**

3. $x^2 - x + 1 = 0$ **1, 1**

4. $7x^2 + 14x - 3 = 0$ **−2, $-\dfrac{3}{7}$**

5. $-2x^2 - 5x = 6$ **$-\dfrac{5}{2}$, 3**

6. $16x^2 + 18x - 12 = 0$ **$-\dfrac{9}{8}$, $-\dfrac{3}{4}$**

Solve each equation. Then find the sum and the product of the roots to check your solutions.

7. $x^2 - 7x = 18$ **9, −2**

8. $25x^2 = 36$ **$-\dfrac{6}{5}$, $\dfrac{6}{5}$**

9. $7p^2 - 11p = 6$ **$-\dfrac{3}{7}$, 2**

10. $3c^2 + 7c - 2 = 0$

$$\frac{-7 + \sqrt{73}}{6}, \frac{-7 - \sqrt{73}}{6}$$

Analyzing Graphs of Quadratic Functions

Since any quadratic function can be described by an equation of the form $f(x) = ax^2 + bx + c$, with $a \neq 0$, any quadratic function can be expressed in the general form $f(x) = a(x - h)^2 + k$. The following conclusions can be made about the graph of $f(x) = a(x - h)^2 + k$.

$y = a(x - h)^2 + k$	a is positive	a is negative
Vertex	(h, k)	(h, k)
Axis of symmetry	$x = h$	$x = h$
Direction of opening	upward	downward
As the value of $\|a\|$ increases, the graph of $y = a(x - h)^2 + k$ narrows.		

Example: Name the vertex, axis of symmetry, and direction of opening for the graph of $f(x) = -2(x - 5)^2$.

This function can be written in the form

$$f(x) = -2(x - 5)^2 + 0.$$

In the case of this equation, $a = -2$, $h = 5$, and $k = 0$. So the vertex is $(5, 0)$, the axis of symmetry is $x = 5$, and since a is negative, the graph opens downward.

Write each equation in the form $f(x) = a(x - h)^2 + k$. Then name the vertex, axis of symmetry, and direction of opening for the graph of each quadratic function.

1. $f(x) = x^2 - 6x + 11$

2. $f(x) = x^2 + 2x + 5$

3. $f(x) = 2x^2 + 4x$

4. $f(x) = -\dfrac{1}{2}x^2 + 2x - 6$

Graph each function.

5. $f(x) = x^2 + 4x - 3$

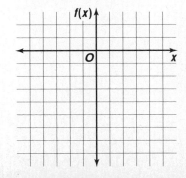

6. $f(x) = -2x^2 + 8x - 5$

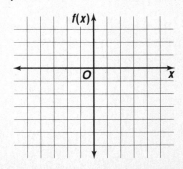

Analyzing Graphs of Quadratic Functions

Since any quadratic function can be described by an equation of the form $f(x) = ax^2 + bx + c$, with $a \neq 0$, any quadratic function can be expressed in the general form $f(x) = a(x - h)^2 + k$. The following conclusions can be made about the graph of $f(x) = a(x - h)^2 + k$.

$y = a(x - h)^2 + k$	a is positive	a is negative
Vertex	(h, k)	(h, k)
Axis of symmetry	$x = h$	$x = h$
Direction of opening	upward	downward
As the value of $|a|$ increases, the graph of $y = a(x - h)^2 + k$ narrows.		

Example: Name the vertex, axis of symmetry, and direction of opening for the graph of $f(x) = -2(x - 5)^2$.

This function can be written in the form

$$f(x) = -2(x - 5)^2 + 0.$$

In the case of this equation, $a = -2$, $h = 5$, and $k = 0$. So the vertex is $(5, 0)$, the axis of symmetry is $x = 5$, and since a is negative, the graph opens downward.

Write each equation in the form $f(x) = a(x - h)^2 + k$. Then name the vertex, axis of symmetry, and direction of opening for the graph of each quadratic function.

1. $f(x) = x^2 - 6x + 11$
   $f(x) = (x - 3)^2 + 2$, $(3, 2)$,
   $x = 3$, upward

2. $f(x) = x^2 + 2x + 5$
   $f(x) = (x + 1)^2 + 4$, $(-1, 4)$,
   $x = 4$, upward

3. $f(x) = 2x^2 + 4x$
   $f(x) = 2(x + 1)^2 - 2$, $(-1, -2)$,
   $x = -1$, downward

4. $f(x) = -\frac{1}{2}x^2 + 2x - 6$
   $f(x) = -\frac{1}{2}(x - 2)^2 - 4$, $(2, -4)$,
   $x = 2$, downward

Graph each function.

5. $f(x) = x^2 + 4x - 3$

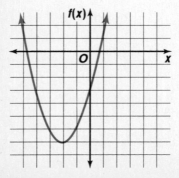

6. $f(x) = -2x^2 + 8x - 5$

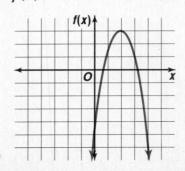

Study Guide

Graphing and Solving Quadratic Inequalities

The graph of the equation $y = x^2 + 3x - 4$ separates the plane into two regions. The graph of $y > x^2 + 3x - 4$ is the region *inside* the parabola. The graph of $y < x^2 + 3x - 4$ is the region *outside* the parabola. The parabola itself is called the boundary of each region. To show that the parabola is part of a graphed inequality, we use a smooth, solid curve. When it is *not* part of the graph, we use a curve made up of dashes.

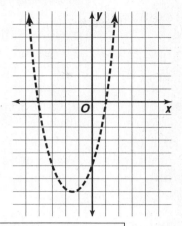

Methods of Solving Quadratic Inequalities	
1. Graphing Method	Using the quadratic function and letting $y = 0$, find the zeros of the function (*x*-intercepts).
2. Algebraic Method	Write the inequality with 0 on one side and a quadratic expression on the other. Next factor the quadratic expression in one variable. Recall that the product of two factors is positive only when both factors are positive or both factors are negative. Also recall that the product of two factors is negative only if one factor is positive and the other is negative.

Graph each inequality.

1. $y \geq x^2 + 5x + 4$

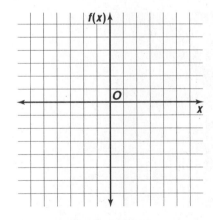

2. $y > -2x^2 + 4x$

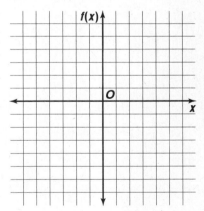

Solve each inequality.

3. $x^2 + 2x < 0$

4. $x^2 - 16 < 0$

5. $0 < 6x - x^2 - 5$

6. $c^2 \leq 4$

7. $2m^2 - m < 1$

8. $y^2 < -8$

Study Guide

Graphing and Solving Quadratic Inequalities

The graph of the equation $y = x^2 + 3x - 4$ separates the plane into two regions. The graph of $y > x^2 + 3x - 4$ is the region *inside* the parabola. The graph of $y < x^2 + 3x - 4$ is the region *outside* the parabola. The parabola itself is called the boundary of each region. To show that the parabola is part of a graphed inequality, we use a smooth, solid curve. When it is *not* part of the graph, we use a curve made up of dashes.

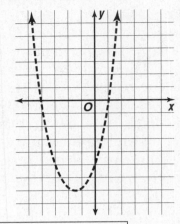

Methods of Solving Quadratic Inequalities	
1. Graphing Method	Using the quadratic function and letting $y = 0$, find the zeros of the function (*x*-intercepts).
2. Algebraic Method	Write the inequality with 0 on one side and a quadratic expression on the other. Next factor the quadratic expression in one variable. Recall that the product of two factors is positive only when both factors are positive or both factors are negative. Also recall that the product of two factors is negative only if one factor is positive and the other is negative.

Graph each inequality.

1. $y \geq x^2 + 5x + 4$

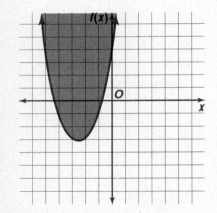

2. $y > -2x^2 + 4x$

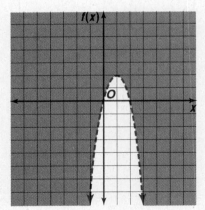

Solve each inequality.

3. $x^2 + 2x < 0$
$\{x|-2 < x < 0\}$

4. $x^2 - 16 < 0$
$\{x|-4 < x < 4\}$

5. $0 < 6x - x^2 - 5$
$\{x|1 < x < 5\}$

6. $c^2 \leq 4$
$\{c|-2 \leq c \leq 2\}$

7. $2m^2 - m < 1$
$\{m|-\frac{1}{2} < m < 1\}$

8. $y^2 < -8$
$\emptyset$

Study Guide

Integration: Statistics
Standard Deviation

The most commonly used measure of variation is called the
standard deviation. The standard deviation for a set of data is
an average measure of how much each value differs from the mean.

Definition of Standard Deviation
From a set of data with n values, where x_1 represents the first term and x_n represents the nth term, if $\bar{x}$ represents the mean, then the standard deviation can be found as follows. $$\text{standard deviation } (SD) = \sqrt{\frac{(x_1 - \bar{x})^2 + (x_2 - \bar{x})^2 + \cdots + (x_n - \bar{x})^2}{n}}$$

Example: Find the standard deviation for {2, 2, 4, 6, 8, 14}.

$$\bar{x} = \frac{2 + 2 + 4 + 6 + 8 + 14}{6} = 6$$ **Find the mean.**

$$SD = \sqrt{\frac{(x_1 - \bar{x})^2 + (x_2 - \bar{x})^2 + \cdots + (x_n - \bar{x})^2}{n}}$$ **Apply the definition of standard deviation.**

$$= \sqrt{\frac{(-4)^2 + (-4)^2 + (-2)^2 + (0)^2 + (2)^2 + (8)^2}{6}}$$ **Write the expression.**

$$= \sqrt{\frac{16 + 16 + 4 + 0 + 4 + 64}{6}}$$

$$= \sqrt{17.33} \text{ or about } 4.2$$

The standard deviation is 4.2.

Find the mean and standard deviation for each set of data.

1. {3, 5, 6, 7, 9, 11, 22}

2. {6, 8, 9, 11, 12, 28, 34, 36}

The average points scored per basketball game in the Eastern Conference
and Western Conference of the National Basketball League are listed below.

Eastern Conference	114	107	103	104	104	105	109
	99	109	111	109	103	104	103
Western Conference	105	106	107	100	106	99	121
	116	107	114	118	107	104	102

3. Find the standard deviation of average points scored for the Eastern Conference.

4. Find the standard deviation of average points scored for the Western Conference.

5. Find the standard deviation for the average points scored for the entire National Basketball League

Study Guide

Integration: Statistics
Standard Deviation

The most commonly used measure of variation is called the
standard deviation. The standard deviation for a set of data is
an average measure of how much each value differs from the mean.

Definition of Standard Deviation
From a set of data with n values, where x_1 represents the first term and x_n represents the nth term, if $\bar{x}$ represents the mean, then the standard deviation can be found as follows. $$\text{standard deviation } (SD) = \sqrt{\frac{(x_1 - \bar{x})^2 + (x_2 - \bar{x})^2 + \cdots + (x_n - \bar{x})^2}{n}}$$

Example: Find the standard deviation for $\{2, 2, 4, 6, 8, 14\}$.

$$\bar{x} = \frac{2 + 2 + 4 + 6 + 8 + 14}{6} = 6$$

Find the mean.

$$SD = \sqrt{\frac{(x_1 - x)^2 + (x_2 - x)^2 + \cdots + (x_n - x)^2}{n}}$$

Apply the definition of
standard deviation.

$$= \sqrt{\frac{(-4)^2 + (-4)^2 + (-2)^2 + (0)^2 + (2)^2 + (8)^2}{6}}$$

Write the expression.

$$= \sqrt{\frac{16 + 16 + 4 + 0 + 4 + 64}{6}}$$

$$= \sqrt{17.33} \text{ or about } 4.2$$

The standard deviation is 4.2.

Find the mean and standard deviation for each set of data.

1. $\{3, 5, 6, 7, 9, 11, 22\}$
   9, 5.8

2. $\{6, 8, 9, 11, 12, 28, 34, 36\}$
   18, 11.7

The average points scored per basketball game in the Eastern Conference
and Western Conference of the National Basketball League are listed below.

Eastern Conference	114	107	103	104	104	105	109
	99	109	111	109	103	104	103

Western Conference	105	106	107	100	106	99	121
	116	107	114	118	107	104	102

3. Find the standard deviation of
   average points scored for the
   Eastern Conference.
   3.8

4. Find the standard deviation of
   average points scored for the
   Western Conference.
   6.5

5. Find the standard deviation for the average points scored for
   the entire National Basketball League. **5.4**

NAME_____ DATE _____

Study Guide

Student Edition
Pages 392–398

Integration: Statistics
The Normal Distribution

One way to analyze data is to consider the frequency with which each value occurs. Often this is done on a bar graph called a **histogram.** Often the frequency distributions are shown by curves of many different shapes. A curve that is bell-shaped and symmetric indicates a **normal distribution.**

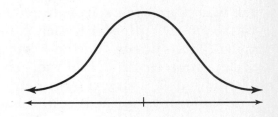

Normal Distribution Properties
1. The graph is maximized at the mean.
2. About 68% of the items are within one standard deviation from the mean. Of the 68%, 34% are greater than the mean and 34% are less than the mean.
3. About 95% of the items are within two standard deviations from the mean. Of the 95%, 47.5% are greater than the mean and 47.5% are less than the mean.
4. About 99% of the items are within three standard deviations from the mean. Of the 99%, 49.5% are greater than the mean and 49.5% are less than the mean.

The number of hours that students studied for final exams was normally distributed. Of the 200 students surveyed, the mean number of hours they studied was 12 hours. The standard deviation was 3 hours.

1. Make the curve to represent the frequency distribution.

2. Of the 200 students surveyed, how many studied less than 9 hours?

3. Of the 200 students surveyed, how many studied between 9 and 15 hours?

4. Of the 200 students surveyed, how many studied at least 3 hours?

5. What percentage of the students studied 3 hours or less?

6. What percentage of the students studied at least 9 hours?

7. How many students studied less than 12 hours?

Study Guide

Integration: Statistics
The Normal Distribution

One way to analyze data is to consider
the frequency with which each value
occurs. Often this is done on a bar graph
called a **histogram.** Often the frequency
distributions are shown by curves of
many different shapes. A curve that is
bell-shaped and symmetric indicates a
normal distribution.

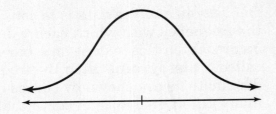

Normal Distribution Properties
1. The graph is maximized at the mean.
2. About 68% of the items are within one standard deviation from the mean. Of the 68%, 34% are greater than the mean and 34% are less than the mean.
3. About 95% of the items are within two standard deviations from the mean. Of the 95%, 47.5% are greater than the mean and 47.5% are less than the mean.
4. About 99% of the items are within three standard deviations from the mean. Of the 99%, 49.5% are greater than the mean and 49.5% are less than the mean.

*The number of hours that students studied for final exams was
normally distributed. Of the 200 students surveyed, the mean number
of hours they studied was 12 hours. The standard deviation was 3 hours.*

1. Make the curve to represent the frequency distribution.

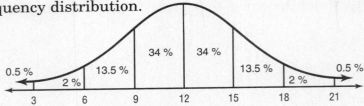

2. Of the 200 students surveyed, how many studied less than 9 hours?
   32

3. Of the 200 students surveyed, how many studied between 9 and 15 hours?
   136

4. Of the 200 students surveyed, how many studied at least 3 hours?
   199

5. What percentage of the students studied 3 hours or less?
   0.5%

6. What percentage of the students studied at least 9 hours?
   84%

7. How many students studied less than 12 hours?
   100

Integration: Geometry
The Distance and Midpoint Formulas

For number lines, you can use absolute value and averages to find distances and locate midpoints. You can do the same in the coordinate plane, though to find distances you need to use the Pythagorean theorem.

Number Line	Coordinate Plane
A: coordinate a B: coordinate b	P: coordinates (x_1, y_1) Q: coordinates (x_2, y_2)
distance: $AB = \|a - b\|$ or $\|b - a\|$	distance: $PQ = \sqrt{(x_2 - x_1)^2 + (y_2 - y_1)^2}$
midpoint: $\dfrac{a + b}{2}$ (average)	midpoint: $\left(\dfrac{x_1 + x_2}{2}, \dfrac{y_1 + y_2}{2}\right)$

Example: Find the distance from P to Q and the midpoint of $\overline{PQ}$ if P has coordinates $(-2, 7)$ and Q has coordinates $(9, 3)$.

You can choose either point for (x_1, y_1).

Use the other point for (x_2, y_2). Let (x_1, y_1) be $(-2, 7)$. Then (x_2, y_2) is $(9, 3)$.

$$PQ = \sqrt{(x_2 - x_1)^2 + (y_2 - y_1)^2} \qquad \text{midpoint of } \overline{PQ} = \left(\frac{x_1 + x_2}{2}, \frac{y_1 + y_2}{2}\right)$$

$$= \sqrt{(9 - (-2))^2 + (3 - 7)^2} \qquad\qquad\qquad = \left(\frac{(-2) + 9}{2}, \frac{7 + 3}{2}\right)$$

$$= \sqrt{121 + 16} \qquad\qquad\qquad\qquad\qquad = \left(\frac{7}{2}, 5\right)$$

$$= \sqrt{137}$$

Find the distance between each pair of points with the given coordinates.

1. $(-3, 4), (6, -11)$

2. $(13, 9), (11, 15)$

3. $(-15, -7), (2, 12)$

4. $\left(\frac{1}{2}, 2\right), \left(-\frac{1}{2}, 1\right)$

5. $\left(\frac{1}{4}, \frac{1}{2}\right), \left(\frac{1}{2}, \frac{1}{4}\right)$

6. $(1.0, -0.31), (-0.2, 0.19)$

Find the midpoint of each line segment if the coordinates of the endpoints are given.

7. $(3, 5), (-6, 11)$

8. $(8, -15), (-7, 13)$

9. $(2.5, -6.1), (7.9, 13.7)$

10. $(-7, -6), (-1, 24)$

11. $(3, -10), (30, -20)$

12. $(-9, 1.7), (-11, 1.3)$

Study Guide

Integration: Geometry
The Distance and Midpoint Formulas

For number lines, you can use absolute value and averages to find distances and locate midpoints. You can do the same in the coordinate plane, though to find distances you need to use the Pythagorean theorem.

Number Line	Coordinate Plane
A: coordinate a B: coordinate b	P: coordinates (x_1, y_1) Q: coordinates (x_2, y_2)
distance: $AB = \|a - b\|$ or $\|b - a\|$	distance: $PQ = \sqrt{(x_2 - x_1)^2 + (y_2 - y_1)^2}$
midpoint: $\dfrac{a + b}{2}$ (average)	midpoint: $\left(\dfrac{x_1 + x_2}{2}, \dfrac{y_1 + y_2}{2}\right)$

Example: Find the distance from P to Q and the midpoint of $\overline{PQ}$ if P has coordinates $(-2, 7)$ and Q has coordinates $(9, 3)$.

You can choose either point for (x_1, y_1).

Use the other point for (x_2, y_2). Let (x_1, y_1) be $(-2, 7)$. Then (x_2, y_2) is $(9, 3)$.

$$PQ = \sqrt{(x_2 - x_1)^2 + (y_2 - y_1)^2} \qquad \text{midpoint of } \overline{PQ} = \left(\frac{x_1 + x_2}{2}, \frac{y_1 + y_2}{2}\right)$$

$$= \sqrt{(9 - (-2))^2 + (3 - 7)^2} \qquad\qquad\quad = \left(\frac{(-2) + 9}{2}, \frac{7 + 3}{2}\right)$$

$$= \sqrt{121 + 16} \qquad\qquad\qquad\qquad\qquad = \left(\frac{7}{2}, 5\right)$$

$$= \sqrt{137}$$

Find the distance between each pair of points with the given coordinates.

1. $(-3, 4), (6, -11)$
   $3\sqrt{34}$

2. $(13, 9), (11, 15)$
   $2\sqrt{10}$

3. $(-15, -7), (2, 12)$
   $5\sqrt{26}$

4. $\left(\frac{1}{2}, 2\right), \left(-\frac{1}{2}, 1\right)$
   $\sqrt{2}$

5. $\left(\frac{1}{4}, \frac{1}{2}\right), \left(\frac{1}{2}, \frac{1}{4}\right)$
   $\frac{1}{4}\sqrt{2}$

6. $(1.0, -0.31), (-0.2, 0.19)$
   1.3

Find the midpoint of each line segment if the coordinates of the endpoints are given.

7. $(3, 5), (-6, 11)$
   $\left(-\frac{3}{2}, 8\right)$

8. $(8, -15), (-7, 13)$
   $\left(\frac{1}{2}, -1\right)$

9. $(2.5, -6.1), (7.9, 13.7)$
   $\left(5.2, 3.8\right)$

10. $(-7, -6), (-1, 24)$
    $(-4, 9)$

11. $(3, -10), (30, -20)$
    $\frac{33}{2}, -15)$

12. $(-9, 1.7), (-11, 1.3)$
    $(-10, 1.5)$

Study Guide

Parabolas

A **parabola** is a curve consisting of all points in the coordinate plane that are the same distance from a given point (the focus) and a given line (the directrix). The chart summarizes important information about parabolas.

Information about Parabolas		
Form of equation	$y = a(x - h)^2 + k$	$x = a(y - k)^2 + h$
Axis of symmetry	$x = h$	$y = k$
Vertex	(h, k)	(h, k)
Focus	$\left(h, k + \frac{1}{4a}\right)$	$\left(h + \frac{1}{4a}, k\right)$
Directrix	$y = k - \frac{1}{4a}$	$x = h - \frac{1}{4a}$
Direction of opening	up $(a > 0)$; down $(a < 0)$	right $(a > 0)$; left $(a < 0)$
Length of latus rectum	$\left|\frac{1}{a}\right|$ units	$\left|\frac{1}{a}\right|$ units

Example: Graph $y = \frac{1}{4}(x - 2)^2 - 3$.

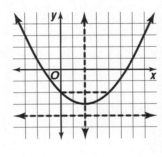

vertex: $(2, -3)$
axis of symmetry: $x = 2$
focus: $(2, -3 + 1)$ or $(2, -2)$
directrix: $y = -3 - 1$ or $y = -4$
direction of opening: upward, since $a > 0$
length of latus rectum: $\left|\frac{1}{\frac{1}{4}}\right|$ or 4 units

Name the coordinates of the vertex and focus, the equations of the axis of symmetry and directrix, and the direction of opening of the parabola with the given equation. Then find the length of the latus rectum.

1. $x^2 = 2y$

2. $x^2 = y + 2$

3. $y = x^2 + 4x + 3$

The coordinates of the focus and the equation of the directrix of a parabola are given. Write an equation for each parabola. Then draw the graph.

4. $(3, 5)$, $y = 1$

5. $(4, -4)$, $y = -6$

6. $(5, -1)$, $x = 3$

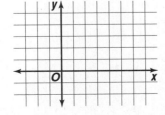

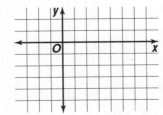

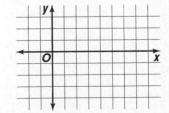

Parabolas

A **parabola** is a curve consisting of all points in the coordinate plane that are the same distance from a given point (the focus) and a given line (the directrix). The chart summarizes important information about parabolas.

Information about Parabolas		
Form of equation	$y = a(x - h)^2 + k$	$x = a(y - k)^2 + h$
Axis of symmetry	$x = h$	$y = k$
Vertex	(h, k)	(h, k)
Focus	$\left(h, k + \frac{1}{4a}\right)$	$\left(h + \frac{1}{4a}, k\right)$
Directrix	$y = k - \frac{1}{4a}$	$x = h - \frac{1}{4a}$
Direction of opening	up ($a > 0$); down ($a < 0$)	right ($a > 0$); left ($a < 0$)
Length of latus rectum	$\left|\frac{1}{a}\right|$ units	$\left|\frac{1}{a}\right|$ units

Example: Graph $y = \frac{1}{4}(x - 2)^2 - 3$.

vertex: $(2, -3)$
axis of symmetry: $x = 2$
focus: $(2, -3 + 1)$ or $(2, -2)$
directrix: $y = -3 - 1$ or $y = -4$
direction of opening: upward, since $a > 0$
length of latus rectum: $\left|\frac{1}{\frac{1}{4}}\right|$ or 4 units

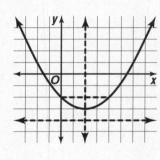

Name the coordinates of the vertex and focus, the equations of the axis of symmetry and directrix, and the direction of opening of the parabola with the given equation. Then find the length of the latus rectum.

1. $x^2 = 2y$
$(0, 0); x = 0; \left(0, \frac{1}{2}\right);$
$y = -\frac{1}{2}$; upward; 2

2. $x^2 = y + 2$
$(0, -2); x = 0; \left(0, -1\frac{3}{4}\right);$
$y = -2\frac{1}{4}$; upward; 1

3. $y = x^2 + 4x + 3$
$(-2, -1); x = -2;$
$\left(-2, -\frac{3}{4}\right); y = -1\frac{1}{4};$
upward; 1

The coordinates of the focus and the equation of the directrix of a parabola are given. Write an equation for each parabola. Then draw the graph.

4. $(3, 5), y = 1$

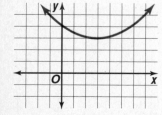

$y = \frac{1}{8}(x - 3)^2 + 3$

5. $(4, -4), y = -6$

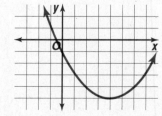

$y = \frac{1}{4}(x - 4)^2 - 5$

6. $(5, -1), x = 3$

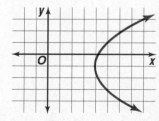

$x = \frac{1}{4}(y + 1)^2 + 4$

Circles

A **circle** is the set of all points in a plane that are equidistant from a given point, called the **center.** The distance from the center to any point on the circle is called the **radius.**

Equation of Circle with Center at (*h, k*), radius *r*
$(x - h)^2 + (y - k)^2 = r^2$

Example: Find the center and radius of the circle whose equation is $x^2 + 2x + y^2 + 4y = 11$. Then graph the circle.

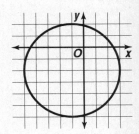

Complete the square for each variable.

$$x^2 + 2x + y^2 + 4y = 11$$
$$x^2 + 2x + \blacksquare + y^2 + 4y + \square = 11 + \blacksquare + \square$$

Write the equation in the form $(x - h)^2 + (y - k)^2 = r^2$

$$x^2 + 2x + 1 + y^2 + 4y + 4 = 11 + 1 + 4$$
$$(x + 1)^2 + (y + 2)^2 = 16$$

The circle has its center at $(-1, -2)$ and a radius of 4.

Find the coordinates of the center and the radius of each circle whose equation is given. Then draw the graph.

1. $(x - 3)^2 + y^2 = 9$

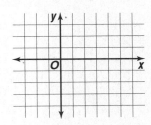

2. $x^2 + (y + 5)^2 = 4$

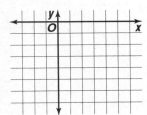

3. $(x - 1)^2 + (y + 3)^2 = 9$

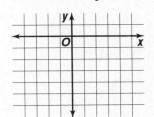

4. $(x - 2)^2 + (y + 4)^2 = 16$

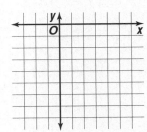

5. $x^2 + 14x + y^2 + 2y = -40$

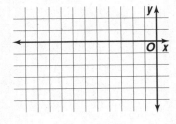

6. $x^2 + y^2 - 10x + 8y + 16 = 0$

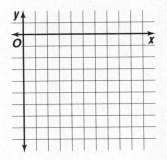

Write an equation for each circle if the coordinates of the center and length of the radius are given.

7. $(-3, 5)$, 7 units

8. $(-4, -6)$, 5 units

Circles

A **circle** is the set of all points in a plane that are equidistant from a given point, called the **center**. The distance from the center to any point on the circle is called the **radius**.

Equation of Circle with Center at (*h, k*), radius *r*
$(x - h)^2 + (y - k)^2 = r^2$

Example: Find the center and radius of the circle whose equation is $x^2 + 2x + y^2 + 4y = 11$. Then graph the circle.

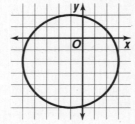

Complete the square for each variable.

$$x^2 + 2x + y^2 + 4y = 11$$
$$x^2 + 2x + \blacksquare + y^2 + 4y + \square = 11 + \blacksquare + \square$$

Write the equation in the form $(x - h)^2 + (y - k)^2 = r^2$

$$x^2 + 2x + 1 + y^2 + 4y + 4 = 11 + 1 + 4$$
$$(x + 1)^2 + (y + 2)^2 = 16$$

The circle has its center at $(-1, -2)$ and a radius of 4.

Find the coordinates of the center and the radius of each circle whose equation is given. Then draw the graph.

1. $(x - 3)^2 + y^2 = 9$

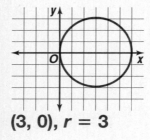

$(3, 0), r = 3$

2. $x^2 + (y + 5)^2 = 4$

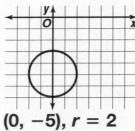

$(0, -5), r = 2$

3. $(x - 1)^2 + (y + 3)^2 = 9$

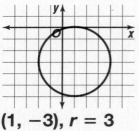

$(1, -3), r = 3$

4. $(x - 2)^2 + (y + 4)^2 = 16$

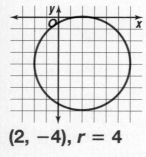

$(2, -4), r = 4$

5. $x^2 + 14x + y^2 + 2y = -40$

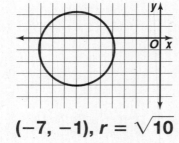

$(-7, -1), r = \sqrt{10}$

6. $x^2 + y^2 - 10x + 8y + 16 = 0$

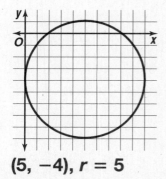

$(5, -4), r = 5$

Write an equation for each circle if the coordinates of the center and length of the radius are given.

7. $(-3, 5)$, 7 units
$$(x + 3)^2 + (y - 5)^2 = 49$$

8. $(-4, -6)$, 5 units
$$(x + 4)^2 + (y + 6)^2 = 25$$

Study Guide

Ellipses

An ellipse is the set of all points in a plane such that the sum of the distances from two given points in the plane, called the **foci,** is constant. An ellipse has two axes of symmetry. The intersection of the two axes is the **center of the ellipse.** The ellipse intersects the axes to define two segments whose endpoints lie on the ellipse. The longer segment is called the **major axis,** and the shorter segment is called the **minor axis.**

Standard Equations for Ellipses with Center at (h, k)		
Horizontal Major Axis:	$\dfrac{(x-h)^2}{a^2} + \dfrac{(y-k)^2}{b^2} = 1$	$(a^2 > b^2)$
Vertical Major Axis:	$\dfrac{(x-h)^2}{b^2} + \dfrac{(y-k)^2}{a^2} = 1$	$(a^2 > b^2)$

Example:

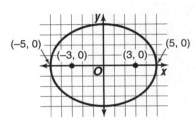

Write the equation of the ellipse.
First find the length of the major axis. The distance between $(-5, 0)$ and $(5, 0)$ is 10 units.

$$2a = 10$$
$$a = 5 \text{ so } a^2 = 25$$

Since the foci are at $(-3, 0)$ and $(3, 0)$, $c = 3$.

$$b^2 = a^2 - c^2$$
$$b^2 = 5^2 - 3^2 \text{ so } b^2 = 16$$

The equation is $\dfrac{x^2}{25} + \dfrac{y^2}{16} = 1$.

Write an equation for each ellipse.

1.

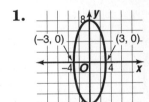

2.

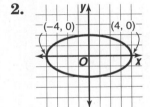

3.

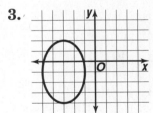

Find the coordinates of the center and foci, and the lengths of the major axis and minor axis for each ellipse whose equation is given. Then draw the graph.

4. $\dfrac{x^2}{4} + \dfrac{y^2}{25} = 1$

5. $9x^2 + 16y^2 = 144$

6. $x^2 + 4y^2 + 24y = -32$

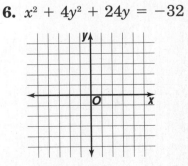

Study Guide

Ellipses

An ellipse is the set of all points in a plane such that the sum of the distances from two given points in the plane, called the **foci,** is constant. An ellipse has two axes of symmetry. The intersection of the two axes is the **center of the ellipse.** The ellipse intersects the axes to define two segments whose endpoints lie on the ellipse. The longer segment is called the **major axis,** and the shorter segment is called the **minor axis.**

Standard Equations for Ellipses with Center at (h, k)		
Horizontal Major Axis:	$\dfrac{(x-h)^2}{a^2} + \dfrac{(y-k)^2}{b^2} = 1$	$(a^2 > b^2)$
Vertical Major Axis:	$\dfrac{(x-h)^2}{b^2} + \dfrac{(y-k)^2}{a^2} = 1$	$(a^2 > b^2)$

Example:

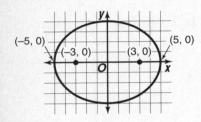

Write the equation of the ellipse.
First find the length of the major axis. The distance between $(-5, 0)$ and $(5, 0)$ is 10 units.

$$2a = 10$$
$$a = 5 \text{ so } a^2 = 25$$

Since the foci are at $(-3, 0)$ and $(3, 0)$, $c = 3$.

$$b^2 = a^2 - c^2$$
$$b^2 = 5^2 - 3^2 \text{ so } b^2 = 16$$

The equation is $\dfrac{x^2}{25} + \dfrac{y^2}{16} = 1$.

Write an equation for each ellipse.

1.

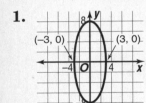

$$\frac{x^2}{9} + \frac{y^2}{64} = 1$$

2.

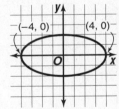

$$\frac{x^2}{16} + \frac{y^2}{4} = 1$$

3.

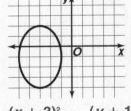

$$\frac{(x+3)^2}{4} + \frac{(y+1)^2}{9} + 1$$

Find the coordinates of the center and foci, and the lengths of the major axis and minor axis for each ellipse whose equation is given. Then draw the graph.

4. $\dfrac{x^2}{4} + \dfrac{y^2}{25} = 1$

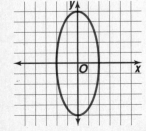

$(0, 0); (0, \pm\sqrt{21}); 10, 4$

5. $9x^2 + 16y^2 = 144$

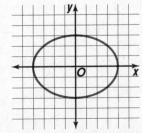

$(0, 0); (\pm\sqrt{7}, 0); 8, 6$

6. $x^2 + 4y^2 + 24y = -32$

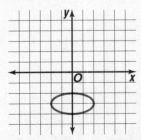

$(0, -3); (\pm\sqrt{3}, 0); 4, 2$

Algebra 2

NAME_____ DATE _____

Study Guide

Student Edition
Pages 440–447

Hyperbolas

A **hyperbola** is the set of all points in a plane such that the absolute value of the difference of the distances from any point on the hyperbola to two given points in the plane, called the **foci,** is constant. Key features of a hyperbola are the foci, vertex, asymptotes, transverse axis, and conjugate axis, shown in the figure. The **center of a hyperbola** is the midpoint of the segment connecting the foci. The lengths *a, b,* and *c* are related by the formula $c^2 = a^2 + b^2$.

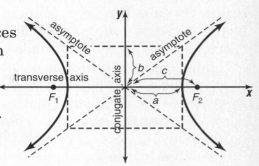

Equation of the Hyperbola	$\frac{(x-h)^2}{a^2} - \frac{(y-k)^2}{b^2} = 1$	$\frac{(y-k)^2}{a^2} - \frac{(x-h)^2}{b^2} = 1$
Slopes of the Asymptotes	$\pm \frac{b}{a}$	$\pm \frac{a}{b}$
Transverse Axis	Horizontal	Vertical
Foci	$(h-c, k), (h+c, k)$	$(h, k-c), (h, k+c)$
Vertices	$(h-a, k), (h+a, k)$	$(h, k-a), (h, k+a)$

Find the coordinates of the vertices and foci and the slopes of the asymptotes for each hyperbola whose equation is given. Then draw the graph.

1. $\frac{x^2}{4} - \frac{y^2}{16} = 1$

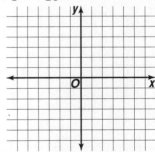

2. $\frac{(y-3)^2}{1} - \frac{(x+2)^2}{9} = 1$

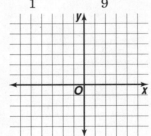

3. $36x^2 - 25y^2 = 900$

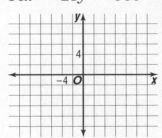

4. $\frac{y^2}{16} - \frac{x^2}{9} = 1$

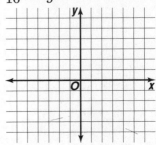

5. $6(x-3)^2 - 4(y+1)^2 = 96$

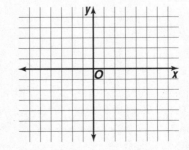

6. $y^2 - 2x^2 + 6y + 4x = 9$

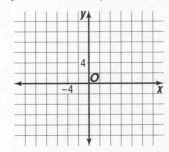

Algebra 2

Hyperbolas

A **hyperbola** is the set of all points in a plane such that the absolute value of the difference of the distances from any point on the hyperbola to two given points in the plane, called the **foci,** is constant. Key features of a hyperbola are the foci, vertex, asymptotes, transverse axis, and conjugate axis, shown in the figure. The **center of a hyperbola** is the midpoint of the segment connecting the foci. The lengths a, b, and c are related by the formula $c^2 = a^2 + b^2$.

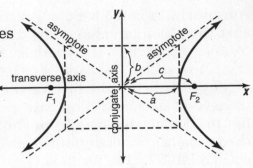

Equation of the Hyperbola	$\frac{(x-h)^2}{a^2} - \frac{(y-k)^2}{b^2} = 1$	$\frac{(y-k)^2}{a^2} - \frac{(x-h)^2}{b^2} = 1$
Slopes of the Asymptotes	$\pm\frac{b}{a}$	$\pm\frac{a}{b}$
Transverse Axis	Horizontal	Vertical
Foci	$(h-c, k), (h+c, k)$	$(h, k-c), (h, k+c)$
Vertices	$(h-a, k), (h+a, k)$	$(h, k-a), (h, k+a)$

Find the coordinates of the vertices and foci and the slopes of the asymptotes for each hyperbola whose equation is given. Then draw the graph.

1. $\dfrac{x^2}{4} - \dfrac{y^2}{16} = 1$

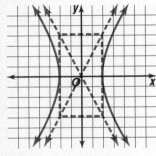

(2, 0), (−2, 0);
(2√5, 0), (−2, √5); ±2

2. $\dfrac{(y-3)^2}{1} - \dfrac{(x+2)^2}{9} = 1$

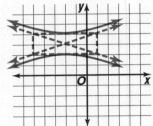

(−2, 4), (−2, 2);
(−2, 3 + √10),
(−2, 3 − √10); ±$\dfrac{1}{3}$

3. $36x^2 - 25y^2 = 900$

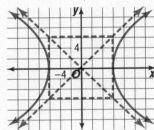

(5, 0), (−5, 0);
(√61, 0), (−√61, 0);
±$\dfrac{6}{5}$

4. $\dfrac{y^2}{16} - \dfrac{x^2}{9} = 1$

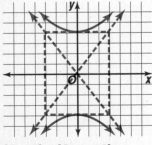

(0, 4), (0, −4);
(0, 5), (0, −5), ±$\dfrac{4}{3}$

5. $6(x-3)^2 - 4(y+1)^2 = 96$

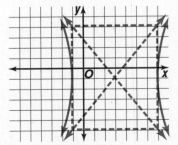

(7, −1), (−1, −1);
(3 − 2√10, −1),
(3 + 2√10, −1); ±$\dfrac{\sqrt{6}}{2}$

6. $y^2 - 2x^2 + 6y + 4x = 9$

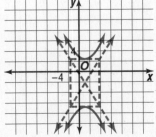

(1, 1), (1, −7);
(1, −3 + 2√6),
(1, −3 − 2√6); ±√2

Algebra 2

Study Guide

Conic Sections

Parabolas, circles, ellipses, and hyperbolas are known as **conic sections.** Any conic section in the coordinate plane can be described by an equation of the form $Ax^2 + Bxy + Cy^2 + Dx + Ey + F = 0$, where A, B, and C are not all zero. When $B = 0$, the coefficients of x^2 and y^2 tell you what kind of conic section the equation will have for its graph.

$A = C$	circle
$A \neq C$, but have same sign	ellipse
$A \neq C$, but have opposite signs	hyperbola
$A = 0$ or $C = 0$, but not both	parabola

Example: Write $x^2 = 4y^2 + 16$ in the form $Ax^2 + Bxy + Cy^2 + Dx + Ey + F = 0$. Tell what kind of conic section the graph will be. Then change the equation to the standard form for that conic section and graph the equation.

$$x^2 = 4y^2 + 16$$
$$x^2 - 4y^2 = 16$$

Since A and C have opposite signs, the graph will be a hyperbola.

Next change $x^2 - 4y^2 = 16$ to the standard form for a hyperbola. Divide each side by 16.

$$\frac{x^2}{16} - \frac{y^2}{4} = 1$$

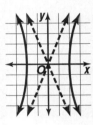

Write each equation in standard form. State whether the graph of the equation is a parabola, a circle, an ellipse, or a hyperbola. Then graph the equation.

1. $x^2 - 2x + y^2 + 8y = 8$

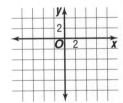

2. $y = x^2 - 2x - 8$

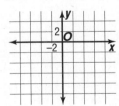

3. $9(x + 4)^2 + 4(y - 1)^2 = 36$

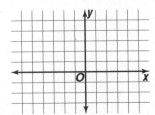

4. $x^2 = 2x + y^2 - 4y + 7$

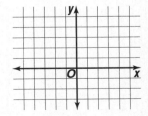

Algebra 2

Conic Sections

Parabolas, circles, ellipses, and hyperbolas are known as **conic sections.** Any conic section in the coordinate plane can be described by an equation of the form $Ax^2 + Bxy + Cy^2 + Dx + Ey + F = 0$, where A, B, and C are not all zero. When $B = 0$, the coefficients of x^2 and y^2 tell you what kind of conic section the equation will have for its graph.

$A = C$	circle
$A \neq C$, but have same sign	ellipse
$A \neq C$, but have opposite signs	hyperbola
$A = 0$ or $C = 0$, but not both	parabola

Example: Write $x^2 = 4y^2 + 16$ in the form $Ax^2 + Bxy + Cy^2 + Dx + Ey + F = 0$. Tell what kind of conic section the graph will be. Then change the equation to the standard form for that conic section and graph the equation.

$$x^2 = 4y^2 + 16$$
$$x^2 - 4y^2 = 16$$

Since A and C have opposite signs, the graph will be a hyperbola.

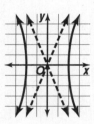

Next change $x^2 - 4y^2 = 16$ to the standard form for a hyperbola. Divide each side by 16.

$$\frac{x^2}{16} - \frac{y^2}{4} = 1$$

Write each equation in standard form. State whether the graph of the equation is a parabola, a circle, an ellipse, or a hyperbola. Then graph the equation.

1. $x^2 - 2x + y^2 + 8y = 8$

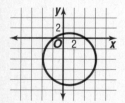

$(x - 1)^2 + (y + 4)^2 = 25$; **circle**

2. $y = x^2 - 2x - 8$

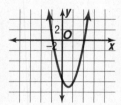

$y = (x - 1)^2 - 9$; **parabola**

3. $9(x + 4)^2 + 4(y - 1)^2 = 36$

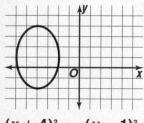

$\dfrac{(x + 4)^2}{4} + \dfrac{(y - 1)^2}{9} = 1$; **ellipse**

4. $x^2 = 2x + y^2 - 4y + 7$

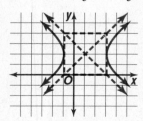

$\dfrac{(x - 1)^2}{4} - \dfrac{(y - 2)^2}{4} = 1$; **hyperbola**

Solving Quadratic Systems

You can use algebra to find exact solutions for systems of quadratic equations. For systems of inequalities, it is usually best to show the solution set with a graph.

Example: Use algebra to find the solutions of the system $\begin{cases} x^2 + y^2 = 25 \\ y - x = 1. \end{cases}$

Solve $y - x = 1$ to get $y = x + 1$.

$x^2 + (x + 1)^2 = 25$	Substitute $x + 1$ for y.
$2x^2 + 2x - 24 = 0$	Simplify. Add -25 to both sides.
$2(x + 4)(x - 3) = 0$	Factor.
$x + 4 = 0$ or $x - 3 = 0$	Zero Product Property
$x = -4 \qquad x = 3$	Solve for x.
$y = -3 \qquad y = 4$	Substitute for x in $y = 1 + x$.

The solutions are $(-4, -3)$ and $(3, 4)$.

Example: Solve the system $\begin{cases} x^2 + y^2 \le 25 \\ \left(x - \dfrac{5}{2}\right)^2 + y^2 \ge \dfrac{25}{4} \end{cases}$ by graphing.

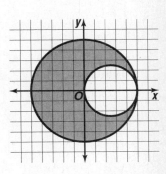

The graph of $x^2 + y^2 \le 25$ consists of all points on or inside the circle with center $(0, 0)$ and radius 5. The graph of $\left(x - \dfrac{5}{2}\right)^2 + y^2 \ge \dfrac{25}{4}$ consists of all points on or outside the circle with center $\left(\dfrac{5}{2}, 0\right)$ and radius $\dfrac{5}{2}$. The solution of the system is the set of points in both regions.

Solve each system of equations, algebraically. Check your solutions with a graphing calculator.

1. $x^2 + y^2 = 9$
$x^2 + y = 3$

2. $x^2 + (y - 5)^2 = 25$
$y = -x^2$

3. $y = x^2 - 1$
$y = x - 3$

Solve each system of inequalities by graphing.

4. $x^2 + y^2 \le 169$
$x^2 + 9y^2 \ge 225$

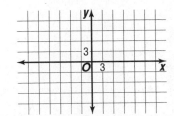

5. $\dfrac{x^2}{16} + \dfrac{y^2}{4} \le 1$

$y > \dfrac{1}{2}x - 2$

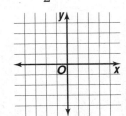

Study Guide

Solving Quadratic Systems

You can use algebra to find exact solutions for systems of quadratic equations. For systems of inequalities, it is usually best to show the solution set with a graph.

Example: Use algebra to find the solutions of the system $\begin{cases} x^2 + y^2 = 25 \\ y - x = 1. \end{cases}$

Solve $y - x = 1$ to get $y = x + 1$.

$x^2 + (x + 1)^2 = 25$	**Substitute $x + 1$ for y.**
$2x^2 + 2x - 24 = 0$	**Simplify. Add -25 to both sides.**
$2(x + 4)(x - 3) = 0$	**Factor.**
$x + 4 = 0$ or $x - 3 = 0$	**Zero Product Property**
$x = -4 \qquad x = 3$	**Solve for x.**
$y = -3 \qquad y = 4$	**Substitute for x in $y = 1 + x$.**

The solutions are $(-4, -3)$ and $(3, 4)$.

Example: Solve the system $\begin{cases} x^2 + y^2 \leq 25 \\ \left(x - \frac{5}{2}\right)^2 + y^2 \geq \frac{25}{4} \end{cases}$ by graphing.

The graph of $x^2 + y^2 \leq 25$ consists of all points on or inside the circle with center $(0, 0)$ and radius 5. The graph of $\left(x - \frac{5}{2}\right)^2 + y^2 \geq \frac{25}{4}$ consists of all points on or outside the circle with center $\left(\frac{5}{2}, 0\right)$ and radius $\frac{5}{2}$. The solution of the system is the set of points in both regions.

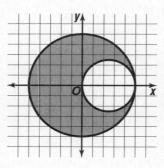

Solve each system of equations, algebraically. Check your solutions with a graphing calculator.

1. $x^2 + y^2 = 9$
$x^2 + y = 3$
**(0, 3), ($\sqrt{5}$, −2),
(−$\sqrt{5}$, −2)**

2. $x^2 + (y - 5)^2 = 25$
$y = -x^2$
(0, 0)

3. $y = x^2 - 1$
$y = x - 3$
(2, −1), (−1, −4)

Solve each system of inequalities by graphing.

4. $x^2 + y^2 \leq 169$
$x^2 + 9y^2 \geq 225$

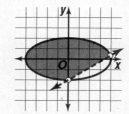

(−12.7, 2.6) (12.7, 2.6)
(−12.7, −2.6) (12.7, −2.6)

5. $\dfrac{x^2}{16} + \dfrac{y^2}{4} \leq 1$
$y > \dfrac{1}{2}x - 2$

Study Guide

Polynomial Functions

A polynomial function is one whose value, for each number a, is equal to the value of a polynomial for the value a of its variable. The function $p(x) = x^3 + 2x^2 - 5x + 7$ is a polynomial function. To find the value of $p(x)$ for a particular value of x, evaluate $x^3 + 2x^2 - 5x + 7$ for value of x.

Example: Find $p(3)$ if $p(x) = x^3 + 2x^2 - 5x + 7$.

$$\begin{aligned} p(3) &= (3)^3 + 2(3)^2 - 5(3) + 7 \qquad &\text{Replace } x \text{ with 3.}\\ &= 27 + 2 \cdot 9 - 15 + 7 &\text{Simplify.}\\ &= 27 + 18 - 15 + 7\\ &= 37 \end{aligned}$$

Find f(−3) for each function.

1. $f(x) = 6x + 10$

2. $f(x) = -x^5 + 4x^2 + 37$

3. $f(x) = x^4 + 2x^3 + 4x - 1$

4. $f(x) = \frac{2}{3}x^4 - x$

5. $f(x) = 7x^3 + \frac{1}{9}x^2 - 50$

6. $f(x) = x^3 - x^2 - x + 4$

Find f(x + h) for each function.

7. $f(x) = \frac{1}{2}x$

8. $f(x) = 5x^2 - 3$

9. $f(x) = x^2 - 7x + 4$

10. $f(x) = x^3 + 4x$

11. $f(x) = x^2 - \frac{2}{5}x$

12. $f(x) = x^3 - x^2$

13. $f(x) = (x - h)^2 + x$

14. $f(x) = x^2 + 2x - h^2$

NAME_____ DATE _____

Study Guide

Polynomial Functions

A polynomial function is one whose value, for each number a, is equal to the value of a polynomial for the value a of its variable. The function $p(x) = x^3 + 2x^2 - 5x + 7$ is a polynomial function. To find the value of $p(x)$ for a particular value of x, evaluate $x^3 + 2x^2 - 5x + 7$ for value of x.

Example: Find $p(3)$ if $p(x) = x^3 + 2x^2 - 5x + 7$.

$$\begin{aligned}
p(3) &= (3)^3 + 2(3)^2 - 5(3) + 7 \\
&= 27 + 2 \cdot 9 - 15 + 7 \\
&= 27 + 18 - 15 + 7 \\
&= 37
\end{aligned}$$

Replace x with 3.
Simplify.

Find f(−3) for each function.

1. $f(x) = 6x + 10$
−8

2. $f(x) = -x^5 + 4x^2 + 37$
316

3. $f(x) = x^4 + 2x^3 + 4x - 1$
14

4. $f(x) = \frac{2}{3}x^4 - x$
57

5. $f(x) = 7x^3 + \frac{1}{9}x^2 - 50$
−238

6. $f(x) = x^3 - x^2 - x + 4$
−29

Find f(x + h) for each function.

7. $f(x) = \frac{1}{2}x$
$\frac{1}{2}x + \frac{1}{2}h$

8. $f(x) = 5x^2 - 3$
$5x^2 + 10xh + 5h^2 - 3$

9. $f(x) = x^2 - 7x + 4$
$x^2 + 2xh + h^2 - 7x - 7h + 4$

10. $f(x) = x^3 + 4x$
$x^3 + 3x^2h + 3xh^2 + h^3 + 4x$

11. $f(x) = x^2 - \frac{2}{5}x$
$x^2 + 2xh + h^2 - \frac{2}{5}x - \frac{2}{5}h$

12. $f(x) = x^3 - x^2$
$x^3 + 3x^2h + 3xh^2 + h^3 - x^2 - 2xh - h^2$

13. $f(x) = (x - h)^2 + x$
$x^2 + x - h$

14. $f(x) = x^2 + 2x - h^2$
$x^2 + 2xh + 2x + 2h$

Algebra 2

Study Guide

The Remainder and Factor Theorems

Two important theorems concerning division of a polynomial by a binomial are the remainder theorem and the factor theorem.

The Remainder Theorem
If a polynomial $f(x)$ is divided by $x - a$, the remainder is the constant $f(a)$, and dividend = quotient · divisor + remainder $f(x) \quad = \quad q(x) \quad · (x - a) + \quad f(a)$ where $q(x)$ is a polynomial with degree one less than the degree of $f(x)$.

The Factor Theorem
The binomial $x - a$ is a factor of the polynomial $f(x)$ if and only if $f(a) = 0$.

Suppose you need to find the value of a polynomial for a particular value, a, of its variable. You can use long division or synthetic substitution to find the remainder that results if you divide the polynomial by $x - a$.

Example: Use synthetic substitution to find $f(1)$ if
$f(x) = x^4 + 3x^2 + 4x - 1$.

$$
\begin{array}{r|rrrrr}
1 & 1 & 0 & 3 & 4 & -1 \\
  &   & 1 & 1 & 4 & 8 \\
\hline
  & 1 & 1 & 4 & 8 & 7
\end{array}
$$

Use the setup for synthetic division by $x - 1$.

The remainder is 7.

Since the remainder is 7, you know that $f(1) = 7$.

Use synthetic substitution to find f(−5) and $f\left(\frac{1}{2}\right)$ for each function.

1. $f(x) = -3x^2 + 5x - 1$

2. $f(x) = x^4 + 11x^2 - 1$

3. $f(x) = -x^3 + 3x^2 - 5$

4. $f(x) = 4x^2 + 6x - 7$

Given a polynomial and one of its factors, find the remaining factors of the polynomial.

5. $x^3 - 4x^2 + 12x - 27; x - 3$

6. $x^3 + 4x^2 - x - 4; x + 4$

Find values for k so that each remainder is 5.

7. $(x^2 + 6x + k) \div (x + 1)$

8. $(2x^3 + 5x^2 + k) \div (x + 2)$

The Remainder and Factor Theorems

Two important theorems concerning division of a polynomial by a binomial are the remainder theorem and the factor theorem.

The Remainder Theorem
If a polynomial $f(x)$ is divided by $x - a$, the remainder is the constant $f(a)$, and
dividend = quotient · divisor + remainder
$f(x) = q(x) \cdot (x - a) + f(a)$
where $q(x)$ is a polynomial with degree one less than the degree of $f(x)$.

The Factor Theorem
The binomial $x - a$ is a factor of the polynomial $f(x)$ if and only if $f(a) = 0$.

Suppose you need to find the value of a polynomial for a particular value, a, of its variable. You can use long division or synthetic substitution to find the remainder that results if you divide the polynomial by $x - a$.

Example: Use synthetic substitution to find $f(1)$ if
$f(x) = x^4 + 3x^2 + 4x - 1$.

$$\begin{array}{r|rrrrr} 1 & 1 & 0 & 3 & 4 & -1 \\ & & 1 & 1 & 4 & 8 \\ \hline & 1 & 1 & 4 & 8 & 7 \end{array}$$

Use the setup for synthetic division by $x - 1$.

The remainder is 7.

Since the remainder is 7, you know that $f(1) = 7$.

Use synthetic substitution to find f(−5) and $f\left(\frac{1}{2}\right)$ for each function.

1. $f(x) = -3x^2 + 5x - 1$
$-101; \dfrac{3}{4}$

2. $f(x) = x^4 + 11x^2 - 1$
$-181; \dfrac{37}{8}$

3. $f(x) = -x^3 + 3x^2 - 5$ **195;** $-\dfrac{35}{8}$

4. $f(x) = 4x^2 + 6x - 7$ **63; −3**

Given a polynomial and one of its factors, find the remaining factors of the polynomial.

5. $x^3 - 4x^2 + 12x - 27; x - 3$
$x^2 - x + 9$

6. $x^3 + 4x^2 - x - 4; x + 4$
$x + 1, x - 1$

Find values for k so that each remainder is 5.

7. $(x^2 + 6x + k) \div (x + 1)$ **10**

8. $(2x^3 + 5x^2 + k) \div (x + 2)$ **1**

Study Guide

Graphing Polynomial Functions and Approximating Zeros

Imagine a point that moves along the graph of a polynomial function. If the point is below the x-axis for a certain value of x and later, for a greater value of x, above the x-axis, the point must have crossed the x-axis somewhere in between.

The Location Principle	Suppose $y = f(x)$ represents a polynomial function and a and b are two numbers such that $f(a) < 0$ and $f(b) > 0$. Then the function has at least one real zero between a and b.

By narrowing in on places where a polynomial function changes from negative to positive values (or vice versa), you can find approximate values for real zeros.

Example: Approximate the real zero of $f(x) = \dfrac{1}{10}x^4 + x^3 - 3x^2 - \dfrac{1}{2}$ to the nearest tenth.

The first table below helps you see that there is a zero between 2 and 3. The second table shows that the graph intersects the x-axis between 2.4 and 2.5, a little closer to 2.5 than to 2.4.

The real zero of $f(x)$ is approximately 2.4.

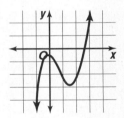

x	$f(x)$		x	$f(x)$
1	−4.4		2.2	−2.029
0	−0.5		2.3	−1.405
1	−2.4		2.4	−0.638
2	−2.9		2.5	0.282
3	7.6			

Approximate the real zeros of each function to the nearest tenth.

1. $f(x) = x^3 - 5x^2 + 6x + 1$

2. $f(x) = 6x^4 - 5x^3 + 2x^2 - 5x - 4$

Graph each function.

3. $f(x) = x^4 - 7x - 3$

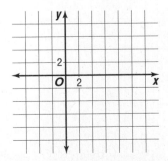

4. $f(x) = 2x^4 - 11x^2 - x + 4$

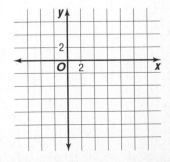

Study Guide

Graphing Polynomial Functions and Approximating Zeros

Imagine a point that moves along the graph of a polynomial function. If the point is below the x-axis for a certain value of x and later, for a greater value of x, above the x-axis, the point must have crossed the x-axis somewhere in between.

The Location Principle	Suppose $y = f(x)$ represents a polynomial function and a and b are two numbers such that $f(a) < 0$ and $f(b) > 0$. Then the function has at least one real zero between a and b.

By narrowing in on places where a polynomial function changes from negative to positive values (or vice versa), you can find approximate values for real zeros.

Example: Approximate the real zero of $f(x) = \frac{1}{10}x^4 + x^3 - 3x^2 - \frac{1}{2}$ to the nearest tenth.

The first table below helps you see that there is a zero between 2 and 3. The second table shows that the graph intersects the x-axis between 2.4 and 2.5, a little closer to 2.5 than to 2.4.

The real zero of $f(x)$ is approximately 2.4.

x	$f(x)$	x	$f(x)$
1	−4.4	2.2	−2.029
0	−0.5	2.3	−1.405
1	−2.4	2.4	−0.638
2	−2.9	2.5	0.282
3	7.6		

Approximate the real zeros of each function to the nearest tenth.

1. $f(x) = x^3 - 5x^2 + 6x + 1$
−0.1

2. $f(x) = 6x^4 - 5x^3 + 2x^2 - 5x - 4$
−0.5 and 1.3

Graph each function.

3. $f(x) = x^4 - 7x - 3$

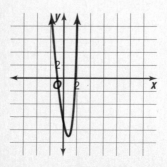

4. $f(x) = 2x^4 - 11x^2 - x + 4$

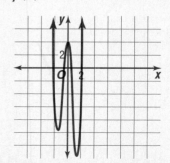

 Algebra 2

Study Guide

Roots and Zeros

There are several methods you can use to find the zeros of a polynomial function.

- Graphing
- Synthetic substitution
- Substituting values and using a calculator

If you know that one zero is imaginary, you can use the complex conjugates theorem to find another zero.

Complex Conjugates Theorem	Suppose a and b are real numbers with $b = 0$. If $a + bi$ is a zero of a polynomial function, then $a - bi$ is also a zero of the function.

You can use Descartes' rule of signs to obtain information about the number of real zeros of a polynomial.

Descartes' Rule of Signs	If $P(x)$ is a polynomial whose terms are arranged in descending powers of the variable, • the number of positive real zeros of $y = P(x)$ is the same as the number of changes in sign of the coefficients of the terms, or is less than this by an even number, and • the number of negative real zeros of $y = P(x)$ is the same as the number of changes in sign of the coefficients of the terms of $P(-x)$, or is less than this number by an even number.

State the number of positive real zeros, negative real zeros, and imaginary zeros for each function.

1. $f(x) = 2x^4 - x^3 - 3x + 7$

2. $P(t) = 16t^3 + 6t^2 - 7t + 3$

Given a function and one of its zeros, find all of the zeros of the function.

3. $f(a) = a^3 - 10a^2 + 34a - 40; 4$

4. $g(x) = x^3 + x^2 + 9x + 9; 3i$

5. $f(x) = x^4 - 5x^3 + 8x^2 - x - 5; 2 - i$

6. $h(x) = x^3 - 5x^2 + 11x - 15; 1 + 2i$

8-4

Study Guide

Roots and Zeros

There are several methods you can use to find the zeros of a polynomial function.

- Graphing
- Synthetic substitution
- Substituting values and using a calculator

If you know that one zero is imaginary, you can use the complex conjugates theorem to find another zero.

Complex Conjugates Theorem	Suppose a and b are real numbers with $b = 0$. If $a + bi$ is a zero of a polynomial function, then $a - bi$ is also a zero of the function.

You can use Descartes' rule of signs to obtain information about the number of real zeros of a polynomial.

Descartes' Rule of Signs	If $P(x)$ is a polynomial whose terms are arranged in descending powers of the variable, • the number of positive real zeros of $y = P(x)$ is the same as the number of changes in sign of the coefficients of the terms, or is less than this by an even number, and • the number of negative real zeros of $y = P(x)$ is the same as the number of changes in sign of the coefficients of the terms of $P(-x)$, or is less than this number by an even number.

State the number of positive real zeros, negative real zeros, and imaginary zeros for each function.

1. $f(x) = 2x^4 - x^3 - 3x + 7$
2 or 0; 0; 2 or 4

2. $P(t) = 16t^3 + 6t^2 - 7t + 3$
2 or 0; 1; 0 or 2

Given a function and one of its zeros, find all of the zeros of the function.

3. $f(a) = a^3 - 10a^2 + 34a - 40; 4$
4, 3 + i, 3 − i

4. $g(x) = x^3 + x^2 + 9x + 9; 3i$
−1, 3i, −3i

5. $f(x) = x^4 - 5x^3 + 8x^2 - x - 5; 2 - i$
$\dfrac{1 + \sqrt{5}}{2}, \dfrac{1 - \sqrt{5}}{2},$ **2 + i, 2 − i**

6. $h(x) = x^3 - 5x^2 + 11x - 15; 1 + 2i$
3, 1 + 2i, 1 − 2i

8-5

Study Guide

Rational Zero Theorem

From the factored form of a polynomial equation, you can look back to say what the original polynomial was. You can also look forward to say what the final solutions will be by setting each factor equal to 0 and solving. Without doing all the multiplication, you can say what the first and last terms of the original polynomial were.

$$(5x + 3)(7x + 2)(4x - 11)(8x - 5) = 0$$

original polynomial

$$(5 \cdot 7 \cdot 4 \cdot 8)x^4 + \cdots + (3 \cdot 2 \cdot -11 \cdot -5)$$

final solutions

$$-\frac{3}{5}, \ -\frac{2}{7}, \ \frac{11}{4}, \ \frac{5}{8}$$

Notice that the coefficient of the x^4 term is the product of the *denominators* of the final solutions. The constant term is similarly related to the product of the *numerators* of the solutions. This example gives some insight into the rational zero theorem.

Rational Zero Theorem	Let $f(x) = a_n x^2 + a_1 x^{n-1} + \cdots + a_{n-1} x + a_n$ represent a polynomial function with integral coefficients. If $\frac{p}{q}$ is a rational number in simplest form and is a zero of $y = f(x)$, then p is a factor of a_n and q is a factor of a_0.

The rational zero theorem allows you to list all possible rational zeros of a polynomial function with integral coefficients. Descartes' rule of signs can help you narrow the field still further.

Example: State all possible rational zeros of
$f(x) = 6x^3 + 11x^2 - 3x - 2$.

The coefficient of x^3 is 6, with has factors ± 1, ± 2, ± 3, and ± 6.

The constant term is -2, which has factors ± 1 and ± 2.

Therefore, the possible rational zeros are
± 1, ± 2, $\pm\frac{1}{2}$, $\pm\frac{1}{3}$, $\pm\frac{2}{3}$, and $\pm\frac{1}{6}$.

Find all of the rational zeros for each function.

1. $f(x) = x^3 + 4x^2 - 25x - 28$

2. $f(x) = x^3 + 6x^2 + 4x + 24$

3. $f(x) = 12x^2 - 7x + 1$

4. $f(x) = x^3 - 9x^2 - 5x + 45$

Find all of the zeros of each function.

5. $f(x) = x^4 + 2x^3 - 11x^2 + 8x - 60$

6. $f(x) = 5x^4 + 28x^3 - 82x^2 + 108x - 32$

NAME_____ DATE _____

Study Guide

Rational Zero Theorem

From the factored form of a polynomial equation, you can look back to say what the original polynomial was. You can also look forward to say what the final solutions will be by setting each factor equal to 0 and solving. Without doing all the multiplication, you can say what the first and last terms of the original polynomial were.

$$(5x + 3)(7x + 2)(4x - 11)(8x - 5) = 0$$

original polynomial

$$(5 \cdot 7 \cdot 4 \cdot 8)x^4 + \cdots + (3 \cdot 2 \cdot -11 \cdot -5)$$

final solutions

$$-\frac{3}{5}, -\frac{2}{7}, \frac{11}{4}, \frac{5}{8}$$

Notice that the coefficient of the x^4 term is the product of the *denominators* of the final solutions. The constant term is similarly related to the product of the *numerators* of the solutions. This example gives some insight into the rational zero theorem.

Rational Zero Theorem	Let $f(x) = a_n x^2 + a_1 x^{n-1} + \cdots + a_{n-1}x + a_n$ represent a polynomial function with integral coefficients. If $\frac{p}{q}$ is a rational number in simplest form and is a zero of $y = f(x)$, then p is a factor of a_n and q is a factor of a_0.

The rational zero theorem allows you to list all possible rational zeros of a polynomial function with integral coefficients. Descartes' rule of signs can help you narrow the field still further.

Example: State all possible rational zeros of
$f(x) = 6x^3 + 11x^2 - 3x - 2.$

The coefficient of x^3 is 6, with has factors $\pm1, \pm2, \pm3$, and ±6.

The constant term is -2, which has factors ±1 and ±2.

Therefore, the possible rational zeros are
$\pm1, \pm2, \pm\frac{1}{2}, \pm\frac{1}{3}, \pm\frac{2}{3},$ and $\pm\frac{1}{6}.$

Find all of the rational zeros for each function.

1. $f(x) = x^3 + 4x^2 - 25x - 28$
−1, 4, −7

2. $f(x) = x^3 + 6x^2 + 4x + 24$
−6

3. $f(x) = 12x^2 - 7x + 1$
$\frac{1}{3}, \frac{1}{4}$

4. $f(x) = x^3 - 9x^2 - 5x + 45$
9

Find all of the zeros of each function.

5. $f(x) = x^4 + 2x^3 - 11x^2 + 8x - 60$
3, 5, ±2*i*

6. $f(x) = 5x^4 + 28x^3 - 82x^2 + 108x - 32$
$\frac{2}{5}, -8, 1 \pm i$

Study Guide

Using Quadratic Techniques to Solve Polynomial Equations

Many equations look very much like quadratic equations when, in fact, they are not. For example, $5(x^{\frac{1}{3}})^2 + x^{\frac{1}{3}} - 4 = 0$ has the rough form of a quadratic equation even though the expression on the left side of the equation is not a polynomial.

Definition of Quadratic Form
An equation is in quadratic form if it is in the form $a[f(x)]^2 + b[f(x)] + c = 0$ where $f(x)$ is some expression in x, and a, b, and c are numbers with $a \neq 0$.

Equations that are in quadratic form can often be solved with the same techniques that work for quadratic equations.

Example: Solve $x^4 - 29x^2 + 100 = 0$.

$$x^4 - 29x^2 + 100 = 0$$
$$(x^2)^2 - 29(x^2) + 100 = 0 \quad \text{Write the equation in quadratic form.}$$
$$(x^2 - 25)(x^2 - 4) = 0 \quad \text{Factor.}$$
$$x^2 - 25 = 0 \text{ or } x^2 - 4 = 0 \quad \text{Use the zero product property.}$$
$$(x + 5)(x - 5) = 0 \text{ or } (x + 2)(x - 2) = 0 \quad \text{Factor each equation.}$$
$$x = -5 \text{ or } x = 5 \text{ or } x = -2 \text{ or } x = 2 \quad \text{Use the zero product property again.}$$

The solutions are -5, -2, 2, and 5.

Write each equation in quadratic form.

1. $x^4 + 6x^2 - 8 = 0$

2. $4p^4 + 6p^2 + 8 = 0$

3. $x^8 + 2x^4 + 1 = 0$

4. $x^{\frac{1}{8}} + 2x^{\frac{1}{16}} + 1 = 0$

Solve each equation.

5. $x^4 = 49$

6. $x^4 - 6x^2 = -8$

7. $m^6 - 16m^3 + 64 = 0$

8. $y^4 - 5y^2 + 4 = 0$

9. $\dfrac{1}{x^2} - \dfrac{7}{x} + 12 = 0$

10. $x - 5\sqrt{x} + 6 = 0$

Study Guide

Using Quadratic Techniques to Solve Polynomial Equations

Many equations look very much like quadratic equations when, in fact, they are not. For example, $5(x^{\frac{1}{3}})^2 + x^{\frac{1}{3}} - 4 = 0$ has the rough form of a quadratic equation even though the expression on the left side of the equation is not a polynomial.

Definition of Quadratic Form
An equation is in quadratic form if it is in the form $a[f(x)]^2 + b[f(x)] + c = 0$ where $f(x)$ is some expression in x, and a, b, and c are numbers with $a \neq 0$.

Equations that are in quadratic form can often be solved with the same techniques that work for quadratic equations.

Example: Solve $x^4 - 29x^2 + 100 = 0$.

$$x^4 - 29x^2 + 100 = 0$$
$$(x^2)^2 - 29(x^2) + 100 = 0 \quad \text{Write the equation in quadratic form.}$$
$$(x^2 - 25)(x^2 - 4) = 0 \quad \text{Factor.}$$
$$x^2 - 25 = 0 \text{ or } x^2 - 4 = 0 \quad \text{Use the zero product property.}$$
$$(x + 5)(x - 5) = 0 \text{ or } (x + 2)(x - 2) = 0 \quad \text{Factor each equation.}$$
$$x = -5 \text{ or } x = 5 \text{ or } x = -2 \text{ or } x = 2 \quad \text{Use the zero product property again.}$$

The solutions are -5, -2, 2, and 5.

Write each equation in quadratic form.

1. $x^4 + 6x^2 - 8 = 0$
   $$(x^2)^2 + 6(x^2) - 8 = 0$$

2. $4p^4 + 6p^2 + 8 = 0$
   $$4(p^2)^2 + 6(p^2) + 8 = 0$$

3. $x^8 + 2x^4 + 1 = 0$
   $$(x^4)^2 + 2(x^4) + 1 = 0$$

4. $x^{\frac{1}{8}} + 2x^{\frac{1}{16}} + 1 = 0$
   $$(x^{\frac{1}{16}})^2 + 2(x^{\frac{1}{16}}) + 1 = 0$$

Solve each equation.

5. $x^4 = 49$
   $$\pm\sqrt{7}, \pm i\sqrt{7}$$

6. $x^4 - 6x^2 = -8$
   $$\pm 2, \pm\sqrt{2}$$

7. $m^6 - 16m^3 + 64 = 0$
   $$2, 1 \pm i\sqrt{3}$$

8. $y^4 - 5y^2 + 4 = 0$
   $$\pm 1, \pm 2$$

9. $\dfrac{1}{x^2} - \dfrac{7}{x} + 12 = 0 \quad \dfrac{1}{3}, \dfrac{1}{4}$

10. $x - 5\sqrt{x} + 6 = 0 \quad \mathbf{4, 9}$

NAME_____ DATE _____

Study Guide

Student Edition
Pages 523–528

Composition of Functions

Composition of Functions
Suppose f and g are functions such that the range of g is a subset of the domain of f. Then the composite function, $f \circ g$, can be described by the equation $[f \circ g](x) = f[g(x)]$.

Example: If $f(x) = x + 7$ and $g(x) = 3 + 2x$, find $[f \circ g](x)$ and $[g \circ f](x)$.

$$[f \circ g](x) = f[3 + 2x] \qquad [g \circ f](x) = g[x + 7]$$
$$= (3 + 2x) + 7 \qquad\qquad = 3 + 2(x + 7)$$
$$= 2x + 10 \qquad\qquad\quad = 2x + 17$$

Find $[f \circ g](x)$ and $[g \circ f](x)$.

1. $f(x) = 2x + 7$
   $g(x) = -5x - 1$

2. $f(x) = x^2 - 1$
   $g(x) = -4x^2$

3. $f(x) = x^2 + 2x$
   $g(x) = x - 9$

4. $f(x) = 5x + 4$
   $g(x) = 3 - x$

5. $f(x) = x^2$
   $g(x) = 2x^2 + 2x - 1$

6. $f(x) = 7x + 6$
   $g(x) = 6x + 7$

If $f(x) = x^2 + 5$, $g(x) = 9x - 1$, and $h(x) = -2x$, find each value.

7. $[f \circ g](-2)$

8. $[h \circ g](-3)$

9. $[f \circ (g \circ h)](2)$

10. $[g \circ h](-3)$

8-7

Study Guide

Composition of Functions

Composition of Functions
Suppose f and g are functions such that the range of g is a subset of the domain of f. Then the composite function, $f \circ g$, can be described by the equation $[f \circ g](x) = f[g(x)]$.

Example: If $f(x) = x + 7$ and $g(x) = 3 + 2x$, find $[f \circ g](x)$ and $[g \circ f](x)$.

$$[f \circ g](x) = f[3 + 2x] \qquad [g \circ f](x) = g[x + 7]$$
$$= (3 + 2x) + 7 \qquad\qquad = 3 + 2(x + 7)$$
$$= 2x + 10 \qquad\qquad\quad = 2x + 17$$

Find $[f \circ g](x)$ and $[g \circ f](x)$.

1. $f(x) = 2x + 7$
   $g(x) = -5x - 1$
   $[f \circ g](x) = -10x + 5$
   $[g \circ f](x) = -10x - 36$

2. $f(x) = x^2 - 1$
   $g(x) = -4x^2$
   $[f \circ g](x) = 16x^4 - 1$
   $[g \circ f](x) = -4x^4 + 8x^2 - 4$

3. $f(x) = x^2 + 2x$
   $g(x) = x - 9$
   $[f \circ g](x) = x^2 - 16x + 63$
   $[g \circ f](x) = x^2 + 2x - 9$

4. $f(x) = 5x + 4$
   $g(x) = 3 - x$
   $[f \circ g](x) = 19 - 5x$
   $[g \circ f](x) = -1 - 5x$

5. $f(x) = x^2$
   $g(x) = 2x^2 + 2x - 1$
   $[f \circ g](x) = 4x^4 + 8x^3 - 4x + 1$
   $[g \circ f](x) = 2x^4 + 2x^2 - 1$

6. $f(x) = 7x + 6$
   $g(x) = 6x + 7$
   $[f \circ g](x) = 42x + 55$
   $[g \circ f](x) = 42x + 43$

If $f(x) = x^2 + 5$, $g(x) = 9x - 1$, and $h(x) = -2x$, find each value.

7. $[f \circ g](-2)$
   366

8. $[h \circ g](-3)$
   56

9. $[f \circ (g \circ h)](2)$
   1374

10. $[g \circ h](-3)$
   53

Algebra 2

Inverse Functions and Relations

The function $I(x) = x$ is called the **identity function,** since for any function f, $[f \circ I](x) = f(x)$ and $[I \circ f](x) = f(x)$. Two functions are **inverse functions** if both their compositions are the identity function.

Definition of Inverse Functions
Two functions, f and g, are inverse functions if and only if both their compositions are the identity function. That is, $[f \circ g](x) = x$ and $[g \circ f](x) = x$.

A special notation is used to show that two functions f and g are inverse functions.

$$g = f^{-1} \text{ and } f = g^{-1}.$$

Suppose f and f^{-1} are inverse functions. Then $f(a) = b$ if and only if $f^{-1}(b) = a$. The inverse function can be found by reversing the order in each pair in the given function or as shown in the example below. In general, the graph of a relation and its inverse are mirror images, or reflections of each other with respect to the graph of the identity function $I(x) = x$.

Example: Find the inverse of $f(x) = 4x + 1$.

Rewrite $f(x)$ as $y = 4x + 1$.

$x = 4y + 1$ **Interchange x and y.**
$4y = x - 1$ **Solve for y.**
$y = \dfrac{x - 1}{4}$

Thus, the inverse of $f(x)$ is the function $f^{-1}(x) = \dfrac{x - 1}{4}$.

Find the inverse of each relation and determine whether the inverse is a function.

1. $f(x) = \dfrac{2}{3}x - \dfrac{1}{4}$ **2.** $h(x) = 5x + \dfrac{1}{4}$

3. $f(x) = \dfrac{2}{3}x + 5$ **4.** $y = x^2 - 8$

5. $g(x) = (x + 10)^2$ **6.** $f(x) = \dfrac{x - 7}{2}$

Find the inverse of each function. Then graph each function and its inverse.

7. $f(x) = 2x + 1$ **8.** $f(x) = x^2 + 2$

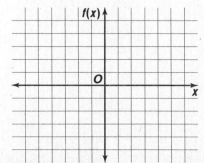

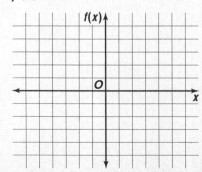

Study Guide

Inverse Functions and Relations

The function $I(x) = x$ is called the **identity function,** since for any function f, $[f \circ I](x) = f(x)$ and $[I \circ f](x) = f(x)$. Two functions are **inverse functions** if both their compositions are the identity function.

Definition of Inverse Functions
Two functions, f and g, are inverse functions if and only if both their compositions are the identity function. That is, $[f \circ g](x) = x$ and $[g \circ f](x) = x$.

A special notation is used to show that two functions f and g are inverse functions.

$$g = f^{-1} \text{ and } f = g^{-1}.$$

Suppose f and f^{-1} are inverse functions. Then $f(a) = b$ if and only if $f^{-1}(b) = a$. The inverse function can be found by reversing the order in each pair in the given function or as shown in the example below. In general, the graph of a relation and its inverse are mirror images, or reflections of each other with respect to the graph of the identity function $I(x) = x$.

Example: Find the inverse of $f(x) = 4x + 1$.

Rewrite $f(x)$ as $y = 4x + 1$.

$x = 4y + 1$ Interchange x and y.
$4y = x - 1$ Solve for y.
$y = \dfrac{x - 1}{4}$

Thus, the inverse of $f(x)$ is the function $f^{-1}(x) = \dfrac{x - 1}{4}$.

Find the inverse of each relation and determine whether the inverse is a function.

1. $f(x) = \dfrac{2}{3}x - \dfrac{1}{4}$ $f^{-1}(x) = \dfrac{3}{2}x + \dfrac{3}{8}$; yes

2. $h(x) = 5x + \dfrac{1}{4}$ $h^{-1}(x) = \dfrac{1}{5}x - \dfrac{1}{20}$; yes

3. $f(x) = \dfrac{2}{3}x + 5$ $f^{-1}(x) = \dfrac{3}{2}x - \dfrac{15}{2}$; yes

4. $y = x^2 - 8$ $y = \pm\sqrt{x + 8}$; no

5. $g(x) = (x + 10)^2$ $g^{-1}(x) = \pm\sqrt{x} - 10$; no

6. $f(x) = \dfrac{x - 7}{2}$ $f^{-1}(x) = 2x + 7$; yes

Find the inverse of each function. Then graph each function and its inverse.

7. $f(x) = 2x + 1$

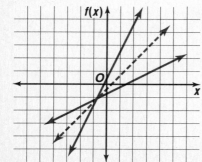

$f^{-1}(x) = \dfrac{x - 1}{2}$

8. $f(x) = x^2 + 2$

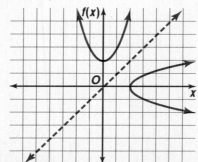

$f^{-1}(x) = \pm\sqrt{x - 2}$

        Algebra 2

Study Guide

Graphing Rational Functions

A rational function is an equation of the form $f(x) = \dfrac{p(x)}{q(x)}$ where $p(x)$ and $q(x)$ are polynomial functions and $q(x) \neq 0$. Functions such as $f(x) = \dfrac{x}{x-2}$ and $f(x) = \dfrac{3}{(x-4)(x-2)}$ are examples of rational functions.

The graph of a rational function has two or more branches. The branches of the graph approach lines called **asymptotes.** First graph the asymptotes. Then plot the points necessary to finish the graph.

Vertical Asymptote	Horizontal Asymptote
The line with the equation $x = a$, if the rational function is undefined when x is a.	The line with the equation $y = b$, if the value of the function approaches b as the value of $|x|$ increases.

Example: Graph $f(x) = \dfrac{x-1}{x}$.

The line with the equation $x = 0$ is a **vertical asymptote** because $f(x)$ is undefined when $x = 0$. As the value of $|x|$ increases, the value of the function approaches 1, as the table shows. The line with equation $y = 1$ is a **horizontal asymptote.**

x	$f(x)$
$\frac{1}{2}$	-1
1	0
2	$\frac{1}{2}$
4	$\frac{3}{4}$
10	$\frac{9}{10}$
$-\frac{1}{2}$	3
-1	2
-2	$\frac{3}{2}$
-4	$\frac{5}{4}$

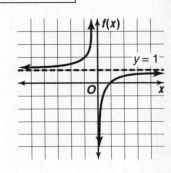

Graph each rational function.

1. $f(x) = \dfrac{3}{x+1}$

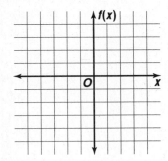

2. $f(x) = \dfrac{2}{x}$

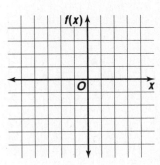

3. $f(x) = \dfrac{2x+1}{x-3}$

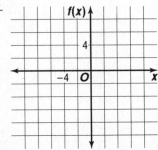

4. $f(x) = \dfrac{2}{(x+3)^2}$

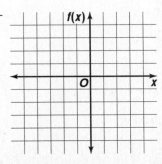

Study Guide

Graphing Rational Functions

A rational function is an equation of the form $f(x) = \dfrac{p(x)}{q(x)}$ where $p(x)$ and $q(x)$ are polynomial functions and $q(x) \neq 0$. Functions such as $f(x) = \dfrac{x}{x-2}$ and $f(x) = \dfrac{3}{(x-4)(x-2)}$ are examples of rational functions.

The graph of a rational function has two or more branches. The branches of the graph approach lines called **asymptotes.** First graph the asymptotes. Then plot the points necessary to finish the graph.

Vertical Asymptote	Horizontal Asymptote
The line with the equation $x = a$, if the rational function is undefined when x is a.	The line with the equation $y = b$, if the value of the function approaches b as the value of $|x|$ increases.

Example: Graph $f(x) = \dfrac{x-1}{x}$.

The line with the equation $x = 0$ is a **vertical asymptote** because $f(x)$ is undefined when $x = 0$. As the value of $|x|$ increases, the value of the function approaches 1, as the table shows. The line with equation $y = 1$ is a **horizontal asymptote.**

x	$f(x)$
$\frac{1}{2}$	-1
1	0
2	$\frac{1}{2}$
4	$\frac{3}{4}$
10	$\frac{9}{10}$
$-\frac{1}{2}$	3
-1	2
-2	$\frac{3}{2}$
-4	$\frac{5}{4}$

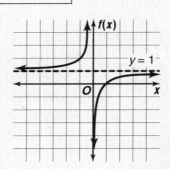

Graph each rational function.

1. $f(x) = \dfrac{3}{x+1}$

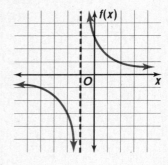

2. $f(x) = \dfrac{2}{x}$

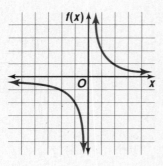

3. $f(x) = \dfrac{2x+1}{x-3}$

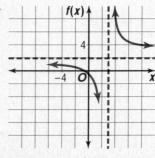

4. $f(x) = \dfrac{2}{(x+3)^2}$

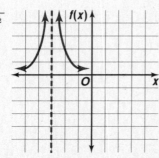

Algebra 2

Study Guide

Direct, Inverse, and Joint Variation

Variables can be related by **direct**, **inverse**, and **joint variation.**

Direct Variation	Inverse Variation	Joint Variation
y varies directly as x if there is some constant k such that $$y = kx.$$	y varies inversely as x if there is some constant k such that $$xy = k.$$	y varies jointly as x and z if there is some number k such that $$y = kxz,$$ where $x \neq 0$ and $z \neq 0$.

Examples:

If y varies directly as x and $y = 16$ when $x = 4$, find x when $y = 20$.

$$\frac{y_1}{x_1} = \frac{y_2}{x_2}$$

$$\frac{16}{4} = \frac{20}{x_2}$$

$$16x_2 = (20)(4)$$

$$x_2 = 5$$

The value of x is 5 when y is 20.

If y varies inversely as x and $y = 5$ when $x = 16$, find y when $x = 20$.

$$\frac{x_1}{y_2} = \frac{x_2}{y_1}$$

$$\frac{16}{y_2} = \frac{20}{5}$$

$$80 = 20y_2$$

$$y_2 = 4$$

The value of y is 4 when x is 20.

If y varies jointly as x and z and $y = 10$ when $x = 2$ and $z = 4$, find y when $x = 4$ and $z = 3$.

$$\frac{y_1}{y_2} = \frac{x_1 z_1}{x_2 z_2}$$

$$\frac{10}{y} = \frac{2 \cdot 4}{4 \cdot 3}$$

$$120 = 8y$$

$$y = 15$$

The value of y is 15 when $x = 4$ and $z = 3$.

Write an equation for each statement. Then solve the equation.

1. Find y when $x = 15$, if y varies inversely as x and $x = 10$ when $y = 12$.

2. Find y when $x = 8$, if x varies directly as y and $y = 9$, when $x = 6$.

3. Find y when $x = 5$ and $z = 3$, if y varies jointly as $x = 3$ and $z = 2$ when $y = 18$.

4. Find x when $y = 9$, if y varies directly as x and $x = 15$ when $y = 5$.

5. Find y when $x = 6$ and $z = 8$, if y varies jointly as $x = 4$ and $z = 2$ when $y = 6$.

6. Find x when $y = 27$, if y varies inversely as x and $x = 9$ when $y = 45$.

7. Find x when $y = 1000$, if y varies directly as x and $y = 50$ when $x = 200$.

8. Find y when $x = 76$, if y varies inversely as x and $y = 100$ when $x = 38$.

NAME_____ DATE _____

Study Guide

Direct, Inverse, and Joint Variation

Variables can be related by **direct**, **inverse**, and **joint variation.**

Direct Variation	Inverse Variation	Joint Variation
y varies directly as x if there is some constant k such that $$y = kx.$$	y varies inversely as x if there is some constant k such that $$xy = k.$$	y varies jointly as x and z if there is some number k such that $$y = kxz,$$ where $x \neq 0$ and $z \neq 0$.

Examples:

If y varies directly as x and $y = 16$ when $x = 4$, find x when $y = 20$.

$$\frac{y_1}{x_1} = \frac{y_2}{x_2}$$

$$\frac{16}{4} = \frac{20}{x_2}$$

$$16x_2 = (20)(4)$$

$$x_2 = 5$$

The value of x is 5 when y is 20.

If y varies inversely as x and $y = 5$ when $x = 16$, find y when $x = 20$.

$$\frac{x_1}{y_2} = \frac{x_2}{y_1}$$

$$\frac{16}{y_2} = \frac{20}{5}$$

$$80 = 20y_2$$

$$y_2 = 4$$

The value of y is 4 when x is 20.

If y varies jointly as x and z and $y = 10$ when $x = 2$ and $z = 4$, find y when $x = 4$ and $z = 3$.

$$\frac{y_1}{y_2} = \frac{x_1 z_1}{x_2 z_2}$$

$$\frac{10}{y} = \frac{2 \cdot 4}{4 \cdot 3}$$

$$120 = 8y$$

$$y = 15$$

The value of y is 15 when $x = 4$ and $z = 3$.

Write an equation for each statement. Then solve the equation.

1. Find y when $x = 15$, if y varies inversely as x and $x = 10$ when $y = 12$.
$$\frac{15}{12} = \frac{10}{y}; \; \textbf{8}$$

2. Find y when $x = 8$, if x varies directly as y and $y = 9$, when $x = 6$.
$$\frac{y}{8} = \frac{9}{6}; \; \textbf{12}$$

3. Find y when $x = 5$ and $z = 3$, if y varies jointly as $x = 3$ and $z = 2$ when $y = 18$.
$$\frac{y}{18} = \frac{5 \cdot 3}{3 \cdot 2}; \; \textbf{45}$$

4. Find x when $y = 9$, if y varies directly as x and $x = 15$ when $y = 5$.
$$\frac{9}{x} = \frac{5}{15}; \; \textbf{27}$$

5. Find y when $x = 6$ and $z = 8$, if y varies jointly as $x = 4$ and $z = 2$ when $y = 6$.
$$\frac{y}{6} = \frac{6 \cdot 8}{4 \cdot 2}; \; \textbf{36}$$

6. Find x when $y = 27$, if y varies inversely as x and $x = 9$ when $y = 45$.
$$\frac{x}{45} = \frac{9}{27}; \; \textbf{15}$$

7. Find x when $y = 1000$, if y varies directly as x and $y = 50$ when $x = 200$.
$$\frac{1000}{x} = \frac{50}{200}; \; \textbf{4000}$$

8. Find y when $x = 76$, if y varies inversely as x and $y = 100$ when $x = 38$.
$$\frac{76}{100} = \frac{38}{y}; \; \textbf{50}$$

9-3

Study Guide

Multiplying and Dividing Rational Expressions

To simplify a rational algebraic expression, divide both numerator and denominator by their GCF. Multiply rational expressions by multiplying the numerators and denominators. Dividing by a rational expression is the same as multiplying by its multiplicative inverse.

Multiplying Rational Expressions
For all rational expressions, $\frac{a}{b}$ and $\frac{c}{d}$, $b \neq 0$, and $d \neq 0$, $\frac{a}{b} \cdot \frac{c}{d} = \frac{ac}{bd}$.

Dividing Rational Expressions
For all rational expressions, $\frac{a}{b}$ and $\frac{c}{d}$, $b \neq 0$, $c \neq 0$, and $d \neq 0$, $\frac{a}{b} \div \frac{c}{d} = \frac{a}{b} \cdot \frac{d}{c}$.

A complex rational expression, also called a **complex fraction,** is an expression whose numerator or denominator, or both, contain rational expressions. To simplify a complex fraction, treat it as a division problem. Remember, all rational expressions must be reduced as much as possible.

Examples: Simplify each expression.

$$\frac{x^2 - 9}{x^2 + x - 12} \cdot \frac{x + 2}{x + 3} = \frac{(x+3)(x-3)}{(x+4)(x-3)} \cdot \frac{x+2}{x+3}$$
$$= \frac{(x+3)(x-3)(x+2)}{(x+4)(x-3)(x+3)}$$
$$= \frac{x+2}{x+4}$$

$$\frac{\dfrac{x^3}{y^3}}{\dfrac{x^2}{y^2}} = \frac{x^3}{y^3} \div \frac{x^2}{y^2}$$
$$= \frac{x^3}{y^3} \cdot \frac{y^2}{x^2}$$
$$= \frac{x^3 y^2}{x^2 y^3}$$
$$= \frac{x}{y}$$

Simplify each expression.

1. $\dfrac{c(c-3)}{c^2 - 25} \cdot \dfrac{c^2 + 4c - 5}{c^2 - 4c + 3}$

2. $\dfrac{(m-3)^2}{m^2 - 6m + 9} \cdot \dfrac{m^3 - 9m}{m^2 - 9}$

3. $\dfrac{x^4 y^2 z^3}{x^2 - 4} \div \dfrac{x^8 y^4 z}{x + 2}$

4. $\dfrac{1}{x+3} \div \dfrac{2x}{(x+2)(x+3)}$

5. $\dfrac{c^3 + 3c^2}{(c+5)^2} \cdot \dfrac{c^2 - 25}{c^2}$

6. $\dfrac{\dfrac{x^2 - 4}{x + 3}}{\dfrac{x^2 - 4x + 4}{x^2 + 3x}}$

7. $\dfrac{\dfrac{b^2 - 100}{b^2}}{\dfrac{3b^2 - 31b + 10}{2b}}$

8. $\dfrac{\dfrac{2x^2 + 9x + 9}{x + 1}}{\dfrac{10x^2 + 19x + 6}{5x^2 + 7x + 2}}$

9. $\dfrac{\dfrac{x^3 y^2 z}{a^2 b^2}}{\dfrac{a^3 x^2 y}{b^2}}$

Study Guide

Multiplying and Dividing Rational Expressions

To simplify a rational algebraic expression, divide both numerator and denominator by their GCF. Multiply rational expressions by multiplying the numerators and denominators. Dividing by a rational expression is the same as multiplying by its multiplicative inverse.

Multiplying Rational Expressions
For all rational expressions, $\frac{a}{b}$ and $\frac{c}{d}$, $b \neq 0$, and $d \neq 0$, $\frac{a}{b} \cdot \frac{c}{d} = \frac{ac}{bd}$.

Dividing Rational Expressions
For all rational expressions, $\frac{a}{b}$ and $\frac{c}{d}$, $b \neq 0$, $c \neq 0$, and $d \neq 0$, $\frac{a}{b} \div \frac{c}{d} = \frac{a}{b} \cdot \frac{d}{c}$.

A complex rational expression, also called a **complex fraction,** is an expression whose numerator or denominator, or both, contain rational expressions. To simplify a complex fraction, treat it as a division problem. Remember, all rational expressions must be reduced as much as possible.

Examples: Simplify each expression.

$$\frac{x^2 - 9}{x^2 + x - 12} \cdot \frac{x + 2}{x + 3} = \frac{(x + 3)(x - 3)}{(x + 4)(x - 3)} \cdot \frac{x + 2}{x + 3}$$

$$= \frac{(x + 3)(x - 3)(x + 2)}{(x + 4)(x - 3)(x + 3)}$$

$$= \frac{x + 2}{x + 4}$$

$$\frac{\frac{x^3}{y^3}}{\frac{x^2}{y^2}} = \frac{x^3}{y^3} \div \frac{x^2}{y^2}$$

$$= \frac{x^3}{y^3} \cdot \frac{y^2}{x^2}$$

$$= \frac{x^3 y^2}{x^2 y^3}$$

$$= \frac{x}{y}$$

Simplify each expression.

1. $\dfrac{c(c - 3)}{c^2 - 25} \cdot \dfrac{c^2 + 4c - 5}{c^2 - 4c + 3}$

$\dfrac{c}{c - 5}$

2. $\dfrac{(m - 3)^2}{m^2 - 6m + 9} \cdot \dfrac{m^3 - 9m}{m^2 - 9}$

m

3. $\dfrac{x^4 y^2 z^3}{x^2 - 4} \div \dfrac{x^8 y^4 z}{x + 2}$

$\dfrac{z^2}{(x - 2)x^4 y^2}$

4. $\dfrac{1}{x + 3} \div \dfrac{2x}{(x + 2)(x + 3)}$

$\dfrac{x + 2}{2x}$

5. $\dfrac{c^3 + 3c^2}{(c + 5)^2} \cdot \dfrac{c^2 - 25}{c^2}$

$\dfrac{(c + 3)(c - 5)}{c + 5}$

6. $\dfrac{\frac{x^2 - 4}{x + 3}}{\frac{x^2 - 4x + 4}{x^2 + 3x}}$

$\dfrac{x(x + 2)}{x - 2}$

7. $\dfrac{\frac{b^2 - 100}{b^2}}{\frac{3b^2 - 31b + 10}{2b}}$

$\dfrac{2b + 20}{b^2(3b - 1)}$

8. $\dfrac{\frac{2x^2 + 9x + 9}{x + 1}}{\frac{10x^2 + 19x + 6}{5x^2 + 7x + 2}}$

$x + 3$

9. $\dfrac{\frac{x^3 y^2 z}{a^2 b^2}}{\frac{a^3 x^2 y}{b^2}}$

$\dfrac{xyz}{a^5}$

NAME_____ DATE _____

Study Guide

Adding and Subtracting Rational Expressions

Use this chart to assist in adding and subtracting rational expressions.

1. To add or subtract rational expressions, they must have the same denominator.
2. If the denominators are different, find the least common denominator (LCD). Find equivalent fractions that have this denominator.
3. Add or subtract the numerators.
4. Combine like terms in the numerator.
5. Factor.
6. Simplify.

Example: Simplify $\dfrac{x+4}{2x-8} - \dfrac{x+12}{4x-16}$.

$$\frac{x+4}{2x-8} - \frac{x+12}{4x-16} = \frac{x+4}{2(x-4)} - \frac{x+12}{4(x-4)} \qquad \text{Factor each denominator.}$$

$$= \frac{2(x+4)}{4(x-4)} - \frac{x+12}{4(x-4)} \qquad \text{The LCD is } 4(x-4).$$

$$= \frac{(2x+8)-(x+12)}{4(x-4)} \qquad \text{Subtract the numerators.}$$

$$= \frac{2x+8-x-12}{4(x-4)}$$

$$= \frac{x-4}{4(x-4)} \text{ or } \frac{1}{4} \qquad \text{Combine like terms and simplify.}$$

Simplify each expression.

1. $\dfrac{-7xy}{3x} + \dfrac{4y^2}{2y}$

2. $c + \dfrac{2}{c+1}$

3. $\dfrac{2}{x-3} - \dfrac{1}{x-1}$

4. $\dfrac{4a}{3bc} + \dfrac{15b}{5ac}$

5. $\dfrac{3}{x+2} + \dfrac{4x+5}{3x+6}$

6. $\dfrac{4}{m+1} + \dfrac{3}{m-2}$

7. $\dfrac{3x+3}{x^2+2x+1} + \dfrac{x-1}{x^2-1}$

8. $\dfrac{7a}{a^2-p^2} - \dfrac{1}{a-p}$

9. $\dfrac{\dfrac{1}{a} + \dfrac{1}{b}}{\dfrac{1}{a} - \dfrac{1}{b}}$

Study Guide

Adding and Subtracting Rational Expressions

Use this chart to assist in adding and subtracting rational expressions.

1. To add or subtract rational expressions, they must have the same denominator.
2. If the denominators are different, find the least common denominator (LCD). Find equivalent fractions that have this denominator.
3. Add or subtract the numerators.
4. Combine like terms in the numerator.
5. Factor.
6. Simplify.

Example: Simplify $\dfrac{x+4}{2x-8} - \dfrac{x+12}{4x-16}$.

$$\frac{x+4}{2x-8} - \frac{x+12}{4x-16} = \frac{x+4}{2(x-4)} - \frac{x+12}{4(x-4)}$$ Factor each denominator.

$$= \frac{2(x+4)}{4(x-4)} - \frac{x+12}{4(x-4)}$$ The LCD is $4(x-4)$.

$$= \frac{(2x+8)-(x+12)}{4(x-4)}$$ Subtract the numerators.

$$= \frac{2x+8-x-12}{4(x-4)}$$

$$= \frac{x-4}{4(x-4)} \text{ or } \frac{1}{4}$$ Combine like terms and simplify.

Simplify each expression.

1. $\dfrac{-7xy}{3x} + \dfrac{4y^2}{2y}$

$-\dfrac{y}{3}$

2. $c + \dfrac{2}{c+1}$

$\dfrac{c^2+c+1}{c+1}$

3. $\dfrac{2}{x-3} - \dfrac{1}{x-1}$

$\dfrac{x+1}{(x-1)(x-3)}$

4. $\dfrac{4a}{3bc} + \dfrac{15b}{5ac}$

$\dfrac{4a^2+9b^2}{3abc}$

5. $\dfrac{3}{x+2} + \dfrac{4x+5}{3x+6}$

$\dfrac{4x+14}{3x+6}$

6. $\dfrac{4}{m+1} + \dfrac{3}{m-2}$

$\dfrac{7m-5}{(m+1)(m-2)}$

7. $\dfrac{3x+3}{x^2+2x+1} + \dfrac{x-1}{x^2-1}$

$\dfrac{4}{x+1}$

8. $\dfrac{7a}{a^2-p^2} - \dfrac{1}{a-p}$

$\dfrac{6a-p}{a^2-p^2}$

9. $\dfrac{\frac{1}{a}+\frac{1}{b}}{\frac{1}{a}-\frac{1}{b}}$

$\dfrac{a+b}{a-b}$

Algebra 2

Solving Rational Equations

An equation that consists of one or more rational expressions is called a **rational equation.** One method of solving a rational equation is to multiply each side of the equation by the least common denominator (LCD) of *all* the denominators. Remember that a rational expression is undefined when the denominator is zero. Be sure to watch for solutions that would produce a denominator of zero. These solutions must be excluded from the final solution set.

Example: Solve $\dfrac{9}{10} + \dfrac{2}{x+1} = \dfrac{2}{5}$

$$\dfrac{9}{10} + \dfrac{2}{x+1} = \dfrac{2}{5}$$

$$10(x+1)\left(\dfrac{9}{10} + \dfrac{2}{x+1}\right) = \left(\dfrac{2}{5}\right)(10)(x+1)$$

$$9(x+1) + 20 = 4(x+1)$$

$$9x + 9 + 20 = 4x + 4$$

$$x = -25$$

$$5x = -5$$

Multiply each side by 10(x + 1), the LCD for all three denominators.

Check: $\dfrac{9}{10} + \dfrac{2}{x+1} = \dfrac{2}{5}$

$$\dfrac{9}{10} + \dfrac{2}{-5+1} \overset{?}{=} \dfrac{2}{5}$$

$$\dfrac{9}{10} + \left(-\dfrac{1}{2}\right) \overset{?}{=} \dfrac{2}{5}$$

$$\dfrac{2}{5} = \dfrac{2}{5} \quad ✔$$

The solution is -5.

Solve each equation. Check your solutions.

1. $\dfrac{2y}{3} - \dfrac{y+3}{6} = 2$

2. $\dfrac{4t-3}{5} - \dfrac{4-2t}{3} = 1$

3. $\dfrac{2x+1}{3} - \dfrac{x-5}{4} = \dfrac{1}{2}$

4. $\dfrac{3m+2}{5m} + \dfrac{2m-1}{2m} = 4$

5. $\dfrac{4}{x-1} = \dfrac{x+1}{12}$

6. $\dfrac{x}{x-2} + \dfrac{4}{x-2} = 10$

7. $\dfrac{3}{4} - \dfrac{3m}{4m+6} = 8$

8. $\dfrac{10}{m^2-1} + \dfrac{2m-5}{m-1} = \dfrac{2m+5}{m+1}$

Solving Rational Equations

An equation that consists of one or more rational expressions is called a **rational equation.** One method of solving a rational equation is to multiply each side of the equation by the least common denominator (LCD) of *all* the denominators. Remember that a rational expression is undefined when the denominator is zero. Be sure to watch for solutions that would produce a denominator of zero. These solutions must be excluded from the final solution set.

Example: Solve $\dfrac{9}{10} + \dfrac{2}{x+1} = \dfrac{2}{5}$

$$\dfrac{9}{10} + \dfrac{2}{x+1} = \dfrac{2}{5}$$

$$10(x+1)\left(\dfrac{9}{10} + \dfrac{2}{x+1}\right) = \left(\dfrac{2}{5}\right)(10)(x+1)$$

$$9(x+1) + 20 = 4(x+1)$$

$$9x + 9 + 20 = 4x + 4$$

$$x = -25$$

$$5x = -5$$

Multiply each side by 10(x + 1), the LCD for all three denominators.

Check:

$$\dfrac{9}{10} + \dfrac{2}{x+1} = \dfrac{2}{5}$$

$$\dfrac{9}{10} + \dfrac{2}{-5+1} \overset{?}{=} \dfrac{2}{5}$$

$$\dfrac{9}{10} + \left(-\dfrac{1}{2}\right) \overset{?}{=} \dfrac{2}{5}$$

$$\dfrac{2}{5} = \dfrac{2}{5} \checkmark$$

The solution is −5.

Solve each equation. Check your solutions.

1. $\dfrac{2y}{3} - \dfrac{y+3}{6} = 2$ **5**

2. $\dfrac{4t-3}{5} - \dfrac{4-2t}{3} = 1$ **2**

3. $\dfrac{2x+1}{3} - \dfrac{x-5}{4} = \dfrac{1}{2}$ $-\dfrac{13}{5}$

4. $\dfrac{3m+2}{5m} + \dfrac{2m-1}{2m} = 4$ $-\dfrac{1}{24}$

5. $\dfrac{4}{x-1} = \dfrac{x+1}{12}$ **±7**

6. $\dfrac{x}{x-2} + \dfrac{4}{x-2} = 10$ $\dfrac{8}{3}$

7. $\dfrac{3}{4} - \dfrac{3m}{4m+6} = 8$ $-\dfrac{87}{64}$

8. $\dfrac{10}{m^2-1} + \dfrac{2m-5}{m-1} = \dfrac{2m+5}{m+1}$ $\dfrac{5}{3}$

Study Guide

Real Exponents and Exponential Functions

Refer to the following definitions and example when working with real exponents. All the properties of rational exponents that you know apply to real exponents as well. Recall that $a^m \cdot a^n = a^{m+n}$, $(a^m)^n = a^{mn}$, and $a^m \div a^n = a^{m-n}$ (when $a \neq 0$).

Definition of Exponential Function
An equation of the form $y = a \cdot b^x$, where $a \neq 0$, $b > 0$, and $b \neq 1$, is called an exponential function with base b.

Property of Equality for Exponential Functions	
Definition	**Example**
Suppose b is a positive number other than 1. Then $b^{x_1} = b^{x_2}$ if and only if $x_1 = x_2$.	Solve $2^5 = 2^{3n-1}$ for n. $2^5 = 2^{3n-1}$ $5 = 3n - 1$ Property of Equality $6 = 3n$ for Exponential Functions $2 = n$

Simplify each expression.

1. $(3^{\sqrt{2}})^{\sqrt{2}}$

2. $8^{\sqrt{5}} \div 2^{\sqrt{5}}$

3. $(m^{\sqrt{28}})^{\sqrt{7}}$

4. $(x^{\sqrt{2}}y^{3\sqrt{2}})^{\sqrt{2}}$

5. $25^{\sqrt{2}} \cdot 125^{\sqrt{2}}$

6. $(c^{\sqrt{6}})^{\sqrt{63}}$

Solve each equation.

7. $2^{x+1} = 2^{2x+3}$

8. $4^{x+1} = 8^{2x+3}$

9. $3^{2x-1} = \dfrac{1}{9}$

10. $2^{2x+1} = 4^{2x+2}$

11. $6^y = 6^{3y+1}$

12. $8^{2n} = 16^{n-3}$

Study Guide

Real Exponents and Exponential Functions

Refer to the following definitions and example when working
with real exponents. All the properties of rational exponents
that you know apply to real exponents as well. Recall that
$a^m \cdot a^n = a^{m+n}$, $(a^m)^n = a^{mn}$, and $a^m \div a^n = a^{m-n}$ (when $a \neq 0$).

Definition of Exponential Function
An equation of the form $y = a \cdot b^x$, where $a \neq 0$, $b > 0$, and $b \neq 1$, is called an exponential function with base b.

Property of Equality for Exponential Functions		
Definition	**Example**	
Suppose b is a positive number other than 1. Then $b^{x_1} = b^{x_2}$ if and only if $x_1 = x_2$.	Solve $2^5 = 2^{3n-1}$ for n. $2^5 = 2^{3n-1}$ $5 = 3n - 1$ $6 = 3n$ $2 = n$	Property of Equality for Exponential Functions

Simplify each expression.

1. $(3^{\sqrt{2}})^{\sqrt{2}}$ **9**

2. $8^{\sqrt{5}} \div 2^{\sqrt{5}}$ **$4^{\sqrt{5}}$**

3. $(m^{\sqrt{28}})^{\sqrt{7}}$ **m^{14}**

4. $(x^{\sqrt{2}}y^{3\sqrt{2}})^{\sqrt{2}}$ **$x^2 y^6$**

5. $25^{\sqrt{2}} \cdot 125^{\sqrt{2}}$ **$5^{5\sqrt{2}}$ or $3125^{\sqrt{2}}$**

6. $(c^{\sqrt{6}})^{\sqrt{63}}$ **$c^{3\sqrt{42}}$**

Solve each equation.

7. $2^{x+1} = 2^{2x+3}$ **-2**

8. $4^{x+1} = 8^{2x+3}$ **$-\dfrac{7}{4}$**

9. $3^{2x-1} = \dfrac{1}{9}$ **$-\dfrac{1}{2}$**

10. $2^{2x+1} = 4^{2x+2}$ **$-\dfrac{3}{2}$**

11. $6^y = 6^{3y+1}$ **$-\dfrac{1}{2}$**

12. $8^{2n} = 16^{n-3}$ **-6**

NAME _____ DATE _____

Study Guide

Logarithms and Logarithmic Functions

Logarithmic functions are the inverses of exponential functions.

Exponential Equation	Logarithmic Equation
$n = b^p$	$p = \log_b n$

Definition of Logarithms	
Definition	**Example**
Suppose $b > 0$ and $b \neq 1$. For $n > 0$, there is a number p such that $\log_b n = p$ if and only if $b^p = n$.	Solve $\log_2 x = 3$ for x. $\log_2 x = 3$ $\quad 2^3 = x \quad$ Definition of Logarithms $\quad\quad x = 8$

You can use the Property of Logarithmic Functions to solve exponential functions involving logarithms.

Property of Equality for Logarithmic Functions	
Definition	**Example**
Suppose $b > 0$ and $b \neq 1$. Then $\log_b x_1 = \log_b x_2$ if and only if $x_1 = x_2$.	Solve $\log_3(2x - 4) = \log_3(7x + 1)$. $\log_3(2x - 4) = \log_3(7x + 1)$ $\quad 2x - 4 = 7x + 1 \quad$ Property of Equality for $\quad\quad -5x = 5 \quad\quad\quad$ Logarithmic Functions $\quad\quad\quad x = -1$

Evaluate each expression.

1. $\log_4 64$

2. $\log_2 64$

3. $\log_{10} 100{,}000$

4. $\log_5 625$

5. $\log_3 27$

6. $\log_{11} 121$

Solve each equation.

7. $\log_5 m = 4$

8. $\log_2 32 = 3x$

9. $\log_3 2c = -2$

10. $\log_4(3x - 1) = \log_4(2x + 3)$

11. $\log_2(x^2 - 6) = \log_2(2x + 2)$

Algebra 2

NAME_____ DATE _____

Study Guide

Student Edition
Pages 605–610

Logarithms and Logarithmic Functions

Logarithmic functions are the inverses of exponential functions.

Exponential Equation	Logarithmic Equation
$n = b^p$	$p = \log_b n$

Definition of Logarithms	
Definition	**Example**
Suppose $b > 0$ and $b \neq 1$. For $n > 0$, there is a number p such that $\log_b n = p$ if and only if $b^p = n$.	Solve $\log_2 x = 3$ for x. $\log_2 x = 3$ $2^3 = x$ Definition of Logarithms $x = 8$

You can use the Property of Logarithmic Functions to solve exponential functions involving logarithms.

Property of Equality for Logarithmic Functions	
Definition	**Example**
Suppose $b > 0$ and $b \neq 1$. Then $\log_b x_1 = \log_b x_2$ if and only if $x_1 = x_2$.	Solve $\log_3(2x - 4) = \log_3(7x + 1)$. $\log_3(2x - 4) = \log_3(7x + 1)$ $2x - 4 = 7x + 1$ Property of Equality for $-5x = 5$ Logarithmic Functions $x = -1$

Evaluate each expression.

1. $\log_4 64$ **3**

2. $\log_2 64$ **6**

3. $\log_{10} 100{,}000$ **5**

4. $\log_5 625$ **4**

5. $\log_3 27$ **3**

6. $\log_{11} 121$ **2**

Solve each equation.

7. $\log_5 m = 4$ **625**

8. $\log_2 32 = 3x$ $\dfrac{5}{3}$

9. $\log_3 2c = -2$ $\dfrac{1}{18}$

10. $\log_4(3x - 1) = \log_4(2x + 3)$
4

11. $\log_2(x^2 - 6) = \log_2(2x + 2)$
4, −2

Algebra 2

Properties of Logarithms

Logarithms are exponents. Thus, the properties of logarithms
can be derived from the properties of exponents.

Properties of Logarithms	
For all positive numbers m, n, and b, where $b \neq 1$.	
Property	**Example**
Product Property $\quad \log_b mn = \log_b m + \log_b n$	Given $\log_3 5 = 1.465$, find $\log_3 25$. $\log_3 25 = \log_3(5 \cdot 5)$ $\quad\quad\quad = \log_3 5 + \log_3 5$ $\quad\quad\quad = 1.465 + 1.465$ or 2.930
Quotient Property $\quad \log_b \dfrac{m}{n} = \log_b m - \log_b n$	Given $\log_6 2 = 0.3869$ and $\log_6 20 = 1.6720$, find $\log_6 0.1$. $\log_6 0.1 = \log_6\left(\dfrac{2}{20}\right)$ $\quad\quad\quad = \log_6 2 - \log_6 20$ $\quad\quad\quad = 0.3869 - 1.6720$ or -1.2851
Power Property $\quad \log_b m^p = p \cdot \log_b m$	Solve $2\log_4 x - \log_4 8 = \log_4 8$. $2\log_4 x - \log_4 8 = \log_4 8$ $\quad 2\log_4 x = \log_4 8 + \log_4 8$ $\quad 2\log_4 x = \log_4 (8 \cdot 8)$ $\quad 2\log_4 x = \log_4 64$ $\quad \log_4 x^2 = \log_4 64$ $\quad\quad\quad x^2 = 64$ $\quad\quad\quad x = \pm 8$

**Use $\log_{12} 3 = 0.4421$ and $\log_{12} 7 = 0.7831$ to evaluate each
expression.**

1. $\log_{12} 21$

2. $\log_{12} \dfrac{7}{3}$

3. $\log_{12} 49$

4. $\log_{12} 36$

5. $\log_{12} 48$

6. $\log_{12} \dfrac{36}{49}$

Solve each equation.

7. $\log_2 4 - \log_2(x + 3) = \log_2 8$

8. $\log_{10}(x + 3) - \log_{10}(2x - 1) = \log_{10} 2$

9. $\log_3(c + 3) - \log_3(4c - 1) = \log_3 5$

10. $\log_2 x - 3\log_2 5 = 2\log_2 10$

Properties of Logarithms

Logarithms are exponents. Thus, the properties of logarithms can be derived from the properties of exponents.

Properties of Logarithms For all positive numbers m, n, and b, where $b \neq 1$.	
Property	**Example**
Product Property $\quad \log_b mn = \log_b m + \log_b n$	Given $\log_3 5 = 1.465$, find $\log_3 25$. $\log_3 25 = \log_3(5 \cdot 5)$ $\quad\quad = \log_3 5 + \log_3 5$ $\quad\quad = 1.465 + 1.465$ or 2.930
Quotient Property $\quad \log_b \dfrac{m}{n} = \log_b m - \log_b n$	Given $\log_6 2 = 0.3869$ and $\log_6 20 = 1.6720$, find $\log_6 0.1$. $\log_6 0.1 = \log_6\left(\dfrac{2}{20}\right)$ $\quad\quad = \log_6 2 - \log_6 20$ $\quad\quad = 0.3869 - 1.6720$ or -1.2851
Power Property $\quad \log_b m^p = p \cdot \log_b m$	Solve $2 \log_4 x - \log_4 8 = \log_4 8$. $2 \log_4 x - \log_4 8 = \log_4 8$ $\quad 2 \log_4 x = \log_4 8 + \log_4 8$ $\quad 2 \log_4 x = \log_4 (8 \cdot 8)$ $\quad 2 \log_4 x = \log_4 64$ $\quad\ \log_4 x^2 = \log_4 64$ $\quad\quad\ x^2 = 64$ $\quad\quad\ x = \pm 8$

Use $\log_{12} 3 = 0.4421$ and $\log_{12} 7 = 0.7831$ to evaluate each expression.

1. $\log_{12} 21$
1.2252

2. $\log_{12} \dfrac{7}{3}$
0.3410

3. $\log_{12} 49$
1.5662

4. $\log_{12} 36$
1.4421

5. $\log_{12} 48$
1.5579

6. $\log_{12} \dfrac{36}{49}$
0.1241

Solve each equation.

7. $\log_2 4 - \log_2(x + 3) = \log_2 8$
$-\dfrac{5}{2}$

8. $\log_{10}(x + 3) - \log_{10}(2x - 1) = \log_{10} 2$
$\dfrac{5}{3}$

9. $\log_3(c + 3) - \log_3(4c - 1) = \log_3 5$
$\dfrac{8}{19}$

10. $\log_2 x - 3 \log_2 5 = 2 \log_2 10$
12,500

Common Logarithms

Logarithms to base 10 are called **common logarithms.** Every logarithm has two parts, the **mantissa** and the **characteristic.** Logarithms depend on the use of scientific notation. The mantissa is the logarithm of a number between 1 and 10. The characteristic is the power of ten that is used when the number is expressed in scientific notation.

A scientific calculator can be used to find common logarithms. Use the ⬜LOG⬜ key.	**Example:** Find log 273. ENTER: 273 ⬜LOG⬜ 2.4361626 The value of log 273 is approximately 2.4362.
In some cases, the calculator will display a negative number. To avoid a negative mantissa, you can add and subtract 10, in effect adding 0.	**Example:** Find log 0.0034. ENTER: 0.0034 ⬜LOG⬜ −2.4685211 The value of log 0.0034 is approximately −2.4685. −2.4685 + 10 − 10 = 7.5315 − 10
Sometimes a logarithm is given and you must find the number. The number is called the **antilogarithm.** If log $x = a$, then $x = $ antilog a. You can use the ⬜INV⬜ and ⬜LOG⬜ keys to find the antilog of a logarithm.	**Example:** If log $x = 3.6355$, find x. ENTER: 3.6355 ⬜INV⬜ ⬜LOG⬜ 4320.161676 The value of x is approximately 4320.

Use a scientific calculator to find the logarithm for each number rounded to four decimal places. Then state the characteristic and the mantissa.

1. 286.1

2. 0.0048

3. 72.68

4. 0.496

5. 6.15

6. 0.0000008

Use a scientific calculator to find the antilogarithm of each logarithm rounded to four decimal places.

7. 2.162

8. −1.42

9. 3.493

10. −2.353

11. 0.681

12. 4.111

Study Guide

Common Logarithms

Logarithms to base 10 are called **common logarithms.** Every logarithm has two parts, the **mantissa** and the **characteristic.** Logarithms depend on the use of scientific notation. The mantissa is the logarithm of a number between 1 and 10. The characteristic is the power of ten that is used when the number is expressed in scientific notation.

A scientific calculator can be used to find common logarithms. Use the $\boxed{\text{LOG}}$ key.	**Example:** Find log 273. ENTER: 273 $\boxed{\text{LOG}}$ 2.4361626 The value of log 273 is approximately 2.4362.
In some cases, the calculator will display a negative number. To avoid a negative mantissa, you can add and subtract 10, in effect adding 0.	**Example:** Find log 0.0034. ENTER: 0.0034 $\boxed{\text{LOG}}$ −2.4685211 The value of log 0.0034 is approximately −2.4685. −2.4685 + 10 − 10 = 7.5315 − 10
Sometimes a logarithm is given and you must find the number. The number is called the **antilogarithm.** If log x = a, then x = antilog a. You can use the $\boxed{\text{INV}}$ and $\boxed{\text{LOG}}$ keys to find the antilog of a logarithm.	**Example:** If log x = 3.6355, find x. ENTER: 3.6355 $\boxed{\text{INV}}$ $\boxed{\text{LOG}}$ 4320.161676 The value of x is approximately 4320.

Use a scientific calculator to find the logarithm for each number rounded to four decimal places. Then state the characteristic and the mantissa.

1. 286.1
   2.4565; 2; 0.4565

2. 0.0048
   −2.3188; −3; 0.6812

3. 72.68
   1.8613; 1; 0.8613

4. 0.496
   −0.3045; −1; 0.6955

5. 6.15
   0.7889; 0; 0.7889

6. 0.0000008
   −6.0969; −7; 0.9031

Use a scientific calculator to find the antilogarithm of each logarithm rounded to four decimal places.

7. 2.162
   145.2112

8. −1.42
   0.0380

9. 3.493
   3111.7163

10. −2.353
    0.0044

11. 0.681
    4.7973

12. 4.111
    12,912.1927

Natural Logarithms

The number e is used extensively in science and mathematics. It is an irrational number whose value is approximately 2.718. e is the base for the **natural logarithms.** All the properties of common logarithms apply also to natural logarithms. You can use a scientific calculator to compute with natural logarithms. The key marked LN is the natural logarithm key.

Example: Find ln 2.856 using a calculator.
ENTER: 2.856 LN 1.0494220
The natural logarithm of 2.856 is approximately 1.0494.

You can also find the antilogarithms of natural logarithms.

Example: Find x if ln x = 2.874.
ENTER: 2.874 2nd e^x 748.169500
So x is about 748.

Use a scientific calculator to find each value, rounded to four decimal places.

1. ln 732

2. ln 1685

3. ln 84,350

4. ln 0.735

5. ln 100

6. ln 0.0824

7. ln 2.388

8. ln 128,245

9. ln 0.00614

10. antiln 1.3475

11. antiln 2.3862

12. antiln 0.5384

13. antiln 0.0813

14. antiln 4.3165

15. antiln 2.4

16. antiln 3.111

17. antiln 0.113

18. antiln 10

10-5

Study Guide

Natural Logarithms

The number e is used extensively in science and mathematics. It is an irrational number whose value is approximately 2.718. e is the base for the **natural logarithms.** All the properties of common logarithms apply also to natural logarithms. You can use a scientific calculator to compute with natural logarithms. The key marked LN is the natural logarithm key.

Example: Find ln 2.856 using a calculator.
   ENTER: 2.856 LN 1.0494220
   The natural logarithm of 2.856 is approximately 1.0494.

You can also find the antilogarithms of natural logarithms.

Example: Find x if ln x = 2.874.
   ENTER: 2.874 2nd e^x 748.169500
   So x is about 748.

Use a scientific calculator to find each value, rounded to four decimal places.

1. ln 732
   6.5958

2. ln 1685
   7.4295

3. ln 84,350
   11.3427

4. ln 0.735
   −0.3079

5. ln 100
   4.6051

6. ln 0.0824
   −2.4962

7. ln 2.388
   0.8705

8. ln 128,245
   11.7617

9. ln 0.00614
   −5.0929

10. antiln 1.3475
    3.8478

11. antiln 2.3862
    10.8721

12. antiln 0.5384
    1.7133

13. antiln 0.0813
    1.0847

14. antiln 4.3165
    74.9259

15. antiln 2.4
    11.0232

16. antiln 3.111
    22.4435

17. antiln 0.113
    1.1196

18. antiln 10
    22026.4658

Algebra 2

NAME_____ DATE _____

Study Guide

Solving Exponential Equations

An equation with a variable in an exponent is called an **exponential equation.** Such an equation can be solved by using the Property of Equality for Logarithmic Functions.	**Example:** Solve $3^x = 16$. $3^x = 16$ $\log 3^x = \log 16$ $x \log 3 = \log 16$ $x = \dfrac{\log 16}{\log 3}$ $x = \dfrac{1.2041}{0.4771}$ $x = 2.5238$
The Change of Base Formula can be used to find logarithms with bases other than 10. The computations can be done using a calculator. **Change of Base Formula** For all positive numbers a, b, and n, where $a \neq 1$ and $b \neq 1$, then $\log_a n = \dfrac{\log_b n}{\log_b a}$.	**Example:** Express $\log_3 35$ in terms of common logarithms. Then find its value. $\log_3 35 = \dfrac{\log 35}{\log 3}$ $= \dfrac{1.5441}{0.4771}$ $= 3.2364$

Approximate the value of each logarithm to three decimal places.

1. $\log_2 4$

2. $\log_5 75$

3. $\log_{1.3} 67$

4. $\log_{12} 2$

5. $\log_{14} 126$

6. $\log_7 896$

Use logarithms to solve each equation.

7. $4^x = 80$

8. $5^y = 10$

9. $5^x = 18.5$

10. $1.3^{2x} = 78$

11. $6^{3x + 1} = 8$

12. $2^x = 5^{x - 2}$

74

Study Guide

Solving Exponential Equations

An equation with a variable in an exponent is called an **exponential equation.** Such an equation can be solved by using the Property of Equality for Logarithmic Functions.	**Example:** Solve $3^x = 16$. $$3^x = 16$$ $$\log 3^x = \log 16$$ $$x \log 3 = \log 16$$ $$x = \frac{\log 16}{\log 3}$$ $$x = \frac{1.2041}{0.4771}$$ $$x = 2.5238$$
The Change of Base Formula can be used to find logarithms with bases other than 10. The computations can be done using a calculator. **Change of Base Formula** For all positive numbers a, b, and n, where $a \neq 1$ and $b \neq 1$, then $\log_a n = \frac{\log_b n}{\log_b a}$.	**Example:** Express $\log_3 35$ in terms of common logarithms. Then find its value. $$\log_3 35 = \frac{\log 35}{\log 3}$$ $$= \frac{1.5441}{0.4771}$$ $$= 3.2364$$

Approximate the value of each logarithm to three decimal places.

1. $\log_2 4$
2.000

2. $\log_5 75$
2.683

3. $\log_{1.3} 67$
16.026

4. $\log_{12} 2$
0.279

5. $\log_{14} 126$
1.833

6. $\log_7 896$
3.493

Use logarithms to solve each equation.

7. $4^x = 80$
3.1611

8. $5^y = 10$
1.4306

9. $5^x = 18.5$
1.8127

10. $1.3^{2x} = 78$
8.3028

11. $6^{3x+1} = 8$
0.0535

12. $2^x = 5^{x-2}$
3.5132

Study Guide

Growth and Decay

Many problems can be solved by applying the following formulas:

Growth and Decay Formula	$y = ne^{kt}$	y is the final amount, n is the initial amount, k is a constant, and t represents time.
Continuously Compounded Interest	$A = Pe^{rt}$	P is the initial investment, r is the annual interest rate, and t is the time in years.
Value of Equipment and Assets in Business	$V_n = P(1 + r)^n$	V_n is the new value, P is the initial value, r is the fixed rate of appreciation or depreciation, and n is the number of years.

Example: Find how long it will take money to double if it is invested at 8% annual interest, compounded continuously.

$$A = Pe^{rt}$$
$$2 = 1e^{0.08t}$$

Substitute 2 for A, 1 for P since the amount is doubled. $r = 0.08$

$$\ln 2 = \ln e^{0.08t}$$

Take the natural log of each side.

$$\ln 2 = 0.08t(\ln e)$$

Power Property of Logarithms

$$\ln 2 = 0.08t$$
$$\frac{\ln 2}{0.08} = t$$
$$8.6643 = t$$

The money will double in approximately 8.66 years.

Solve.

1. Carl plans to invest $500 at 8.25% interest, compounded continously. How long will it take for his money to triple?

2. A certain strain of bacteria grows from 40 to 326 in 120 minutes. Find k for the growth formula.

3. A $40,000 car depreciates at a constant rate of 12% per year. In how many years will the car be worth $12,000?

Study Guide

Growth and Decay

Many problems can be solved by applying the following formulas:

Growth and Decay Formula	$y = ne^{kt}$	y is the final amount, n is the initial amount, k is a constant, and t represents time.
Continuously Compounded Interest	$A = Pe^{rt}$	P is the initial investment, r is the annual interest rate, and t is the time in years.
Value of Equipment and Assets in Business	$V_n = P(1 + r)^n$	V_n is the new value, P is the initial value, r is the fixed rate of appreciation or depreciation, and n is the number of years.

Example: Find how long it will take money to double if it is invested at 8% annual interest, compounded continuously.

$$A = Pe^{rt}$$
$$2 = 1e^{0.08t}$$
$$\ln 2 = \ln e^{0.08t}$$
$$\ln 2 = 0.08t(\ln e)$$
$$\ln 2 = 0.08t$$
$$\frac{\ln 2}{0.08} = t$$
$$8.6643 = t$$

Substitute 2 for A, 1 for P since the amount is doubled. $r = 0.08$

Take the natural log of each side.

Power Property of Logarithms

The money will double in approximately 8.66 years.

Solve.

1. Carl plans to invest $500 at 8.25% interest, compounded continuously. How long will it take for his money to triple?
   13.316 years

2. A certain strain of bacteria grows from 40 to 326 in 120 minutes. Find k for the growth formula.
   0.0175

3. A $40,000 car depreciates at a constant rate of 12% per year. In how many years will the car be worth $12,000?
   9.42 years

NAME_____ DATE _____

Study Guide

Arithmetic Sequences

A set of numbers in a specific order is called a **sequence.** Each number in a sequence is called a **term.** The first term is symbolized by a_1 and the second term by a_2, so that, in general, a_n represents the nth term. An **arithmetic sequence** is a sequence in which each term, after the first, is found by adding a constant, called the *common difference,* to the previous term.

nth Term of an Arithmetic Sequence
The nth term, a_n, of an arithmetic sequence with first term a_1 and common difference d is given by the formula $a_n = a_1 + (n - 1)d$, where n is a positive integer.

Example: Find the tenth term, a_{10}, of the arithmetic sequence with $a_1 = 7$ and $d = 3$.

$$a_n = a_1 + (n - 1)d$$
$$a_{10} = 7 + (10 - 1)3$$
$$= 7 + 27$$
$$= 34$$

The tenth term is 34.

Find the indicated term in each arithmetic sequence.

1. a_{14} for $a_1 = 4, d = 6$ **2.** a_{12} for $a_1 = -4, d = -2$ **3.** a_{15} for $a_1 = 5, d = -3$

4. a_{10} for $0, -3, -6, -9, \cdots$ **5.** a_{12} for $4, 10, 16, 22, \cdots$ **6.** a_{21} for $10, 6, 2, -2, \cdots$

Find the missing terms in each arithmetic sequence.

7. $5, \underline{\quad}, \underline{\quad}, \underline{\quad}, -3$ **8.** $-7, \underline{\quad}, \underline{\quad}, \underline{\quad}, 1$ **9.** $\underline{\quad}, \underline{\quad}, 42, \underline{\quad}, 60$

10. $18, \underline{\quad}, \underline{\quad}, \underline{\quad}, -2$ **11.** $\underline{\quad}, \underline{\quad}, 3, \underline{\quad}, -11$ **12.** $\underline{\quad}, 10, \underline{\quad}, \underline{\quad}, 4, \underline{\quad}$

Study Guide

Arithmetic Sequences

A set of numbers in a specific order is called a **sequence**. Each number in a sequence is called a **term.** The first term is symbolized by a_1 and the second term by a_2, so that, in general, a_n represents the nth term. An **arithmetic sequence** is a sequence in which each term, after the first, is found by adding a constant, called the *common difference,* to the previous term.

nth Term of an Arithmetic Sequence
The nth term, a_n, of an arithmetic sequence with first term a_1 and common difference d is given by the formula $a_n = a_1 + (n - 1)d$, where n is a positive integer.

Example: Find the tenth term, a_{10}, of the arithmetic sequence with $a_1 = 7$ and $d = 3$.

$$a_n = a_1 + (n - 1)d$$
$$a_{10} = 7 + (10 - 1)3$$
$$= 7 + 27$$
$$= 34$$

The tenth term is 34.

Find the indicated term in each arithmetic sequence.

1. a_{14} for $a_1 = 4, d = 6$
82

2. a_{12} for $a_1 = -4, d = -2$
−26

3. a_{15} for $a_1 = 5, d = -3$
−37

4. a_{10} for $0, -3, -6, -9, \cdots$
−27

5. a_{12} for $4, 10, 16, 22, \cdots$
70

6. a_{21} for $10, 6, 2, -2, \cdots$
−70

Find the missing terms in each arithmetic sequence.

7. $5, \underline{\textbf{3}}, \underline{\textbf{1}}, \underline{\textbf{−1}}, -3$

8. $-7, \underline{\textbf{−5}}, \underline{\textbf{−3}}, \underline{\textbf{−1}}, 1$

9. $\underline{\textbf{24}}, \underline{\textbf{33}}, 42, \underline{\textbf{51}}, 60$

10. $18, \underline{\textbf{13}}, \underline{\textbf{8}}, \underline{\textbf{3}}, -2$

11. $\underline{\textbf{17}}, \underline{\textbf{10}}, 3, \underline{\textbf{−4}}, -11$

12. $\underline{\textbf{12}}, 10, \underline{\textbf{8}}, \underline{\textbf{6}}, 4, \underline{\textbf{2}}$

11-2

Study Guide

Arithmetic Series

The indicated sum of the terms of a sequence is called a **series**. The symbol S_n is used to represent the sum of the first n terms of a series. Since $a_n = a_1 + (n - 1)d$, substitute this into the formula

$S_n = \frac{n}{2}(a_1 + a_n)$ and get another formula for S_n,

$S_n = \frac{n}{2}[2a_1 + (n - 1)d]$.

Sum of an Arithmetic Series
The sum, S_n, of the first n terms of an arithmetic series is given by the following formula. $$S_n = \frac{n}{2}(a_1 + a_n)$$

Example: Find the sum of the first 20 terms of an arithmetic series where $a_1 = 10$ and $d = 3$.

$$S_n = \frac{n}{2}[2a_1 + (n - 1)d]$$

$$S_{20} = \frac{20}{2}[2(10) + (20 - 1)3]$$

$$= 770$$

Sigma notation can also be used to express an arithmetic series.

Example: Find $\sum\limits_{k=1}^{4} (2k - 3)$.

$$\sum_{k=1}^{4} (2k - 3) = \underbrace{2(1) - 3}_{-1} + \underbrace{2(2) - 3}_{1} + \underbrace{2(3) - 3}_{3} + \underbrace{2(4) - 3}_{5}$$

$$= 8$$

Find S_n for each arithmetic series described.

1. $a_1 = 12, a_n = 100, n = 12$

2. $a_1 = 50, a_n = -50, n = 15$

3. $a_1 = 42, n = 8, d = 6$

4. $a_1 = 4, n = 20, d = 2\frac{1}{2}$

5. $8 + 6 + 4 + \cdots + -10$

6. $3 + 6 + 9 + \cdots + 99$

7. $\sum\limits_{n=1}^{20} (2n + 1)$

8. $\sum\limits_{n=5}^{25} x - 1$

9. the first 50 positive odd integers

10. the first 100 positive multiples of 5

Find the first three terms of each arithmetic series.

11. $a_1 = 7, a_n = 83, S_n = 900$

12. $a_1 = 5, a_n = 200, S_n = 4100$

Arithmetic Series

The indicated sum of the terms of a sequence is called a **series**. The symbol S_n is used to represent the sum of the first n terms of a series. Since $a_n = a_1 + (n-1)d$, substitute this into the formula

$S_n = \frac{n}{2}(a_1 + a_n)$ and get another formula for S_n,

$S_n = \frac{n}{2}[2a_1 + (n-1)d].$

> **Sum of an Arithmetic Series**
>
> The sum, S_n, of the first n terms of an arithmetic series is given by the following formula.
>
> $$S_n = \frac{n}{2}(a_1 + a_n)$$

Example: Find the sum of the first 20 terms of an arithmetic series where $a_1 = 10$ and $d = 3$.

$$S_n = \frac{n}{2}[2a_1 + (n-1)d]$$

$$S_{20} = \frac{20}{2}[2(10) + (20-1)3]$$

$$= 770$$

Sigma notation can also be used to express an arithmetic series.

Example: Find $\sum_{k=1}^{4} (2k - 3)$.

$$\sum_{k=1}^{4} (2k-3) = \underbrace{2(1)-3}_{-1} + \underbrace{2(2)-3}_{1} + \underbrace{2(3)-3}_{3} + \underbrace{2(4)-3}_{5}$$

$$= 8$$

Find S_n for each arithmetic series described.

1. $a_1 = 12, a_n = 100, n = 12$
672

2. $a_1 = 50, a_n = -50, n = 15$
−300

3. $a_1 = 42, n = 8, d = 6$
126

4. $a_1 = 4, n = 20, d = 2\frac{1}{2}$
$55\frac{1}{2}$

5. $8 + 6 + 4 + \cdots + -10$
−10

6. $3 + 6 + 9 + \cdots + 99$
1683

7. $\sum_{n=1}^{20} (2n+1)$
340

8. $\sum_{n=5}^{25} x - 1$
294

9. the first 50 positive odd integers
2500

10. the first 100 positive multiples of 5
25,250

Find the first three terms of each arithmetic series.

11. $a_1 = 7, a_n = 83, S_n = 900$
7, 11, 15

12. $a_1 = 5, a_n = 200, S_n = 4100$
5, 10, 15

Geometric Sequences

A **geometric sequence** is a sequence in which each term after the first can be found by multiplying the preceding term by a constant, called the **common ratio.** The common ratio, r, can be found by dividing any term by the preceding term. The terms between any two nonconsecutive terms of a geometric sequence are called **geometric means.**

nth Term of the Geometric Sequence
The nth term, a_n, of a geometric sequence with first term a_1 and common ratio r is given by either of the following formulas. $$a_n = a_{n-1}r \text{ or } a_n = a_1 r^{n-1}$$

Example: Write the first four terms of a geometric sequence in which $a_1 = 3$ and $r = 2$. Find each term using the formula $a_n = a_1 r^{n-1}$.

a_1	a_2	a_3	a_4
3	$3 \cdot 2$	$3 \cdot 2^2$	$3 \cdot 2^3$
3	6	12	24

The first four terms are 3, 6, 12, and 24.

Find the nth term of each geometric sequence.

1. $a_1 = -10, r = 4, n = 2$

2. $a_1 = 4, r = 3, n = 9$

3. $a_1 = -14, r = -\frac{1}{2}, n = 5$

4. $a_1 = -6, r = -\frac{1}{2}, n = 8$

5. $a_3 = 9, r = -3, n = 7$

6. $a_4 = 16, r = 2, n = 10$

7. $a_5 = -1, r = -1, n = 100$

8. $a_3 = \frac{3}{8}, r = \frac{1}{2}, n = 6$

9. $a_4 = \frac{1}{81}, r = \frac{1}{3}, n = 5$

10. $a_1 = 8, r = \frac{2}{3}, n = 5$

11. $a_3 = \frac{1}{10}, r = \frac{1}{10}, n = 6$

12. $a_4 = -54, r = -3, n = 6$

Study Guide

Geometric Sequences

A **geometric sequence** is a sequence in which each term after the first can be found by multiplying the preceding term by a constant, called the **common ratio.** The common ratio, r, can be found by dividing any term by the preceding term. The terms between any two nonconsecutive terms of a geometric sequence are called **geometric means.**

nth Term of the Geometric Sequence
The nth term, a_n, of a geometric sequence with first term a_1 and common ratio r is given by either of the following formulas.
$a_n = a_{n-1} r$ or $a_n = a_1 r^{n-1}$

Example: Write the first four terms of a geometric sequence in which $a_1 = 3$ and $r = 2$. Find each term using the formula $a_n = a_1 r^{n-1}$.

a_1	a_2	a_3	a_4
3	$3 \cdot 2$	$3 \cdot 2^2$	$3 \cdot 2^3$
3	6	12	24

The first four terms are 3, 6, 12, and 24.

Find the nth term of each geometric sequence.

1. $a_1 = -10, r = 4, n = 2$

   -40

2. $a_1 = 4, r = 3, n = 9$

   26,244

3. $a_1 = -14, r = -\dfrac{1}{2}, n = 5$

   $-\dfrac{7}{8}$

4. $a_1 = -6, r = -\dfrac{1}{2}, n = 8$

   $\dfrac{3}{64}$

5. $a_3 = 9, r = -3, n = 7$

   729

6. $a_4 = 16, r = 2, n = 10$

   1024

7. $a_5 = -1, r = -1, n = 100$

   -1

8. $a_3 = \dfrac{3}{8}, r = \dfrac{1}{2}, n = 6$

   $\dfrac{3}{64}$

9. $a_4 = \dfrac{1}{81}, r = \dfrac{1}{3}, n = 5$

   $\dfrac{1}{243}$

10. $a_1 = 8, r = \dfrac{2}{3}, n = 5$

    $\dfrac{128}{81}$

11. $a_3 = \dfrac{1}{10}, r = \dfrac{1}{10}, n = 6$

    $\dfrac{1}{10,000}$

12. $a_4 = -54, r = -3, n = 6$

    -486

Algebra 2

11-4

Study Guide

Geometric Series

The indicated sum of the terms of a geometric sequence is called a **geometric series.**

Sum of a Geometric Series
The sum S_n of the first n terms of a geometric series is given by $S_n = \dfrac{a_1 - a_1 r^n}{1 - r}$ or $S_n = \dfrac{a_1(1 - r^n)}{1 - r}$, where $r \neq 1$.

Example: Find the sum of the first seven terms of the geometric series for which $a_1 = 4$ and $r = -3$.

$$S_n = \frac{a_1 - a_1 r^n}{1 - r}$$

$$S_7 = \frac{4 - 4(-3)^7}{1 - (-3)}$$

$$= 2188$$

The sum of the first seven terms is 2188.

Sigma notation can also be used to express a geometric series.

Example: Write $\displaystyle\sum_{j=1}^{5} 2(3^j)$ in expanded form and find the sum.

$$\sum_{j=1}^{5} 2(3^j) = 2(3^1) + 2(3^2) + 2(3^3) + 2(3^4) + 2(3^5)$$

$$= 6 + 18 + 54 + 162 + 486$$

$$= 726$$

Find the sum of each geometric series.

1. $6 + 18 + 54 + \cdots$ to 6 terms

2. $10 + 5 + \dfrac{5}{2} + \cdots$ to 5 terms

3. $a_1 = 3, r = \dfrac{1}{3}, n = 4$

4. $a_1 = 8, r = -2, n = 7$

5. $a_1 = 2, r = -3, a_5 = 162$

6. $a_1 = \dfrac{2}{3}, r = 6, a_5 = 864$

Write the terms of each geometric series and find the sum.

7. $\displaystyle\sum_{j=1}^{4} 3j$

8. $\displaystyle\sum_{j=4}^{8} 2^j$

Express each series in sigma notation and find the sum.

9. $1 + 3 + 9 + 27 + 81$

10. $1 - 2 + 4 - 8 + 16 - 32$

Algebra 2

Geometric Series

The indicated sum of the terms of a geometric sequence is called
a **geometric series.**

Sum of a Geometric Series
The sum S_n of the first n terms of a geometric series is given by $$S_n = \frac{a_1 - a_1 r^n}{1 - r} \text{ or } S_n = \frac{a_1(1 - r^n)}{1 - r}, \text{ where } r \neq 1.$$

Example: Find the sum of the first seven terms of the geometric
series for which $a_1 = 4$ and $r = -3$.

$$S_n = \frac{a_1 - a_1 r^n}{1 - r}$$

$$S_7 = \frac{4 - 4(-3)^7}{1 - (-3)}$$

$$= 2188$$

The sum of the first seven terms is 2188.

Sigma notation can also be used to express a geometric series.

Example: Write $\sum_{j=1}^{5} 2(3^j)$ in expanded form and find the sum.

$$\sum_{j=1}^{5} 2(3^j) = 2(3^1) + 2(3^2) + 2(3^3) + 2(3^4) + 2(3^5)$$

$$= 6 + 18 + 54 + 162 + 486$$

$$= 726$$

Find the sum of each geometric series.

1. $6 + 18 + 54 + \cdots$ to 6 terms

  2184

2. $10 + 5 + \frac{5}{2} + \cdots$ to 5 terms

  $19\frac{3}{8}$

3. $a_1 = 3, r = \frac{1}{3}, n = 4$

  $4\frac{4}{9}$

4. $a_1 = 8, r = -2, n = 7$

  344

5. $a_1 = 2, r = -3, a_5 = 162$

  122

6. $a_1 = \frac{2}{3}, r = 6, a_5 = 864$

  $1036\frac{2}{3}$

Write the terms of each geometric series and find the sum.

7. $\sum_{j=1}^{4} 3j$

  $3 \cdot 1 + 3 \cdot 2 + 3 \cdot 3 + 3 \cdot 4 = 30$

8. $\sum_{j=4}^{8} 2^j$

  $2^4 + 2^5 + 2^6 + 2^7 + 2^8 = 496$

Express each series in sigma notation and find the sum.

9. $1 + 3 + 9 + 27 + 81$

  $\sum_{j=1}^{5} 3^{j-1} = 113$

10. $1 - 2 + 4 - 8 + 16 - 32$

  $\sum_{j=1}^{6} (-2)^{j-1} = -21$

Study Guide

Infinite Geometric Series

An infinite geometric series is a geometric series in which the number of terms is unlimited. In an infinite geometric series for which $|r| < 1$, the values of the terms approach zero as n increases. The sum of the first n terms approaches a specific number, S, which is called the sum of the infinite geometric series.

Sum of an Infinite Geometric Series
The sum, S, of an infinite geometric series, where the common ratio is $-1 < r < 1$, is given by the following formula. $$S = \frac{a_1}{1 - r}$$

Example: Find the sum of the infinite geometric series

$$20 - 10 + 5 - 2\frac{1}{2} + 1\frac{1}{4} + \cdots$$

$$a_2 = a_1 r$$

$$-10 = 20r$$

$$-\frac{1}{2} = r$$

$$S = \frac{20}{1 - \left(-\frac{1}{2}\right)} \text{ or } \frac{40}{3}$$

The sum is $\frac{40}{3}$.

Find the sum of each infinite geometric series, if it exists.

1. $a_1 = -7, r = \frac{5}{8}$

2. $a_1 = 4, r = \frac{1}{2}$

3. $\frac{2}{9} + \frac{5}{27} + \frac{25}{162} + \cdots$

4. $15 + 10 + 6\frac{2}{3} + \cdots$

5. $a_1 = 6, r = \frac{2}{5}$

6. $18 - 9 + 4\frac{1}{2} - 2\frac{1}{4} + \cdots$

7. $\frac{1}{10} + \frac{1}{20} + \frac{1}{40} + \cdots$

8. $6 - 12 + 24 - 48 + \cdots$

Find the first four terms of each infinite geometric series described.

9. $S = -16, r = \frac{1}{4}$

10. $S = 48, r = -\frac{2}{3}$

11. $S = \frac{33}{4}, r = \frac{1}{3}$

12. $S = 5, r = \frac{1}{5}$

13. $S = \frac{20}{3}, r = -\frac{1}{2}$

14. $S = \frac{1}{12}, r = -\frac{1}{3}$

Study Guide

Infinite Geometric Series

An infinite geometric series is a geometric series in which the number of terms is unlimited. In an infinite geometric series for which $|r| < 1$, the values of the terms approach zero as n increases. The sum of the first n terms approaches a specific number, S, which is called the sum of the infinite geometric series.

Sum of an Infinite Geometric Series
The sum, S, of an infinite geometric series, where the common ratio is $-1 < r < 1$, is given by the following formula. $$S = \frac{a_1}{1 - r}$$

Example: Find the sum of the infinite geometric series

$$20 - 10 + 5 - 2\frac{1}{2} + 1\frac{1}{4} + \cdots$$

$$a_2 = a_1 r$$

$$-10 = 20r$$

$$-\frac{1}{2} = r$$

$$S = \frac{20}{1 - \left(-\frac{1}{2}\right)} \text{ or } \frac{40}{3}$$

The sum is $\frac{40}{3}$.

Find the sum of each infinite geometric series, if it exists.

1. $a_1 = -7, r = \frac{5}{8}$

 $-18\frac{2}{3}$

2. $a_1 = 4, r = \frac{1}{2}$

 8

3. $\frac{2}{9} + \frac{5}{27} + \frac{25}{162} + \cdots$

 $1\frac{1}{3}$

4. $15 + 10 + 6\frac{2}{3} + \cdots$

 45

5. $a_1 = 6, r = \frac{2}{5}$

 10

6. $18 - 9 + 4\frac{1}{2} - 2\frac{1}{4} + \cdots$

 12

7. $\frac{1}{10} + \frac{1}{20} + \frac{1}{40} + \cdots$

 $\frac{1}{5}$

8. $6 - 12 + 24 - 48 + \cdots$

 does not exist

Find the first four terms of each infinite geometric series described.

9. $S = -16, r = \frac{1}{4}$

 $-12, -3, -\frac{3}{4}, -\frac{3}{16}$

10. $S = 48, r = -\frac{2}{3}$

 $80, -\frac{160}{3}, \frac{320}{9}, -\frac{640}{27}$

11. $S = \frac{33}{4}, r = \frac{1}{3}$

 $\frac{11}{2}, \frac{11}{6}, \frac{11}{18}, \frac{11}{54}$

12. $S = 5, r = \frac{1}{5}$

 $4, \frac{4}{5}, \frac{4}{25}, \frac{4}{125}$

13. $S = \frac{20}{3}, r = -\frac{1}{2}$

 $10, -5, \frac{5}{2}, -\frac{5}{4}$

14. $S = \frac{1}{12}, r = -\frac{1}{3}$

 $\frac{1}{9}, -\frac{1}{27}, \frac{1}{81}, -\frac{1}{243}$

Study Guide

Recursion and Special Sequences

A recursive sequence is a sequence in which each succeeding term is formulated from one or more previous terms. A **recursive formula** for a sequence describes how to find the nth term from the term(s) before it.

Parts of a Recursive Formula
1. the value of the first term(s)
2. a recursive equation that shows how to find each term from the term(s) before it

Example: Find the first six terms of the sequence where $f(0) = 4$ and $f(n + 1) = f(n) + 3$.

$f(0) = 4$
$f(1) = f(0) + 3 = 4 + 3 = 7$
$f(2) = f(1) + 3 = 7 + 3 = 10$
$f(3) = f(2) + 3 = 10 + 3 = 13$
$f(4) = f(3) + 3 = 13 + 3 = 16$
$f(5) = f(4) + 3 = 16 + 3 = 19$

A special type of recursion is **iteration.** Iteration is the process of composing a function with itself repeatedly.

Example: Find the first four iterates of $f(x) = 3x + 5$ for an initial value of $x_0 = 1$.

$f(x_0) = f(1) = 3(1) + 5 = 8$
$f(x_1) = f(8) = 3(8) + 5 = 29$
$f(x_2) = f(29) = 3(29) + 5 = 92$
$f(x_3) = f(92) = 3(92) + 5 = 281$

Find the first six terms of each sequence.

1. $f(0) = 1; f(2) = 1; f(n + 1) = f(n) + f(n - 1)$ where $n \geq 2$.

2. $f(1) = 1; f(n + 1) = \dfrac{1}{1 + f(n)}$

3. $f(0) = 3; f(n + 1) = f(n) + 2n$

4. $f(0) = 5; f(n + 1) = f(n) + 2$

5. $f(0) = 1; f(n + 1) = (n + 1) \cdot f(n)$

6. $f(1) = 13; f(n + 1) = f(n) - n + 3$

Find the first three iterates of each function, using the given initial value.

7. $f(x) = x - 1; x_0 = 4$

8. $f(x) = 2x^2 + 5; x_0 = -4$

9. $f(x) = x^2 - 3x; x_0 = 1$

10. $f(x) = 4x - 6; x_0 = -5$

11. $f(x) = x^2 + 2x + 1; x_0 = -2$

12. $f(x) = 4x^2 - 9; x_0 = -1$

Study Guide

Recursion and Special Sequences

A recursive sequence is a sequence in which each succeeding term is formulated from one or more previous terms. A **recursive formula** for a sequence describes how to find the nth term from the term(s) before it.

Parts of a Recursive Formula
1. the value of the first term(s)
2. a recursive equation that shows how to find each term from the term(s) before it

Example: Find the first six terms of the sequence where $f(0) = 4$ and $f(n + 1) = f(n) + 3$.
$f(0) = 4$
$f(1) = f(0) + 3 = 4 + 3 = 7$
$f(2) = f(1) + 3 = 7 + 3 = 10$
$f(3) = f(2) + 3 = 10 + 3 = 13$
$f(4) = f(3) + 3 = 13 + 3 = 16$
$f(5) = f(4) + 3 = 16 + 3 = 19$

A special type of recursion is **iteration.** Iteration is the process of composing a function with itself repeatedly.

Example: Find the first four iterates of $f(x) = 3x + 5$ for an initial value of $x_0 = 1$.
$f(x_0) = f(1) = 3(1) + 5 = 8$
$f(x_1) = f(8) = 3(8) + 5 = 29$
$f(x_2) = f(29) = 3(29) + 5 = 92$
$f(x_3) = f(92) = 3(92) + 5 = 281$

Find the first six terms of each sequence.

1. $f(0) = 1; f(2) = 1; f(n + 1) = f(n) + f(n - 1)$ where $n \geq 2$.
1, 1, 2, 3, 5, 8

2. $f(1) = 1; f(n + 1) = \dfrac{1}{1 + f(n)}$
$1, \dfrac{1}{2}, \dfrac{2}{3}, \dfrac{3}{5}, \dfrac{5}{8}, \dfrac{8}{13}$

3. $f(0) = 3; f(n + 1) = f(n) + 2n$
3, 3, 5, 9, 15, 23

4. $f(0) = 5; f(n + 1) = f(n) + 2$
5, 7, 9, 11, 13, 15

5. $f(0) = 1; f(n + 1) = (n + 1) \cdot f(n)$
1, 1, 2, 6, 24, 120

6. $f(1) = 13; f(n + 1) = f(n) - n + 3$
13, 15, 16, 16, 15, 13

Find the first three iterates of each function, using the given initial value.

7. $f(x) = x - 1; x_0 = 4$
3, 2, 1

8. $f(x) = 2x^2 + 5; x_0 = -4$
37, 2743, 1,548,103

9. $f(x) = x^2 - 3x; x_0 = 1$
−2, 10, 70

10. $f(x) = 4x - 6; x_0 = -5$
−26, −110, −446

11. $f(x) = x^2 + 2x + 1; x_0 = -2$
1, 4, 25

12. $f(x) = 4x^2 - 9; x_0 = -1$
−5, 91, 33,115

Algebra 2

Fractals

A fractal is a geometric figure that has self-similarity, is created using a recursive process, and is infinite in its structure. Fractal geometry provides models for many of nature's designs and patterns.

Example: Air bubbles in fluids are an example of fractals in science.

a. Find the number of bubbles in the 6th stage if the recursive formula for the increase in the number of bubbles per stage is $a_n = 1$, $a_{n+1} = 3a_n - 1$.

$a_1 = 1$
$a_2 = 3(1) - 1 = 2$
$a_3 = 3(2) - 1 = 5$
$a_4 = 3(5) - 1 = 14$
$a_5 = 3(14) - 1 = 41$
$a_6 = 3(41) - 1 = 122$

b. Draw a diagram of the first four stages of this air bubble example.

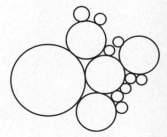

Draw the next stage of the fractal formed by replacing each segment with the pattern shown.

1.

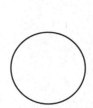

2.

3. Tree branches are an example of fractial geometry. Find the number of branches at stage 5 if the recursive formula is $a_1 = 1$ and $a_{n+1} = 2a_n + 1$.

4. Describe an example of fractals found in the human body.

NAME_____ DATE _____

Study Guide

Fractals

A fractal is a geometric figure that has self-similarity, is created using a recursive process, and is infinite in its structure. Fractal geometry provides models for many of nature's designs and patterns.

Example: Air bubbles in fluids are an example of fractals in science.

    a. Find the number of bubbles in the 6th stage if the recursive formula for the increase in the number of bubbles per stage is $a_n = 1$, $a_{n+1} = 3a_n - 1$.

$$a_1 = 1$$
$$a_2 = 3(1) - 1 = 2$$
$$a_3 = 3(2) - 1 = 5$$
$$a_4 = 3(5) - 1 = 14$$
$$a_5 = 3(14) - 1 = 41$$
$$a_6 = 3(41) - 1 = 122$$

    b. Draw a diagram of the first four stages of this air bubble example.

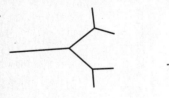

Draw the next stage of the fractal formed by replacing each segment with the pattern shown.

1.

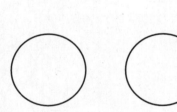

2.

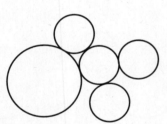 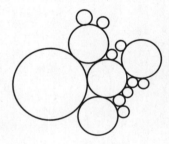

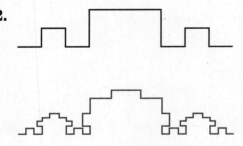

3. Tree branches are an example of fractial geometry. Find the number of branches at stage 5 if the recursive formula is $a_1 = 1$ and $a_{n+1} = 2a_n + 1$. **$a_5 = 2(15) + 1 = 31$ branches**

4. Describe an example of fractals found in the human body.
Examples of fractals in the human body include the blood vessels: arteries, capillaries, and veins.

 Algebra 2

Study Guide

The Binomial Theorem

The binomial expression $(a + b)$ can be raised to various powers.
There are patterns to be found in the powers of $(a + b)$ listed below.

$$(a + b)^0 = 1a^0b^0$$
$$(a + b)^1 = 1a^1b^0 + 1a^0b^1$$
$$(a + b)^2 = 1a^2b^0 + 2a^1b^1 + 1a^0b^2$$
$$(a + b)^3 = 1a^3b^0 + 3a^2b^1 + 3a^1b^2 + 1a^0b^3$$
$$(a + b)^4 = 1a^4b^0 + 4a^3b^1 + 6a^2b^2 + 4a^1b^3 + 1a^0b^4.$$

Next look at just the numerical coefficients
and the pattern becomes obvious. This is
known as Pascal's Triangle. Each new row
is formed by adding elements of the
previous row in pairs. Each row begins
and ends with one.

$(a + b)^0$					1				
$(a + b)^1$				1		1			
$(a + b)^2$			1		2		1		
$(a + b)^3$		1		3		3		1	
$(a + b)^4$	1		4		6		4		1

The Binomial Theorem summarizes these
patterns.

The Binomial Theorem	Definition of n Factorial
If n is a positive integer, then $$(a + b)^n = 1a^nb^0 + \frac{n}{1}a^{n-1}b^1 + \frac{n(n-1)}{1 \cdot 2}a^{n-2}b^2 + \cdots + 1a^0b^n.$$	If n is a positive integer, the expression $n!$ (n factorial) is defined as follows: $n! = n(n-1)(n-2) \cdots 1$

Use a calculator to evaluate each expression.

1. $\dfrac{12!}{3!5!}$

2. $\dfrac{13!10!}{6!17!}$

3. $\dfrac{20!4!}{18!3!}$

4. $\dfrac{18!2!}{20!}$

5. $\dfrac{16!}{12!}$

6. $\dfrac{12!}{6!6!}$

7. $9!$

8. $\dfrac{12!}{8!4!}$

Expand each binomial.

9. $(m + t)^6$

10. $(4m + 2y)^4$

11. $(2 - q)^5$

12. $(x - y)^3$

Find the indicated term of each expression.

13. fourth term of $(2a + b)^5$

14. fifth term of $(y - 5)^6$

Study Guide

The Binomial Theorem

The binomial expression $(a + b)$ can be raised to various powers. There are patterns to be found in the powers of $(a + b)$ listed below.

$$(a + b)^0 = 1a^0b^0$$
$$(a + b)^1 = 1a^1b^0 + 1a^0b^1$$
$$(a + b)^2 = 1a^2b^0 + 2a^1b^1 + 1a^0b^2$$
$$(a + b)^3 = 1a^3b^0 + 3a^2b^1 + 3a^1b^2 + 1a^0b^3$$
$$(a + b)^4 = 1a^4b^0 + 4a^3b^1 + 6a^2b^2 + 4a^1b^3 + 1a^0b^4.$$

Next look at just the numerical coefficients and the pattern becomes obvious. This is known as Pascal's Triangle. Each new row is formed by adding elements of the previous row in pairs. Each row begins and ends with one.

$$
\begin{array}{cc}
(a + b)^0 & 1 \\
(a + b)^1 & 1 \quad 1 \\
(a + b)^2 & 1 \quad 2 \quad 1 \\
(a + b)^3 & 1 \quad 3 \quad 3 \quad 1 \\
(a + b)^4 & 1 \quad 4 \quad 6 \quad 4 \quad 1 \\
\end{array}
$$

The Binomial Theorem summarizes these patterns.

The Binomial Theorem	Definition of *n* Factorial
If *n* is a positive integer, then $(a + b)^n = 1a^nb^0 + \dfrac{n}{1}a^{n-1}b^1 + \dfrac{n(n-1)}{1 \cdot 2}a^{n-2}b^2 + \cdots + 1a^0b^n.$	If *n* is a positive integer, the expression $n!$ (*n* factorial) is defined as follows: $n! = n(n-1)(n-2) \cdots 1$

Use a calculator to evaluate each expression.

1. $\dfrac{12!}{3!5!}$ **665,280**

2. $\dfrac{13!10!}{6!17!}$ **$\dfrac{3}{34}$**

3. $\dfrac{20!4!}{18!3!}$ **1520**

4. $\dfrac{18!2!}{20!}$ **$\dfrac{1}{190}$**

5. $\dfrac{16!}{12!}$ **43,680**

6. $\dfrac{12!}{6!6!}$ **924**

7. $9!$ **362,880**

8. $\dfrac{12!}{8!4!}$ **495**

Expand each binomial.

9. $(m + t)^6$
$m^6 + 6m^5t + 15m^4t^2 + 20m^3t^3 + 15m^2t^4 + 6mt^5 + t^6$

10. $(4m + 2y)^4$
$256m^4 + 512m^3y + 384m^2y^2 + 128my^3 + 16y^4$

11. $(2 - q)^5$ **$32 - 80q + 80q^2 - 40q^3 + 10q^4 - q^5$**

12. $(x - y)^3$
$x^3 - 3x^2y + 3xy^2 - y^3$

Find the indicated term of each expression.

13. fourth term of $(2a + b)^5$
$40a^2b^3$

14. fifth term of $(y - 5)^6$
$9375y^2$

 Algebra 2

12-1

Study Guide

The Counting Principle

If the outcome of one event does not affect the outcome of another event and vice versa, the events are called **independent** events. If their outcomes do affect one another, they are **dependent** events.

Fundamental Counting Principle
If event M can occur in m ways and is followed by event N that can occur in n ways, then the event M followed by the event N can occur in $m \cdot n$ ways.

Example: How many 3-digit numbers can be formed from the digits 1, 2, 3, 4, and 5 if each digit can be used repeatedly?

The use of a digit in one place-value position does not affect whether it may be used in another. There are 5 ways to choose a digit to occupy each of the three place-value positions. Therefore, by the fundamental counting principle, the total number of three-digit numbers possible is $5 \cdot 5 \cdot 5$, or 125.

Solve.

1. The letters A, B, C, and D are used to form four-letter passwords for entering a computer file. How many passwords are possible if letters can be repeated any number of times?

2. How many ways can the first five letters of the alphabet be arranged if each is used only once?

3. A restaurant serves 5 main dishes, 3 salads and 4 desserts. How many different meals could be ordered if each has a main dish, a salad, and a dessert?

4. How many different ways can 4 different books be arranged on the shelf?

5. How many 5-digit even numbers can be formed using the digits 4, 6, 7, 2, 8 if digits can be repeated any number of times?

6. How many 4-digit positive even integers are there?

7. How many license plate numbers consisting of three letters followed by three numbers are possible when repetition is allowed?

8. How many combinations are possible using the information in problem 7 if no repetition is allowed?

Study Guide

The Counting Principle

If the outcome of one event does not affect the outcome of another event and vice versa, the events are called **independent** events. If their outcomes do affect one another, they are **dependent** events.

Fundamental Counting Principle
If event M can occur in m ways and is followed by event N that can occur in n ways, then the event M followed by the event N can occur in $m \cdot n$ ways.

Example: How many 3-digit numbers can be formed from the digits 1, 2, 3, 4, and 5 if each digit can be used repeatedly?

The use of a digit in one place-value position does not affect whether it may be used in another. There are 5 ways to choose a digit to occupy each of the three place-value positions. Therefore, by the fundamental counting principle, the total number of three-digit numbers possible is $5 \cdot 5 \cdot 5$, or 125.

Solve.

1. The letters A, B, C, and D are used to form four-letter passwords for entering a computer file. How many passwords are possible if letters can be repeated any number of times?
256

2. How many ways can the first five letters of the alphabet be arranged if each is used only once?
120

3. A restaurant serves 5 main dishes, 3 salads and 4 desserts. How many different meals could be ordered if each has a main dish, a salad, and a dessert?
60

4. How many different ways can 4 different books be arranged on the shelf?
24

5. How many 5-digit even numbers can be formed using the digits 4, 6, 7, 2, 8 if digits can be repeated any number of times?
2500

6. How many 4-digit positive even integers are there?
4500

7. How many license plate numbers consisting of three letters followed by three numbers are possible when repetition is allowed?
17,576,000

8. How many combinations are possible using the information in problem 7 if no repetition is allowed?
11,232,000

NAME_____ DATE_____

Study Guide

Permutations

An arrangement of things in a certain order is called a **permutation.** In a permutation, the *order* is important. The arrangement of n objects in a line is called a **linear permutation.** The number of linear permutations of n objects taken r at a time is denoted by the symbol $P(n, r)$. If all of the objects are clearly distinguishable, then changing even one object in a permutation leads to a different permutation. The value of $P(n, r)$ is given by the formula

$$P(n, r) = \frac{n!}{(n - r)!}$$

If not all the objects are distinguishable, that fact must be taken into account in counting the permutations. For example, if p of the objects are indistinguishable and another q of the objects are also indistinguishable, then the number of distinguishable linear permutations of the n objects is $\frac{n!}{p!q!}$.

Example: Five people line up for a photo. Among them are two sets of dressed-alike identical twins. How many of the possible lineups would be distinguishable by the photographer?

The number of distinguishable lineups is $\frac{5!}{2!2!}$, or 30.

If n distinct objects are arranged in a circle, they form a **circular permutation.** There are only $(n - 1)!$ circular permutations of n objects. If n objects are in a circular arrangement, but the position of the objects is related to a fixed point, then there are $n!$ permutations. Because of the fixed point, the permutations are now considered linear.

How many different ways can the letters of each word be arranged?

1. MONDAY

2. MOM

3. STEREO

Solve.

4. How many ways can 8 members of a family be seated side-by-side in a movie theater if the father is seated on the aisle?

5. How many ways can 3 books be placed on a shelf if chosen from a selection of 7 different books?

6. The bride and groom and 8 members of the bridal party are seated around a round table. The bride and groom have specific seats. In how many ways can the bridal party be seated around the table?

7. How many ways can 6 charms be placed on a bracelet that has no clasp?

8. How many ways can 6 charms be placed on a bracelet if there is a clasp?

9. How many ways can 8 campers be seated around a campfire?

NAME_____ DATE _____

Study Guide

Permutations

An arrangement of things in a certain order is called a **permutation.** In a permutation, the *order* is important. The arrangement of n objects in a line is called a **linear permutation.** The number of linear permutations of n objects taken r at a time is denoted by the symbol $P(n, r)$. If all of the objects are clearly distinguishable, then changing even one object in a permutation leads to a different permutation. The value of $P(n, r)$ is given by the formula

$$P(n, r) = \frac{n!}{(n - r)!}$$

If not all the objects are distinguishable, that fact must be taken into account in counting the permutations. For example, if p of the objects are indistinguishable and another q of the objects are also indistinguishable, then the number of distinguishable linear permutations of the n objects is $\frac{n!}{p!q!}$.

Example: Five people line up for a photo. Among them are two sets of dressed-alike identical twins. How many of the possible lineups would be distinguishable by the photographer?

The number of distinguishable lineups is $\frac{5!}{2!2!}$, or 30.

If n distinct objects are arranged in a circle, they form a **circular permutation.** There are only $(n - 1)!$ circular permutations of n objects. If n objects are in a circular arrangement, but the position of the objects is related to a fixed point, then there are $n!$ permutations. Because of the fixed point, the permutations are now considered linear.

How many different ways can the letters of each word be arranged?

1. MONDAY
   720

2. MOM
   3

3. STEREO
   360

Solve.

4. How many ways can 8 members of a family be seated side-by-side in a movie theater if the father is seated on the aisle?
   5040

5. How many ways can 3 books be placed on a shelf if chosen from a selection of 7 different books?
   210

6. The bride and groom and 8 members of the bridal party are seated around a round table. The bride and groom have specific seats. In how many ways can the bridal party be seated around the table?
   40,320

7. How many ways can 6 charms be placed on a bracelet that has no clasp?
   60

8. How many ways can 6 charms be placed on a bracelet if there is a clasp?
   360

9. How many ways can 8 campers be seated around a campfire?
   5040

Study Guide

Combinations

A **combination** is a selection of objects where the order is not important. (Remember that order *is* important in a permutation.) The number of combinations of n objects taken r at a time is denoted by the symbol $C(n, r)$. To find $C(n, r)$, use the following formula:

$$C(n, r) = \frac{n!}{(n - r)!\,r!}$$

Example: From a group of 8 men and 6 women, how many committees of 4 men and 3 women can be formed? Order is not considered.

$$C(8, 4) \cdot C(6, 3) = \frac{8!}{(8 - 4)!\,4!} \cdot \frac{6!}{(6 - 3)!\,3!}$$

$$= \frac{8 \cdot 7 \cdot 6 \cdot 5 \cdot \cancel{4} \cdot \cancel{3} \cdot \cancel{2} \cdot \cancel{1}}{4 \cdot 3 \cdot 2 \cdot 1 \cdot \cancel{4} \cdot \cancel{3} \cdot \cancel{2} \cdot \cancel{1}} \cdot \frac{6 \cdot 5 \cdot 4 \cdot \cancel{3} \cdot \cancel{2} \cdot \cancel{1}}{3 \cdot 2 \cdot 1 \cdot \cancel{3} \cdot \cancel{2} \cdot \cancel{1}}$$

$$= 70 \cdot 20 \text{ or } 1400$$

Determine whether each situation involves a permutation or a combination.

1. arrangement of 10 books on a shelf

2. selection of a committee of 3 from 10 people

3. a hand of 6 cards from a deck of 52 cards

4. arrangement of 8 people around a circular table

5. a subset of 12 elements contained in a set of 26

6. a guest list of 3 friends that your family has said you can invite to dinner

Solve.

7. There are 15 different books. How many groups of 6 books can be selected?

8. From a group of 10 men and 12 women, how many committees of 5 men and 6 women can be formed?

9. How many tennis teams of 6 players can be formed from 14 players without regard to position played?

10. From a standard deck of 52 cards, how many ways can 5 cards be drawn?

Study Guide

Combinations

A **combination** is a selection of objects where the order is not important. (Remember that order *is* important in a permutation.) The number of combinations of n objects taken r at a time is denoted by the symbol $C(n, r)$. To find $C(n, r)$, use the following formula:

$$C(n, r) = \frac{n!}{(n - r)! r!}$$

Example: From a group of 8 men and 6 women, how many committees of 4 men and 3 women can be formed? Order is not considered.

$$C(8, 4) \cdot C(6, 3) = \frac{8!}{(8 - 4)! 4!} \cdot \frac{6!}{(6 - 3)! 3!}$$

$$= \frac{8 \cdot 7 \cdot 6 \cdot 5 \cdot 4 \cdot 3 \cdot 2 \cdot 1}{4 \cdot 3 \cdot 2 \cdot 1 \cdot 4 \cdot 3 \cdot 2 \cdot 1} \cdot \frac{6 \cdot 5 \cdot 4 \cdot 3 \cdot 2 \cdot 1}{3 \cdot 2 \cdot 1 \cdot 3 \cdot 2 \cdot 1}$$

$$= 70 \cdot 20 \text{ or } 1400$$

Determine whether each situation involves a permutation or a combination.

1. arrangement of 10 books on a shelf
   permutation

2. selection of a committee of 3 from 10 people
   combination

3. a hand of 6 cards from a deck of 52 cards
   combination

4. arrangement of 8 people around a circular table
   permutation

5. a subset of 12 elements contained in a set of 26
   combination

6. a guest list of 3 friends that your family has said you can invite to dinner
   combination

Solve.

7. There are 15 different books. How many groups of 6 books can be selected?
   455

8. From a group of 10 men and 12 women, how many committees of 5 men and 6 women can be formed?
   232,848

9. How many tennis teams of 6 players can be formed from 14 players without regard to position played?
   3003

10. From a standard deck of 52 cards, how many ways can 5 cards be drawn?
    2,598,960

NAME_____ DATE _____

Study Guide

Probability

When a die is tossed, only six outcomes are possible. The die will show 1, 2, 3, 4, 5, or 6. The desired outcome is called a **success.** Any other outcome is called a **failure.** Probabilities and odds give you a way of gauging the chance of success or failure.

Probability of Success and Failure	
Definition	**Example**
If an event can succeed in s ways and fail in f ways, then the **probability of success,** $P(s)$, and the **probability of failure,** $P(f)$, are as follows. $P(s) = \frac{s}{s+f}$ and $P(f) = \frac{f}{s+f}$.	A bag contains 3 red marbles and 5 green marbles. If one marble is chosen at random, what is the probability that it will be red? $P(\text{red marble}) = \frac{s}{s+f}$ Drawing a red marble is a success. Drawing a green marble is a failure. $= \frac{3}{3+5}$ $= \frac{3}{8}$ The probability of selecting a red marble is $\frac{3}{8}$ or 0.375.
Odds	
Definition	**Example**
The **odds** of the successful outcome of an event is expressed as the ratio of the number of ways it can succeed to the number of ways it can fail. Odds is the ratio of s to f or $\frac{s}{f}$.	What are the odds of drawing a 5 from a standard deck of 52 cards? Odds $= \frac{4}{48}$ A 5 can appear 4 ways. Other numbers can appear in 48 ways. The odds of getting a 5 are 4 to 48 (or 1 to 12).

One bag of candy gummy fish contains 15 red gummy fish, 10 yellow gummy fish, and 6 green gummy fish. Find the probability of each selection.

1. picking a red gummy fish

2. not picking a yellow gummy fish

3. picking a green gummy fish

4. not picking a red gummy fish

Solve.

5. In a bag there are 5 math questions and 4 science questions. Ardie picks a question from the bag. What are the odds of not picking a science question?

6. What are the odds that a person chosen at random got a passing grade on an algebra test if the scores were 3 A's, 4 B's, 10 C's, 2 D's, and 2 F's?

NAME_____ DATE _____

Study Guide

Probability

When a die is tossed, only six outcomes are possible. The die will show 1, 2, 3, 4, 5, or 6. The desired outcome is called a **success.** Any other outcome is called a **failure.** Probabilities and odds give you a way of gauging the chance of success or failure.

Probability of Success and Failure	
Definition	**Example**
If an event can succeed in *s* ways and fail in *f* ways, then the **probability of success,** $P(s)$, and the **probability of failure,** $P(f)$, are as follows. $P(s) = \frac{s}{s+f}$ and $P(f) = \frac{f}{s+f}$	A bag contains 3 red marbles and 5 green marbles. If one marble is chosen at random, what is the probability that it will be red? $P(\text{red marble}) = \frac{s}{s+f}$ Drawing a red marble is a success. Drawing a green marble is a failure. $= \frac{3}{3+5}$ $= \frac{3}{8}$ The probability of selecting a red marble is $\frac{3}{8}$ or 0.375.
Odds	
Definition	**Example**
The **odds** of the successful outcome of an event is expressed as the ratio of the number of ways it can succeed to the number of ways it can fail. Odds is the ratio of *s* to *f* or $\frac{s}{f}$.	What are the odds of drawing a 5 from a standard deck of 52 cards? Odds $= \frac{4}{48}$ A 5 can appear 4 ways. Other numbers can appear in 48 ways. The odds of getting a 5 are 4 to 48 (or 1 to 12).

One bag of candy gummy fish contains 15 red gummy fish, 10 yellow gummy fish, and 6 green gummy fish. Find the probability of each selection.

1. picking a red gummy fish
   $\frac{15}{31}$

2. not picking a yellow gummy fish
   $\frac{21}{31}$

3. picking a green gummy fish
   $\frac{6}{31}$

4. not picking a red gummy fish
   $\frac{16}{31}$

Solve.

5. In a bag there are 5 math questions and 4 science questions. Ardie picks a question from the bag. What are the odds of not picking a science question?
   $\frac{5}{4}$

6. What are the odds that a person chosen at random got a passing grade on an algebra test if the scores were 3 A's, 4 B's, 10 C's, 2 D's, and 2 F's?
   $\frac{19}{2}$

Study Guide

Multiplying Probabilities

To calculate the probability that event A *and* event B will occur,
you need to know whether the events are independent or dependent.

Probability of Two Events	
Independent Events	**Example**
If two events A and B are independent, then the probability of both events occurring is found as follows. $P(A \text{ and } B) = P(A)P(B)$	A bag contains 5 red marbles and 4 white marbles. A marble is to be selected and replaced in the bag. A second selection is then made. What is the probability of selecting 2 red marbles? These events are independent because the first marble selected is replaced. The outcome is not affected by the results of the first selection. $P(\text{both reds}) = P(\text{red}) \cdot P(\text{red})$ $= \dfrac{5}{9} \cdot \dfrac{5}{9} = \dfrac{25}{81}$ The probability is $\dfrac{25}{81}$ or approximately 0.309.
Dependent Events	**Example**
If two events A and B are dependent, then the probability of both events occurring is found as follows. $P(A \text{ and } B) = P(A) \cdot P(B \text{ following } A)$	There are 7 dimes and 9 pennies in a wallet. Suppose two coins are to be selected at random, without replacing the first one. Find the probability of picking a penny and then a dime. Because the coins are not replaced, the events are dependent. Thus, $P(A \text{ and } B) = P(A) \cdot P(B \text{ following } A)$. $P(\text{penny and dime}) = P(\text{penny}) \cdot P(\text{dime following penny})$ $= \dfrac{9}{16} \cdot \dfrac{7}{15} = \dfrac{21}{80}$ The probability is $\dfrac{21}{80}$ or 0.2625.

Determine if each event is independent or dependent. Then find the probability.

1. A box contains 5 triangles, 6 circles, and 4 squares. If a figure is removed, replaced, and a second is picked, what is the probability that a triangle and then a circle will be picked?

2. What is the probability of drawing two cards showing odd numbers from a set of cards that show the first 20 counting numbers if the first card is not replaced before the second is chosen?

3. A jar contains 7 lemon jawbreakers, 3 cherry jawbreakers, and 8 rainbow jawbreakers. What is the probability of selecting 2 lemon jawbreakers in succession providing the jawbreaker drawn first is then replaced before the second is drawn?

4. There are 3 quarters, 4 dimes, and 7 nickels in a change purse. Suppose 3 coins are to be selected without replacement. What is the probability of selecting a quarter, then a dime, and then a nickel?

NAME_____ DATE_____

Study Guide

Multiplying Probabilities

To calculate the probability that event A *and* event B will occur,
you need to know whether the events are independent or dependent.

Probability of Two Events	
Independent Events	**Example**
If two events A and B are independent, then the probability of both events occurring is found as follows. P(A and B) = P(A)P(B)	A bag contains 5 red marbles and 4 white marbles. A marble is to be selected and replaced in the bag. A second selection is then made. What is the probability of selecting 2 red marbles? These events are independent because the first marble selected is replaced. The outcome is not affected by the results of the first selection. P(both reds) = P(red) · P(red) $= \dfrac{5}{9} \cdot \dfrac{5}{9} = \dfrac{25}{81}$ The probability is $\dfrac{25}{81}$ or approximately 0.309.
Dependent Events	**Example**
If two events A and B are dependent, then the probability of both events occurring is found as follows. P(A and B) = P(A) · P(B following A)	There are 7 dimes and 9 pennies in a wallet. Suppose two coins are to be selected at random, without replacing the first one. Find the probability of picking a penny and then a dime. Because the coins are not replaced, the events are dependent. Thus, P(A and B) = P(A) · P(B following A). P(penny and dime) = P(penny) · P(dime following penny) $= \dfrac{9}{16} \cdot \dfrac{7}{15} = \dfrac{21}{80}$ The probability is $\dfrac{21}{80}$ or 0.2625.

*Determine if each event is independent or dependent. Then
find the probability.*

1. A box contains 5 triangles, 6 circles, and 4 squares. If a figure is removed, replaced, and a second is picked, what is the probability that a triangle and then a circle will be picked?

   independent, $\dfrac{2}{15}$ or about 0.133

2. What is the probability of drawing two cards showing odd numbers from a set of cards that show the first 20 counting numbers if the first card is not replaced before the second is chosen?

   dependent, $\dfrac{9}{38}$ or about 0.237

3. A jar contains 7 lemon jawbreakers, 3 cherry jawbreakers, and 8 rainbow jawbreakers. What is the probability of selecting 2 lemon jawbreakers in succession providing the jawbreaker drawn first is then replaced before the second is drawn?

   independent, $\dfrac{49}{324}$ or about 0.151

4. There are 3 quarters, 4 dimes, and 7 nickels in a change purse. Suppose 3 coins are to be selected without replacement. What is the probability of selecting a quarter, then a dime, and then a nickel?

   dependent, $\dfrac{1}{26}$ or about 0.038

NAME_____ DATE _____

Study Guide

Adding Probabilities

Events that cannot occur at the same time are called **mutually exclusive. Inclusive events** are not mutually exclusive. Therefore, the two events can occur at the same time.

Mutually Exclusive Events	Example
The probability of one or the other of two mutually exclusive events A and B occurring is the sum of their individual probabilities. $P(A \text{ or } B) = P(A) + P(B)$	What is the probability of drawing a jack or a king from a standard deck of 52 cards? $P(A \text{ or } B) = P(A) + P(B)$ There are 4 jacks in a deck of 52 or $\frac{4}{52} = \frac{1}{13}$. $= \frac{1}{13} + \frac{1}{13}$ There are 4 kings in a deck of 52 or $\frac{4}{52} = \frac{1}{13}$. $= \frac{2}{13}$ The probability of picking a jack or a king is $\frac{2}{13}$ or about 0.154.

Inclusive Events	Example
The probability of one or the other of two inclusive events A and B occurring is the sum of the individual probabilities decreased by the probability of both occurring. $P(A \text{ or } B) = P(A) + P(B) - P(A \text{ and } B)$	A card is selected from a standard deck of 52 cards. What is the probability that it is a red card or an ace? $P(\text{red or ace}) = P(\text{red}) + P(\text{ace}) - P(\text{red ace})$ $= \frac{26}{52} + \frac{4}{52} - \frac{2}{52}$ There are 2 red aces. Thus, these events are inclusive. $= \frac{28}{52}$ or $\frac{7}{13}$ The probability of selecting a red card or an ace is $\frac{7}{13}$.

State whether the events are inclusive or mutually exclusive. Then find the probability

1. Three cards are selected from a standard deck of 52 cards. What is the probability of selecting a king, a queen, or a red card?

2. A bag contains 45 dyed eggs: 15 yellow, 12 green, and 18 red. What is the probability of selecting a green or a red egg?

3. The letters from the words LOVE and LIVE are placed on cards and put in a box. What is the probability of selecting an L or O from the box?

4. The letters of the alphabet are placed in a bag. What is the probability of selecting a vowel or the letters QUIZ?

12-6

Study Guide

Adding Probabilities

Events that cannot occur at the same time are called **mutually exclusive. Inclusive events** are not mutually exclusive. Therefore, the two events can occur at the same time.

Mutually Exclusive Events	Example
The probability of one or the other of two mutually exclusive events A and B occurring is the sum of their individual probabilities. $P(A \text{ or } B) = P(A) + P(B)$	What is the probability of drawing a jack or a king from a standard deck of 52 cards? $P(A \text{ or } B) = P(A) + P(B)$ There are 4 jacks in a deck of 52 or $\frac{4}{52} = \frac{1}{13}$. $\quad\quad = \frac{1}{13} + \frac{1}{13}$ There are 4 kings in a deck of 52 or $\frac{4}{52} = \frac{1}{13}$. $\quad\quad = \frac{2}{13}$ The probability of picking a jack or a king is $\frac{2}{13}$ or about 0.154.
Inclusive Events	**Example**

The probability of one or the other of two inclusive events A and B occurring is the sum of the individual probabilities decreased by the probability of both occurring.
 	
$P(A \text{ or } B) = P(A) + P(B) -$
$P(A \text{ and } B)$
	A card is selected from a standard deck of 52 cards. What is the probability that it is a red card or an ace?
	$P(\text{red or ace}) = P(\text{red}) + P(\text{ace}) - P(\text{red ace})$
	$\quad\quad = \frac{26}{52} + \frac{4}{52} - \frac{2}{52}$ There are 2 red aces.
	  Thus, these events are
	  inclusive.
	$\quad\quad = \frac{28}{52} \text{ or } \frac{7}{13}$
	The probability of selecting a red card or an ace is $\frac{7}{13}$.

State whether the events are inclusive or mutually exclusive. Then find the probability.

1. Three cards are selected from a standard deck of 52 cards. What is the probability of selecting a king, a queen, or a red card?

   inclusive, $\frac{15}{26}$ or about 0.577

2. A bag contains 45 dyed eggs: 15 yellow, 12 green, and 18 red. What is the probability of selecting a green or a red egg?

   mutually exclusive, $\frac{2}{3}$ or about 0.667

3. The letters from the words LOVE and LIVE are placed on cards and put in a box. What is the probability of selecting an L or O from the box?

   inclusive, $\frac{3}{8}$ or 0.375

4. The letters of the alphabet are placed in a bag. What is the probability of selecting a vowel or the letters QUIZ?

   inclusive, $\frac{7}{26}$ or about 0.269

NAME_____ DATE _____

Study Guide

Student Edition
Pages 752–757

Binomial Experiments and Simulations

Problems that can be solved using binomial expansion are called **binomial experiments.** A binomial experiment exists if and only if the following conditions occur.

1. There are exactly two possible outcomes for any trial.
2. There is a fixed number of trials.
3. The trials are independent.
4. The probability for a given outcome is the same for each trial.

Example: What is the probability that 4 coins show heads and 1 shows tails when 5 coins are tossed?

There are only two possible outcomes: heads (H) and tails (T). The tosses of 5 coins are independent events. When $(H + T)^5$ is expanded, the term containing H^4T^1, which represents 4 heads and 1 tail, is used to get the desired probabilities. The coefficient of H^4T^1 is $C(5, 4)$.

$P(4 \text{ heads, } 1 \text{ tail}) = C(5, 4) \, H^4T^1$ Replace H with $P(H)$ which is $\frac{1}{2}$.

$\qquad\qquad\qquad\qquad = \frac{5!}{4!1!} \left(\frac{1}{2}\right)^4 \left(\frac{1}{2}\right)^1$ or $\frac{5}{32}$ Replace T with $P(T)$ which is $\frac{1}{2}$.

The probability of 4 heads and 1 tail is $\frac{5}{32}$ or approximately 0.156.

Find each probability if a coin is tossed five times.

1. $P(2 \text{ heads})$

2. $P(\text{at least 2 heads})$

Mike guesses on all 10 questions of a true-false test. Find each probability.

3. Mike gets exactly 8 correct.

4. Mike gets at most 3 correct.

5. A die is tossed 4 times. What is the probability of tossing exactly two sixes?

6. A die is tossed 6 times. What is the probability of getting exactly one 3?

Algebra 2

Study Guide

Binomial Experiments and Simulations

Problems that can be solved using binomial expansion are
called **binomial experiments.** A binomial experiment exists
if and only if the following conditions occur.

1. There are exactly two possible outcomes for any trial.
2. There is a fixed number of trials.
3. The trials are independent.
4. The probability for a given outcome is the same for each trial.

Example: What is the probability that 4 coins show heads and
1 shows tails when 5 coins are tossed?

There are only two possible outcomes: heads (H) and
tails (T). The tosses of 5 coins are independent events.
When $(H + T)^5$ is expanded, the term containing H^4T^1,
which represents 4 heads and 1 tail, is used to get the
desired probabilities. The coefficient of H^4T^1 is $C(5, 4)$.

$P(4 \text{ heads}, 1 \text{ tail}) = C(5, 4) H^4T^1$ Replace H with $P(H)$ which is $\frac{1}{2}$.

$\qquad\qquad\qquad = \frac{5!}{4!1!} \left(\frac{1}{2}\right)^4 \left(\frac{1}{2}\right)^1$ or $\frac{5}{32}$ Replace T with $P(T)$ which is $\frac{1}{2}$.

The probability of 4 heads and 1 tail is $\frac{5}{32}$ or
approximately 0.156.

Find each probability if a coin is tossed five times.

1. $P(2 \text{ heads})$

$\frac{5}{16}$ or 0.3125

2. $P(\text{at least 2 heads})$

$\frac{13}{16}$ or 0.8125

***Mike guesses on all 10 questions of a true-false test. Find
each probability.***

3. Mike gets exactly 8 correct.

$\frac{45}{1024}$ or 0.044

4. Mike gets at most 3 correct.

$\frac{11}{64}$ or 0.172

5. A die is tossed 4 times. What is the
probability of tossing exactly two sixes?

$\frac{25}{216}$ or 0.116

6. A die is tossed 6 times. What is the
probability of getting exactly one 3?

$\frac{3125}{7776}$ or 0.402

12-8

Study Guide

Sampling and Testing Hypotheses

A sample of size n is random when every possible sample of size n has an equal chance of being selected.

Example: Determine whether this situation represents a random sampling.

To determine how people in the U.S. feel about mass transit, we decide to stop people at a commuter train station and ask their opinion.

No; we would be questioning only people who actually use a mass-transit facility. The sample would not include people who prefer to ride a bike, drive a car, or walk.

The sampling error is the difference between the sample results and the true population results. If the percentage of people in a sample responding in a certain way is p and the size of the sample is n, then 95% of the time, the percentage of the population responding in that same way will be within $p \pm$ ME where ME $= 2\sqrt{\dfrac{p(1-p)}{n}}$.

Example: Find the margin of sampling error in this situation and explain what it indicates about the results.

A high-school counselor sent a letter to each member of the preceding year's graduating class of 172 members, asking how well he or she was doing in college. 83% said that they were "having a great year" or "doing well."

$$\text{ME} = 2\sqrt{\frac{0.83(1-0.83)}{1072}} = 2(0.01147) \approx 2.3\%$$

This 2.3% means that there is a 95% probability that between 80.8% and 85.2% of the population believes they are "having a great year" or "doing well."

Determine whether this situation represents a random sampling. Write yes or no and explain.

1. Asking people in Phoenix, Arizona, to determine the average rainfall for the United States

2. Obtaining a variety of tree types in North America from all of the U.S. National Forests

Find the margin of sampling error in Exercises 3 and 4. Explain what it indicates about the results.

3. A survey by the makers of Sneezarrest capsules claimed that in a poll of 200 doctors, 90% of the physicians surveyed preferred their product.

4. A study of 50,000 drivers in Indiana, Illinois, and Ohio showed that 68% preferred a speed limit of 75 mph over 65 mph on highways and country roads.

Study Guide

Sampling and Testing Hypotheses

A sample of size n is random when every possible sample of size n has
an equal chance of being selected.

Example: Determine whether this situation represents a random sampling.

To determine how people in the U.S. feel about mass transit, we
decide to stop people at a commuter train station and ask their opinion.

No; we would be questioning only people who actually use a mass-transit
facility. The sample would not include people who prefer to ride a bike,
drive a car, or walk.

The sampling error is the difference between the sample results and
the true population results. If the percentage of people in a sample
responding in a certain way is p and the size of the sample is n, then
95% of the time, the percentage of the population responding in that

same way will be within $p \pm$ ME where ME $= 2\sqrt{\dfrac{p(1-p)}{n}}$.

Example: Find the margin of sampling error in this situation and
explain what it indicates about the results.

A high-school counselor sent a letter to each member of
the preceding year's graduating class of 172 members,
asking how well he or she was doing in college. 83% said
that they were "having a great year" or "doing well."

$$\text{ME} = 2\sqrt{\frac{0.83(1-0.83)}{1072}} = 2(0.01147) \approx 2.3\%$$

This 2.3% means that there is a 95% probability that
between 80.8% and 85.2% of the population believes they
are "having a great year" or "doing well."

Determine whether this situation represents a random sampling. Write yes or no and explain.

1. Asking people in Phoenix, Arizona, to determine the average
   rainfall for the United States No; it rains less in Phoenix
   than most places in the U.S.

2. Obtaining a variety of tree types in North America from all of the
   U.S. National Forests Yes; there are National Forests in
   about every state in the U.S.

Find the margin of sampling error in Exercises 3 and 4. Explain what it indicates about the results.

3. A survey by the makers of Sneezarrest capsules claimed that in a poll
   of 200 doctors, 90% of the physicians surveyed preferred their product. ME = 1.3%
   There is a 95% probability that 88.7–91.3% of the doctors preferred
   Sneezarrest.

4. A study of 50,000 drivers in Indiana, Illinois, and Ohio showed
   that 68% preferred a speed limit of 75 mph over 65 mph on
   highways and country roads. ME = 0.4% There is a 95% probability that
   67.6–68.4% preferred a 75 mph speed limit on highways.

An Introduction to Trigonometry

Trigonometry can be used to find the missing measures of triangles. Refer to the diagram at the right. The **hypotenuse** of triangle ABC is side AB, and its length is c units. The side opposite angle A is side BC. Its length is a units. The side **adjacent** to angle A is side AC. Its length is b units.

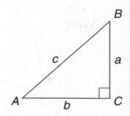

Using the figure, trigonometric values can be defined in the following way.

$$\sin A = \frac{\text{opposite side}}{\text{hypotenuse}} = \frac{a}{c} \qquad \cos A = \frac{\text{adjacent side}}{\text{hypotenuse}} = \frac{b}{c} \qquad \tan A = \frac{\text{opposite side}}{\text{adjacent side}} = \frac{a}{b}$$

$$\csc A = \frac{\text{hypotenuse}}{\text{opposite side}} = \frac{c}{a} \qquad \sec A = \frac{\text{hypotenuse}}{\text{adjacent side}} = \frac{c}{b} \qquad \cot A = \frac{\text{adjacent side}}{\text{opposite side}} = \frac{b}{a}$$

Example: Find the sine, cosine, tangent, cosecant, secant, and cotangent of angle A rounded to four decimal places.

$$\sin A = \frac{6}{10} \text{ or } 0.6000 \qquad \csc A = \frac{10}{6} \text{ or } 1.6667$$

$$\cos A = \frac{8}{10} \text{ or } 0.8000 \qquad \sec A = \frac{10}{8} \text{ or } 1.2500$$

$$\tan A = \frac{6}{8} \text{ or } 0.7500 \qquad \cot A = \frac{8}{6} \text{ or } 1.3333$$

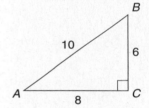

Solve. Round measures of sides and angles to the nearest tenth.

1. If $c = 21$ and $a = 15$, find b.

2. If $a = 32$ and $b = 15$, find A.

3. If $A = 32°$ and $c = 8$, find b.

4. If $a = 5$ and $b = 10$, find A, B, and c.

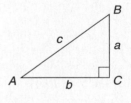

5. A 150-foot rope is tied from the top of a 100-foot-tall pole to a stake in the ground. What is the angle between the rope and the ground?

6. A 6-foot-long pipe is propped on a 3-foot-tall packing crate that sits on level ground. One foot of the pipe extends above the top edge of the crate and the other end rests on the ground. What angle does the pipe form with the ground?

Study Guide

An Introduction to Trigonometry

Trigonometry can be used to find the missing measures of triangles. Refer to the diagram at the right. The **hypotenuse** of triangle ABC is side AB, and its length is c units. The side opposite angle A is side BC. Its length is a units. The side **adjacent** to angle A is side AC. Its length is b units.

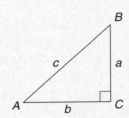

Using the figure, trigonometric values can be defined in the following way.

$$\sin A = \frac{\text{opposite side}}{\text{hypotenuse}} = \frac{a}{c} \qquad \cos A = \frac{\text{adjacent side}}{\text{hypotenuse}} = \frac{b}{c} \qquad \tan A = \frac{\text{opposite side}}{\text{adjacent side}} = \frac{a}{b}$$

$$\csc A = \frac{\text{hypotenuse}}{\text{opposite side}} = \frac{c}{a} \qquad \sec A = \frac{\text{hypotenuse}}{\text{adjacent side}} = \frac{c}{b} \qquad \cot A = \frac{\text{adjacent side}}{\text{opposite side}} = \frac{b}{a}$$

Example: Find the sine, cosine, tangent, cosecant, secant, and cotangent of angle A rounded to four decimal places.

$$\sin A = \frac{6}{10} \text{ or } 0.6000 \qquad \csc A = \frac{10}{6} \text{ or } 1.6667$$

$$\cos A = \frac{8}{10} \text{ or } 0.8000 \qquad \sec A = \frac{10}{8} \text{ or } 1.2500$$

$$\tan A = \frac{6}{8} \text{ or } 0.7500 \qquad \cot A = \frac{8}{6} \text{ or } 1.3333$$

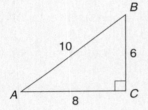

Solve. Round measures of sides and angles to the nearest tenth.

1. If $c = 21$ and $a = 15$, find b.
   14.7

2. If $a = 32$ and $b = 15$, find A.
   64.9°

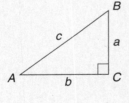

3. If $A = 32°$ and $c = 8$, find b.
   6.8

4. If $a = 5$ and $b = 10$, find A, B, and c.
   26.6°, 63.4°, 11.2

5. A 150-foot rope is tied from the top of a 100-foot-tall pole to a stake in the ground. What is the angle between the rope and the ground?
   41.8°

6. A 6-foot-long pipe is propped on a 3-foot-tall packing crate that sits on level ground. One foot of the pipe extends above the top edge of the crate and the other end rests on the ground. What angle does the pipe form with the ground?
   53.1°

NAME_____ DATE _____

Study Guide

Angles and Their Measure

An angle in **standard position** is an angle that has its vertex at the origin, and one ray, called the **initial ray,** along the positive x-axis. The second ray of the angle is called the **terminal side.** If you think of the terminal side starting from the same position as the initial ray and rotating counterclockwise about O to its final position, the angle generated is positive. Angles in standard position that have the same terminal side are called **coterminal angles.**

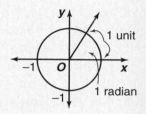

A circle with center at the origin and with a radius of 1 unit is a **unit circle.** An angle in standard position that intercepts an arc 1 unit long on the unit circle is defined to have a measure of 1 **radian.**

Conversions	Examples
Degrees to radians: Multiply by $\frac{\pi \text{ radians}}{180°}$.	Change 45° to radians. $45°\left(\frac{\pi \text{ radians}}{180°}\right) = \frac{45\pi}{180}$ or $\frac{\pi}{4}$ radians
Radians to degrees: Multiply by $\frac{180°}{\pi \text{ radians}}$.	Change $\frac{5\pi}{3}$ radians to degrees. $\frac{5\pi}{3}$ radians $\left(\frac{180°}{\pi \text{ radians}}\right) = \frac{900\pi}{3\pi}$ or 300°

Change each degree measure to radian measure.

1. 140°

2. −860°

3. 1200°

4. −300°

5. −405°

6. 280°

Change each radian measure to degree measure.

7. $\frac{-3\pi}{5}$

8. $\frac{11\pi}{3}$

9. $\frac{2\pi}{7}$

10. $-4\frac{1}{2}\pi$

11. $\frac{-12\pi}{5}$

12. $\frac{8\pi}{5}$

13. $\frac{3\pi}{2}$

14. $\frac{\pi}{5}$

15. $-\frac{\pi}{3}$

93

Study Guide

Angles and Their Measure

An angle in **standard position** is an angle that has its vertex at the origin, and one ray, called the **initial ray,** along the positive x-axis. The second ray of the angle is called the **terminal side.** If you think of the terminal side starting from the same position as the initial ray and rotating counterclockwise about O to its final position, the angle generated is positive. Angles in standard position that have the same terminal side are called **coterminal angles.**

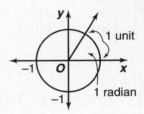

A circle with center at the origin and with a radius of 1 unit is a **unit circle.** An angle in standard position that intercepts an arc 1 unit long on the unit circle is defined to have a measure of 1 **radian.**

Conversions	Examples
Degrees to radians: Multiply by $\dfrac{\pi \text{ radians}}{180°}$.	Change 45° to radians. $45°\left(\dfrac{\pi \text{ radians}}{180°}\right) = \dfrac{45\pi}{180}$ or $\dfrac{\pi}{4}$ radians
Radians to degrees: Multiply by $\dfrac{180°}{\pi \text{ radians}}$.	Change $\dfrac{5\pi}{3}$ radians to degrees. $\dfrac{5\pi}{3}$ radians $\left(\dfrac{180°}{\pi \text{ radians}}\right) = \dfrac{900\pi}{3\pi}$ or 300°

Change each degree measure to radian measure.

1. 140°
   $\dfrac{7\pi}{9}$

2. −860°
   $\dfrac{-43\pi}{9}$

3. 1200°
   $\dfrac{20\pi}{3}$

4. −300°
   $\dfrac{-5\pi}{3}$

5. −405°
   $\dfrac{-9\pi}{4}$

6. 280°
   $\dfrac{14\pi}{9}$

Change each radian measure to degree measure.

7. $\dfrac{-3\pi}{5}$
   −108°

8. $\dfrac{11\pi}{3}$
   660°

9. $\dfrac{2\pi}{7}$
   $51\dfrac{3}{7}°$

10. $-4\dfrac{1}{2}\pi$
    −810°

11. $\dfrac{-12\pi}{5}$
    −432°

12. $\dfrac{8\pi}{5}$
    288°

13. $\dfrac{3\pi}{2}$
    270°

14. $\dfrac{\pi}{5}$
    36°

15. $-\dfrac{\pi}{3}$
    −60°

Study Guide

Trigonometric Functions of General Angles

Trigonometric identities are true for *all* values of the variable(s) for which the expressions are defined.

> The following trigonometric identities hold for all values of θ except those for which any function is undefined.
>
> $\tan \theta = \dfrac{\sin \theta}{\cos \theta}$ $\sec \theta = \dfrac{1}{\cos \theta}$
>
> $\cot \theta = \dfrac{\cos \theta}{\sin \theta}$ $\csc \theta = \dfrac{1}{\sin \theta}$ $\cot \theta = \dfrac{1}{\tan \theta}$

Example: Find $\tan 150°$

$$\tan 150° = \frac{\sin 150°}{\cos 150°} \quad \textbf{Definition of tangent}$$

$$= \frac{\frac{1}{2}}{-\frac{\sqrt{3}}{2}} \quad \textbf{Substitute values for sin 150° and cos 150°.}$$

$$= -\frac{1}{\sqrt{3}} \text{ or } -\frac{\sqrt{3}}{3}$$

Find the exact value of each trigonometric function.

1. $\tan(-510°)$

2. $\csc \dfrac{11\pi}{4}$

3. $\sin(-90°)$

4. $\cot 1665°$

5. $\cot 30°$

6. $\tan 315°$

7. $\csc \dfrac{\pi}{4}$

8. $\tan \dfrac{4\pi}{3}$

9. $\cot 1110°$

10. $\cos 270°$

11. $\csc(-45°)$

12. $\sin 30°$

13. $\sec 2\pi$

14. $\cot(-30°)$

15. $\csc 3\pi$

Study Guide

Trigonometric Functions of General Angles

Trigonometric identities are true for *all* values of the variable(s)
for which the expressions are defined.

> The following trigonometric identities hold for all values of
> θ except those for which any function is undefined.
>
> $\tan \theta = \dfrac{\sin \theta}{\cos \theta}$ $\qquad$ $\sec \theta = \dfrac{1}{\cos \theta}$
>
> $\cot \theta = \dfrac{\cos \theta}{\sin \theta}$ $\qquad$ $\csc \theta = \dfrac{1}{\sin \theta}$ $\qquad$ $\cot \theta = \dfrac{1}{\tan \theta}$

Example: Find $\tan 150°$

$$\tan 150° = \frac{\sin 150°}{\cos 150°} \quad \textbf{Definition of tangent}$$

$$= \frac{\frac{1}{2}}{-\frac{\sqrt{3}}{2}} \quad \textbf{Substitute values for sin 150° and cos 150°.}$$

$$= -\frac{1}{\sqrt{3}} \text{ or } -\frac{\sqrt{3}}{3}$$

Find the exact value of each trigonometric function.

1. $\tan(-510°)$
$\dfrac{\sqrt{3}}{3}$

2. $\csc \dfrac{11\pi}{4}$
$\sqrt{2}$

3. $\sin(-90°)$
-1

4. $\cot 1665°$
1

5. $\cot 30°$
$\sqrt{3}$

6. $\tan 315°$
-1

7. $\csc \dfrac{\pi}{4}$
$\sqrt{2}$

8. $\tan \dfrac{4\pi}{3}$
$\sqrt{3}$

9. $\cot 1110°$
$\sqrt{3}$

10. $\cos 270°$
0

11. $\csc(-45°)$
$-\sqrt{2}$

12. $\sin 30°$
$\dfrac{1}{2}$

13. $\sec 2\pi$
1

14. $\cot(-30°)$
$-\sqrt{3}$

15. $\csc 3\pi$
undefined

13-4

Study Guide

Law of Sines

You can use any of the following formulas
to find the area of any $\triangle ABC$, including
triangles that are not right triangles.

$\text{area} = \dfrac{1}{2}ab \sin C$

$\text{area} = \dfrac{1}{2}bc \sin A$

$\text{area} = \dfrac{1}{2}ac \sin B$

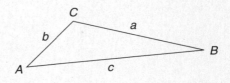

Example: Find the area of $\triangle ABC$ if $a = 10$, $b = 14$, and $C = 40°$.

$$\text{area} = \dfrac{1}{2}ab \sin C$$

$$= \dfrac{1}{2}(10)(14)\sin 40°$$

$$= 44.9951$$

To the nearest square unit, the area is 45 square units.

From the formulas above, we can deduce the **Law of Sines:**

$$\dfrac{\sin A}{a} = \dfrac{\sin B}{b} = \dfrac{\sin C}{c}$$

The law of sines can be used to solve right triangles.

Example: If $a = 12$, $b = 9$, and $A = 28°$, find B.

$$\dfrac{\sin A}{a} = \dfrac{\sin B}{b}$$

$$\dfrac{\sin 28°}{12} = \dfrac{\sin B}{9}$$

$$\sin B = \dfrac{9 \sin 28°}{12}$$

$$\sin B = 0.3521$$

$$B = 20.45°$$

**Find the area of each triangle described below. Round
answers to the nearest tenth.**

1. $a = 10$, $b = 10$, $c = 40°$

2. $a = 6$, $c = 14$, $B = 41°$

**Solve each triangle described below. Round measures of
sides and angles to the nearest tenth.**

3. $B = 71°$, $c = 8$, $b = 16$

4. $A = 40°$, $B = 14°$, $a = 52$

95

Study Guide

Law of Sines

You can use any of the following formulas to find the area of any $\triangle ABC$, including triangles that are not right triangles.

$$\text{area} = \frac{1}{2}ab \sin C$$

$$\text{area} = \frac{1}{2}bc \sin A$$

$$\text{area} = \frac{1}{2}ac \sin B$$

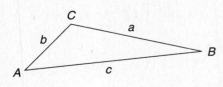

Example: Find the area of $\triangle ABC$ if $a = 10$, $b = 14$, and $C = 40°$.

$$\text{area} = \frac{1}{2}ab \sin C$$

$$= \frac{1}{2}(10)(14)\sin 40°$$

$$= 44.9951$$

To the nearest square unit, the area is 45 square units.

From the formulas above, we can deduce the **Law of Sines:**

$$\frac{\sin A}{a} = \frac{\sin B}{b} = \frac{\sin C}{c}$$

The law of sines can be used to solve right triangles.

Example: If $a = 12$, $b = 9$, and $A = 28°$, find B.

$$\frac{\sin A}{a} = \frac{\sin B}{b}$$

$$\frac{\sin 28°}{12} = \frac{\sin B}{9}$$

$$\sin B = \frac{9 \sin 28°}{12}$$

$$\sin B = 0.3521$$

$$B = 20.45°$$

Find the area of each triangle described below. Round answers to the nearest tenth.

1. $a = 10$, $b = 10$, $c = 40°$
   32.1 square units

2. $a = 6$, $c = 14$, $B = 41°$
   27.6 square units

Solve each triangle described below. Round measures of sides and angles to the nearest tenth.

3. $B = 71°$, $c = 8$, $b = 16$
   $C = 28.2°$, $A = 80.8°$, $a = 16.7$

4. $A = 40°$, $B = 14°$, $a = 52$
   $b = 19.6$, $c = 65.5$, $C = 126°$

NAME_____ DATE _____

Study Guide

Law of Cosines

Law of Cosines
Let $\triangle ABC$ be any triangle with a, b, and c representing the measures of sides opposite angles with measurements A, B, and C, respectively. Then, the following equations are true. $a^2 = b^2 + c^2 - 2bc \cos A$ $b^2 = a^2 + c^2 - 2ac \cos B$ $c^2 = a^2 + b^2 - 2ab \cos C$

Use the law of cosines to solve a triangle in the following cases.
1. To find the length of the third side of any triangle if the lengths of two sides and the measurement of the included angle are given.
2. To find the measurement of an angle of a triangle if the lengths of three sides are given.

Example: A hiker walks 3 miles due east from his house. He then turns 45° and walks 2 miles northeast. How far will he have to walk to get home?

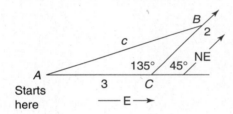

$c^2 = a^2 + b^2 - 2ab \cos C$
$c^2 = 2^2 + 3^2 - 2(2)(3) \cos 135°$
$c^2 \approx 4 + 9 - 12(-0.7071)$
$c^2 \approx 21.4852$
$c \approx 4.6$
He will have to walk about 4.6 miles.

Solve each triangle described below. Round measures of sides and angles to the nearest tenth.

1. $a = 14$, $c = 20$, $B = 38°$

2. $A = 60°$, $c = 17$, $b = 12$

3. $a = 4$, $b = 6$, $c = 3$

4. $A = 20°$, $b = 100$, $c = 84$

5. A diver leaps 2.5 feet off the board and jackknifes 10 feet into the water at an angle of 20°. How far from the edge of the board does she enter the water?

6. Some children set up a tepee in the woods. The poles are 7 feet long, and the children want the distance between adjacent poles to be 4 feet at the base. How wide must the angle be between the poles?

96

NAME_____ DATE _____

Study Guide

Law of Cosines

Law of Cosines
Let $\triangle ABC$ be any triangle with a, b, and c representing the measures of sides opposite angles with measurements A, B, and C, respectively. Then, the following equations are true. $$a^2 = b^2 + c^2 - 2bc \cos A$$ $$b^2 = a^2 + c^2 - 2ac \cos B$$ $$c^2 = a^2 + b^2 - 2ab \cos C$$

Use the law of cosines to solve a triangle in the following cases.
1. To find the length of the third side of any triangle if the lengths of two sides and the measurement of the included angle are given.
2. To find the measurement of an angle of a triangle if the lengths of three sides are given.

Example: A hiker walks 3 miles due east from his house. He then turns 45° and walks 2 miles northeast. How far will he have to walk to get home?

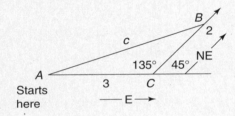

$c^2 = a^2 + b^2 - 2ab \cos C$
$c^2 = 2^2 + 3^2 - 2(2)(3) \cos 135°$
$c^2 \approx 4 + 9 - 12(-0.7071)$
$c^2 \approx 21.4852$
$c \approx 4.6$
He will have to walk about 4.6 miles.

Solve each triangle described below. Round measures of sides and angles to the nearest tenth.

1. $a = 14$, $c = 20$, $B = 38°$
   $b = 12.4$, $A = 43.9°$, $C = 98.1°$

2. $A = 60°$, $c = 17$, $b = 12$
   $a = 15.1$, $B = 43.4°$, $C = 76.6°$

3. $a = 4$, $b = 6$, $c = 3$
   $A = 36.3°$, $B = 117.3°$, $C = 26.4°$

4. $A = 20°$, $b = 100$, $c = 84$
   $a = 35.6$, $B = 73.7°$, $C = 86.3°$

5. A diver leaps 2.5 feet off the board and jackknifes 10 feet into the water at an angle of 20°. How far from the edge of the board does she enter the water?
   7.7 feet

6. Some children set up a tepee in the woods. The poles are 7 feet long, and the children want the distance between adjacent poles to be 4 feet at the base. How wide must the angle be between the poles?
   33.2°

Algebra 2

NAME _____ DATE _____

Study Guide

Circular Functions

If (x, y) is the point on the unit circle at which the terminal ray of an angle θ in standard position intersects the unit circle, then $\cos \theta = x$ and $\sin \theta = y$.

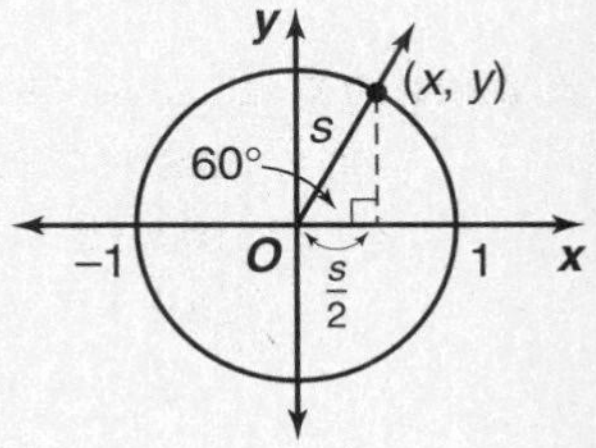

Example: Find $\cos 60°$. Look at the diagram at the right. The dashed line segment cuts the x-axis and the terminal side of the angle to form a $30°$–$60°$ right triangle. The length of the radius of the circle is 1 unit. Thus,

$$s = 1 \text{ unit and } \frac{s}{2} = \frac{1}{2} \text{ unit.}$$

The x-coordinate of the point (x, y) is $\frac{1}{2}$.

Therefore, $\cos 60° = \frac{1}{2}$.

Every $360°$ or 2π radians through which the terminal side of an angle rotates corresponds to a complete rotation around the unit circle. When comparing the sine and cosine tables, you see that every $360°$ or 2π radians, the sine and cosine functions repeat their values. The sine and cosine functions are therefore called **periodic functions.**

Periodic Function	
Definition	**Example**
A function is called **periodic** if there is a number a such that $f(x) = f(x + a)$ for all x in the domain of the function. The least positive value of a for which $f(x) = f(x + a)$ is called the **period** of the function.	Find the value of the function $\sin 570°$. $\sin 570° = \sin (210 + 360)° \quad 570 = 210 + 360$ $\qquad = \sin 210° \qquad\quad$ The sine function has a period of $360°$. $\qquad = -\frac{1}{2} \qquad\qquad\quad \sin \theta$ is negative in the third quadrant.

For each of the following, find the least positive angle measurement that is coterminal.

1. $-90°$

2. $1000°$

3. $\dfrac{20\pi}{7}$

Find the value of each function.

4. $\cos(-420)°$

5. $\cos 2280°$

6. $\sin(-510)°$

7. $\sin 495°$

8. $\cos\left(-2\frac{1}{2}\pi\right)$

9. $\cos\left(\dfrac{11\pi}{4}\right)$

10. $\sin\left(\dfrac{5\pi}{3}\right)$

11. $\sin\left(-\dfrac{3\pi}{4}\right)$

Algebra 2

Study Guide

Circular Functions

If (x, y) is the point on the unit circle at which the terminal ray of an angle θ in standard position intersects the unit circle, then $\cos \theta = x$ and $\sin \theta = y$.

Example: Find $\cos 60°$. Look at the diagram at the right. The dashed line segment cuts the x-axis and the terminal side of the angle to form a $30°$–$60°$ right triangle. The length of the radius of the circle is 1 unit. Thus,

$$s = 1 \text{ unit and } \frac{s}{2} = \frac{1}{2} \text{ unit.}$$

The x-coordinate of the point (x, y) is $\frac{1}{2}$.

Therefore, $\cos 60° = \frac{1}{2}$.

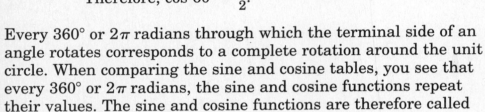

Every $360°$ or 2π radians through which the terminal side of an angle rotates corresponds to a complete rotation around the unit circle. When comparing the sine and cosine tables, you see that every $360°$ or 2π radians, the sine and cosine functions repeat their values. The sine and cosine functions are therefore called **periodic functions.**

Periodic Function	
Definition	**Example**
A function is called **periodic** if there is a number a such that $f(x) = f(x + a)$ for all x in the domain of the function. The least positive value of a for which $f(x) = f(x + a)$ is called the **period** of the function.	Find the value of the function $\sin 570°$. $\sin 570° = \sin (210 + 360)°$ $570 = 210 + 360$ $\qquad\quad = \sin 210°$ The sine function has $\qquad\quad = -\dfrac{1}{2}$ a period of $360°$. $\qquad\qquad\qquad\qquad$ $\sin \theta$ is negative in $\qquad\qquad\qquad\qquad$ the third quadrant.

For each of the following, find the least positive angle measurement that is coterminal.

1. $-90°$
   270°

2. $1000°$
   280°

3. $\dfrac{20\pi}{7}$
   $\dfrac{6\pi}{7}$

Find the value of each function.

4. $\cos(-420)°$
   0.5

5. $\cos 2280°$
   −0.5

6. $\sin(-510)°$
   −0.5

7. $\sin 495°$ $\dfrac{\sqrt{2}}{2}$

8. $\cos\left(-2\frac{1}{2}\pi\right)$
   0

9. $\cos\left(\dfrac{11\pi}{4}\right)$
   $-\dfrac{\sqrt{2}}{2}$

10. $\sin\left(\dfrac{5\pi}{3}\right)$
    $-\dfrac{\sqrt{3}}{2}$

11. $\sin\left(-\dfrac{3\pi}{4}\right)$
    $-\dfrac{\sqrt{2}}{2}$

Study Guide

Inverse Trigonometric Functions

The inverse of a trigonometric function is not a function. However, for functions with properly restricted domains, the inverse is a function. The values in these restricted domains are called **principal values.** Capital letters are used to distinguish trigonometric functions with restricted domains from those with unrestricted domains.

Function	Restrictions	Inverse
$y = \text{Cos } x$	$0 \leq x \leq \pi$	$y = \text{Cos}^{-1} x$ or $y = \text{Arccos } x$
$y = \text{Sin } x$	$-\dfrac{\pi}{2} \leq x \leq \dfrac{\pi}{2}$	$y = \text{Sin}^{-1} x$ or $y = \text{Arcsin } x$
$y = \text{Tan } x$	$-\dfrac{\pi}{2} < x < \dfrac{\pi}{2}$	$y = \text{Tan}^{-1} x$ or $y = \text{Arctan } x$

Example: Find $\text{Cos}^{-1}\left(-\dfrac{\sqrt{3}}{2}\right)$.

Let $\theta = \text{Cos}^{-1}\left(-\dfrac{\sqrt{3}}{2}\right)$.

Then, $\text{Cos } \theta = -\dfrac{\sqrt{3}}{2}$ and $\theta = \dfrac{5\pi}{6}$.

Find each value.

1. $\cot(\text{Tan}^{-1} 2)$

2. $\text{Arctan}(-1)$

3. $\text{Cot}^{-1} 1$

4. $\cos\left(\text{Sin}^{-1} -\dfrac{\sqrt{2}}{2}\right)$

5. $\text{Sin}^{-1} -\dfrac{\sqrt{3}}{2}$

6. $\sin\left(\text{Arcsin} \dfrac{\sqrt{3}}{2}\right)$

7. $\tan\left(\text{Arcsin} -\dfrac{5}{7}\right)$

8. $\sin\left(\text{Tan}^{-1} \dfrac{5}{12}\right)$

9. $\sin[\text{Arctan} (-\sqrt{2})]$

10. $\text{Arccos}\left(-\dfrac{\sqrt{3}}{2}\right)$

11. $\text{Arcsin}\left(\dfrac{\sqrt{3}}{2}\right)$

12. $\text{Arccot} -\dfrac{\sqrt{3}}{3}$

Study Guide

Inverse Trigonometric Functions

The inverse of a trigonometric function is not a function. However, for functions with properly restricted domains, the inverse is a function. The values in these restricted domains are called **principal values.** Capital letters are used to distinguish trigonometric functions with restricted domains from those with unrestricted domains.

Function	Restrictions	Inverse
$y = \text{Cos } x$	$0 \leq x \leq \pi$	$y = \text{Cos}^{-1} x$ or $y = \text{Arccos } x$
$y = \text{Sin } x$	$-\frac{\pi}{2} \leq x \leq \frac{\pi}{2}$	$y = \text{Sin}^{-1} x$ or $y = \text{Arcsin } x$
$y = \text{Tan } x$	$-\frac{\pi}{2} < x < \frac{\pi}{2}$	$y = \text{Tan}^{-1} x$ or $y = \text{Arctan } x$

Example: Find $\text{Cos}^{-1}\left(-\frac{\sqrt{3}}{2}\right)$.

Let $\theta = \text{Cos}^{-1}\left(-\frac{\sqrt{3}}{2}\right)$.

Then, $\text{Cos } \theta = -\frac{\sqrt{3}}{2}$ and $\theta = \frac{5\pi}{6}$.

Find each value.

1. $\cot(\text{Tan}^{-1} 2)$
$\dfrac{1}{2}$

2. $\text{Arctan}(-1)$
−45°

3. $\text{Cot}^{-1} 1$
45°

4. $\cos\left(\text{Sin}^{-1} -\frac{\sqrt{2}}{2}\right)$
$\dfrac{\sqrt{2}}{2}$

5. $\text{Sin}^{-1} -\frac{\sqrt{3}}{2}$
−60°

6. $\sin\left(\text{Arcsin } \frac{\sqrt{3}}{2}\right)$
$\dfrac{\sqrt{3}}{2}$

7. $\tan\left(\text{Arcsin } -\frac{5}{7}\right)$
$-\dfrac{5\sqrt{6}}{12}$

8. $\sin\left(\text{Tan}^{-1} \frac{5}{12}\right)$
$\dfrac{5}{13}$

9. $\sin[\text{Arctan } (-\sqrt{2})]$
$-\dfrac{\sqrt{6}}{3}$

10. $\text{Arccos}\left(-\frac{\sqrt{3}}{2}\right)$
150°

11. $\text{Arcsin}\left(\frac{\sqrt{3}}{2}\right)$
45°

12. $\text{Arccot } -\frac{\sqrt{3}}{3}$
−60°

Study Guide

Graphing Trigonometric Functions

The chart below shows useful information about common trigonometric functions. Study the chart.

Function	Period	Zeros	Max.	Min.
sine (sin)	360°	0°, 180°, 360°, ⋯	1	−1
cosine (cos)	360°	90°, 270°, ⋯	1	−1
tangent (tan)	180°	0°, 180°, ⋯	none	none
cotangent (cot)	180°	90°, 270°, ⋯	none	none
secant (sec)	360°	none	−1 (rel.)	1 (rel.)
cosecant (csc)	360°	none	−1 (rel.)	1 (rel.)

When graphing trigonometric functions, it helps to remember that for $y = a \sin b\theta$, $y = a \cos b\theta$, $|a|$ is the amplitude, and $\dfrac{360°}{|b|}$ is the period of the function.

Example: State the period and amplitude for $y = \dfrac{1}{2} \cos \dfrac{1}{2}\theta$.

$$\text{amplitude} = \frac{1}{2} \qquad\qquad \text{period} = \frac{360°}{\frac{1}{2}} = 720°$$

State the amplitude (if it exists) and period for each function. Then graph each function.

1. $y = 2 \cos \theta$

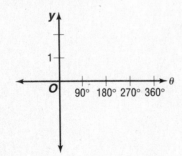

2. $y = -3 \sin \theta$

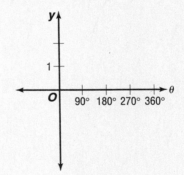

3. $y = \csc 3\theta$

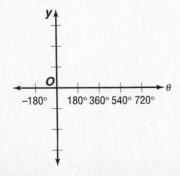

4. $y = 2 \tan \dfrac{\theta}{2}$

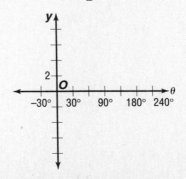

Study Guide

Graphing Trigonometric Functions

The chart below shows useful information about common trigonometric functions. Study the chart.

Function	Period	Zeros	Max.	Min.
sine (sin)	360°	0°, 180°, 360°, ⋯	1	−1
cosine (cos)	360°	90°, 270°, ⋯	1	−1
tangent (tan)	180°	0°, 180°, ⋯	none	none
cotangent (cot)	180°	90°, 270°, ⋯	none	none
secant (sec)	360°	none	−1 (rel.)	1 (rel.)
cosecant (csc)	360°	none	−1 (rel.)	1 (rel.)

When graphing trigonometric functions, it helps to remember that for $y = a \sin b\theta$, $y = a \cos b\theta$, $|a|$ is the amplitude, and $\dfrac{360°}{|b|}$ is the period of the function.

Example: State the period and amplitude for $y = \dfrac{1}{2} \cos \dfrac{1}{2} \theta$.

$$\text{amplitude} = \frac{1}{2} \qquad \text{period} = \frac{360°}{\frac{1}{2}} = 720°$$

State the amplitude (if it exists) and period for each function.
Then graph each function.

1. $y = 2 \cos \theta$ **2; 360° or 2π**

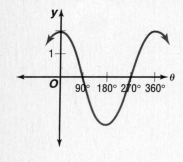

2. $y = -3 \sin \theta$ **3; 360° or 2π**

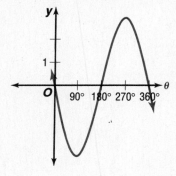

3. $y = \csc 3\theta$ **no amplitude;**
120° or $\dfrac{2}{3}\pi$

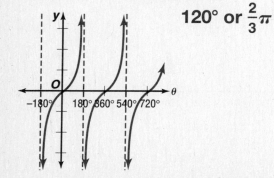

4. $y = 2 \tan \dfrac{\theta}{2}$ **no amplitude;**
360° or 2π

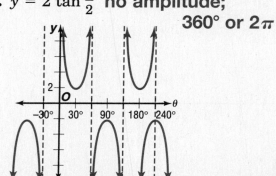

Algebra 2

Trigonometric Identities

An equation that is true for all values of the variables for which
it is defined is called an **identity**.

Basic Trigonometric Identities
The following equations are trigonometric identities. They hold for all values of θ except those for which an expression in the equation is undefined. $\sin^2 \theta + \cos^2 \theta = 1$ $1 + \tan^2 \theta = \sec^2 \theta$ $1 + \cot^2 \theta = \csc^2 \theta$

Example: If $\tan a = -\dfrac{3}{5}$, find $\cos a$ for values of a between 90° and 180°.

$$\sec^2 a = 1 + \tan^2 a \qquad \textbf{Trigonometric identity}$$

$$\sec^2 a = 1 + \left(-\frac{3}{5}\right)^2$$

$$\left(\frac{1}{\cos a}\right)^2 = \frac{34}{25} \qquad \textbf{sec } a = \frac{1}{\cos a}$$

$$\cos^2 a = \frac{25}{34}$$

$$\cos a = -\sqrt{\frac{25}{34}} \qquad \textbf{cos } a \text{ is negative for values of } a$$
$$\text{between 90° and 180°.}$$

$$\cos a = \frac{-5\sqrt{34}}{34}$$

Solve for values of θ between 0° and 90°.

1. If $\sin \theta = \dfrac{3}{7}$, find $\tan \theta$.

2. If $\cos \theta = \dfrac{\sqrt{3}}{2}$, find $\csc \theta$.

3. If $\sin \theta = \dfrac{3}{5}$, find $\cos \theta$.

4. If $\sin \theta = \dfrac{1}{3}$, find $\sec \theta$.

Simplify each expression.

5. $\dfrac{\tan \theta \csc \theta}{\sec \theta}$

6. $\dfrac{\cot^2 x - 1}{1 + \cot^2 x}$

7. $\dfrac{\sin^2 \theta - \cot \theta \tan \theta}{\cot \theta \sin \theta}$

8. $\dfrac{\cos \theta}{\sec \theta - \tan \theta}$

Study Guide

Trigonometric Identities

An equation that is true for all values of the variables for which it is defined is called an **identity**.

Basic Trigonometric Identities
The following equations are trigonometric identities. They hold for all values of θ except those for which an expression in the equation is undefined. $\sin^2 \theta + \cos^2 \theta = 1$ $1 + \tan^2 \theta = \sec^2 \theta$ $1 + \cot^2 \theta = \csc^2 \theta$

Example: If $\tan a = -\dfrac{3}{5}$, find $\cos a$ for values of a between 90° and 180°.

$$\sec^2 a = 1 + \tan^2 a \qquad \textbf{Trigonometric identity}$$

$$\sec^2 a = 1 + \left(-\frac{3}{5}\right)^2$$

$$\left(\frac{1}{\cos a}\right)^2 = \frac{34}{25} \qquad \textbf{sec } a = \frac{1}{\cos a}$$

$$\cos^2 a = \frac{25}{34}$$

$$\cos a = -\sqrt{\frac{25}{34}} \qquad \textbf{cos } a \text{ is negative for values of } a$$
$$\text{between 90° and 180°.}$$

$$\cos a = \frac{-5\sqrt{34}}{34}$$

Solve for values of θ between 0° and 90°.

1. If $\sin \theta = \dfrac{3}{7}$, find $\tan \theta$.

$\dfrac{3\sqrt{10}}{20}$

2. If $\cos \theta = \dfrac{\sqrt{3}}{2}$, find $\csc \theta$.

2

3. If $\sin \theta = \dfrac{3}{5}$, find $\cos \theta$.

$\dfrac{4}{5}$

4. If $\sin \theta = \dfrac{1}{3}$, find $\sec \theta$.

$\dfrac{3}{4}\sqrt{2}$

Simplify each expression.

5. $\dfrac{\tan \theta \csc \theta}{\sec \theta}$

1

6. $\dfrac{\cot^2 x - 1}{1 + \cot^2 x}$

$1 - 2 \sin^2 \theta$ (or $\cos^2 \theta - \sin^2 \theta$ or $2 \cos^2 \theta - 1$)

7. $\dfrac{\sin^2 \theta - \cot \theta \tan \theta}{\cot \theta \sin \theta}$

$-\cos \theta$

8. $\dfrac{\cos \theta}{\sec \theta - \tan \theta}$

$1 + \sin \theta$

14-3

Study Guide

Verifying Trigonometric Identities

The basic trigonometric identities along with the definitions of the trigonometric functions can be used to verify other identities. Verifying an identity is like checking the solution to an equation. To verify that the expressions on each side are equal, you must simplify one or both sides **separately** until they are the same.

Example: Verify $\tan^2 x - \sin^2 x = \tan^2 x \sin^2 x$.

$$\tan^2 x - \sin^2 x \overset{?}{=} \tan^2 x \sin^2 x$$

$$\frac{\sin^2 x}{\cos^2 x} - \sin^2 x \overset{?}{=} \tan^2 x \sin^2 x \qquad \tan x = \frac{\sin x}{\cos x}$$

$$\left(\frac{1}{\cos^2 x} - 1\right) \sin^2 x \overset{?}{=} \tan^2 x \sin^2 x \qquad \text{Distributive property}$$

$$(\sec^2 x - 1)\sin^2 x \overset{?}{=} \tan^2 x \sin^2 x \qquad \sec x \frac{1}{\cos x}$$

$$(\tan^2 x)\sin^2 x = \tan^2 x \sin^2 x \qquad 1 + \tan^2 x = \sec^2 x$$

Verify that each of the following is an identity.

1. $\tan \beta(\cot \beta + \tan \beta) = \sec^2 \beta$

2. $\tan^2 \theta \cos^2 \theta = 1 - \cos^2 \theta$

3. $\csc x \sec x = \cot x + \tan x$

4. $\cos^2 x + \tan^2 x \cos^2 x = 1$

5. $\tan \theta \sin \theta = \dfrac{1 - \cos^2 \theta}{\cos \theta}$

6. $\sin \alpha(\csc \alpha - \sin \alpha) = \cos^2 \alpha$

Verifying Trigonometric Identities

The basic trigonometric identities along with the definitions of the trigonometric functions can be used to verify other identities. Verifying an identity is like checking the solution to an equation. To verify that the expressions on each side are equal, you must simplify one or both sides **separately** until they are the same.

Example: Verify $\tan^2 x - \sin^2 x = \tan^2 x \sin^2 x$.

$$\tan^2 x - \sin^2 x \overset{?}{=} \tan^2 x \sin^2 x$$

$$\frac{\sin^2 x}{\cos^2 x} - \sin^2 x \overset{?}{=} \tan^2 x \sin^2 x \qquad \tan x = \frac{\sin x}{\cos x}$$

$$\left(\frac{1}{\cos^2 x} - 1\right) \sin^2 x \overset{?}{=} \tan^2 x \sin^2 x \qquad \text{Distributive property}$$

$$(\sec^2 x - 1)\sin^2 x \overset{?}{=} \tan^2 x \sin^2 x \qquad \sec x \,\, \frac{1}{\cos x}$$

$$(\tan^2 x)\sin^2 x = \tan^2 x \sin^2 x \qquad 1 + \tan^2 x = \sec^2 x$$

Verify that each of the following is an identity.

1. $\tan \beta(\cot \beta + \tan \beta) = \sec^2 \beta$

$$\tan \beta\left(\frac{1}{\tan \beta} + \tan \beta\right) \overset{?}{=} \sec^2 \beta$$

$$1 + \tan^2 \beta \overset{?}{=} \sec^2 \beta$$

$$\sec^2 \beta = \sec^2 \beta$$

2. $\tan^2 \theta \cos^2 \theta = 1 - \cos^2 \theta$

$$\left(\frac{\sin^2 \theta}{\cos^2 \theta}\right) \cos^2 \theta \overset{?}{=} 1 - \cos^2 \theta$$

$$\sin^2 \theta \overset{?}{=} 1 - \cos^2 \theta$$

$$1 - \cos^2 \theta = 1 - \cos^2 \theta$$

3. $\csc x \sec x = \cot x + \tan x$

$$\left(\frac{1}{\sin x}\right)\left(\frac{1}{\cos x}\right) \overset{?}{=} \frac{\cos x}{\sin x} + \frac{\sin x}{\cos x}$$

$$\frac{1}{\sin x \cos x} \overset{?}{=} \frac{\cos^2 x + \sin^2 x}{\sin x \cos x}$$

$$\frac{1}{\sin x \cos x} = \frac{1}{\sin x \cos x}$$

4. $\cos^2 x + \tan^2 x \cos^2 x = 1$

$$\cos^2 x + \left(\frac{\sin^2 x}{\cos^2 x}\right) \cos^2 x \overset{?}{=} 1$$

$$\cos^2 x + \sin^2 x \overset{?}{=} 1$$

$$1 = 1$$

5. $\tan \theta \sin \theta = \dfrac{1 - \cos^2 \theta}{\cos \theta}$

$$\tan \theta \sin \theta \overset{?}{=} \frac{\sin^2 \theta}{\cos \theta}$$

$$\tan \theta \sin \theta \overset{?}{=} \frac{\sin \theta}{\cos \theta} \cdot \sin \theta$$

$$\tan \theta \sin \theta = \tan \theta \sin \theta$$

6. $\sin \alpha(\csc \alpha - \sin \alpha) = \cos^2 \alpha$

$$\sin \alpha \csc \alpha - \sin^2 \alpha \overset{?}{=} \cos^2 \alpha$$

$$\sin \alpha\left(\frac{1}{\sin \alpha}\right) - \sin^2 \alpha \overset{?}{=} \cos^2 \alpha$$

$$1 - \sin^2 \alpha \overset{?}{=} \cos^2 \alpha$$

$$\cos^2 \alpha = \cos^2 \alpha$$

14-4

Study Guide

Sum and Difference of Angles Formulas

It is often helpful to use formulas for the trigonometric values of the difference or sum of two angles.

Sum and Difference Angle Formulas
The following identities hold for all values of α and β.
$\cos(\alpha + \beta) = \cos\alpha\cos\beta - \sin\alpha\sin\beta$
$\cos(\alpha - \beta) = \cos\alpha\cos\beta + \sin\alpha\sin\beta$
$\sin(\alpha + \beta) = \sin\alpha\cos\beta + \cos\alpha\sin\beta$
$\sin(\alpha - \beta) = \sin\alpha\cos\beta - \cos\alpha\sin\beta$

Example: Evaluate $\sin 15°$.

$$\sin 15° = \sin(45° - 30°)$$
$$= \sin 45° \cos 30° - \cos 45° \sin 30°$$
$$= \frac{\sqrt{2}}{2} \cdot \frac{\sqrt{3}}{2} - \frac{\sqrt{2}}{2} \cdot \frac{1}{2}$$
$$= \frac{\sqrt{6} - \sqrt{2}}{4}$$

$\sin(\alpha - \beta) = \sin\alpha\cos\beta - \cos\alpha\sin\beta$

Find the exact value of each expression.

1. $\cos 75°$

2. $\sin 255°$

3. $\cos(-15°)$

4. $\sin 75° - \sin 15°$

5. $\sin 10° \cos 80° + \cos 10° \sin 80°$

6. $\cos 20° \cos 40° - \sin 20° \sin 40°$

7. $\sin 60° \cos 15° - \cos 60° \sin 15°$

8. $\cos 105° \cos 15° + \sin 105° \sin 15°$

Verify that each of the following is an identity.

9. $\sin(90° - \theta) = \cos\theta$

10. $\sin(\theta + 270°) = -\cos\theta$

Algebra 2

Study Guide

Sum and Difference of Angles Formulas

It is often helpful to use formulas for the trigonometric values of the difference or sum of two angles.

Sum and Difference Angle Formulas
The following identities hold for all values of α and β.
$\cos(\alpha + \beta) = \cos \alpha \cos \beta - \sin \alpha \sin \beta$
$\cos(\alpha - \beta) = \cos \alpha \cos \beta + \sin \alpha \sin \beta$
$\sin(\alpha + \beta) = \sin \alpha \cos \beta + \cos \alpha \sin \beta$
$\sin(\alpha - \beta) = \sin \alpha \cos \beta - \cos \alpha \sin \beta$

Example: Evaluate $\sin 15°$.

$$\sin 15° = \sin(45° - 30°)$$
$$= \sin 45° \cos 30° - \cos 45° \sin 30° \qquad \sin(\alpha - \beta) = \sin \alpha \cos \beta - \cos \alpha \sin \beta$$
$$= \frac{\sqrt{2}}{2} \cdot \frac{\sqrt{3}}{2} - \frac{\sqrt{2}}{2} \cdot \frac{1}{2}$$
$$= \frac{\sqrt{6} - \sqrt{2}}{4}$$

Find the exact value of each expression.

1. $\cos 75°$ $\dfrac{\sqrt{6} - \sqrt{2}}{4}$

2. $\sin 255°$ $\dfrac{\sqrt{2} - \sqrt{6}}{4}$

3. $\cos(-15°)$ $\dfrac{\sqrt{6} + \sqrt{2}}{4}$

4. $\sin 75° - \sin 15°$ $\dfrac{\sqrt{2}}{2}$

5. $\sin 10° \cos 80° + \cos 10° \sin 80°$ **1**

6. $\cos 20° \cos 40° - \sin 20° \sin 40°$ $\dfrac{1}{2}$

7. $\sin 60° \cos 15° - \cos 60° \sin 15°$ $\dfrac{\sqrt{2}}{2}$

8. $\cos 105° \cos 15° + \sin 105° \sin 15°$ **0**

Verify that each of the following is an identity.

9. $\sin(90° - \theta) = \cos \theta$
$$\sin 90° \cos \theta - \cos 90° \sin \theta \overset{?}{=} \cos \theta$$
$$1(\cos \theta) - 0(\sin \theta) \overset{?}{=} \cos \theta$$
$$\cos \theta = \cos \theta$$

10. $\sin(\theta + 270°) = -\cos \theta$
$$\sin \theta \cos 270° + \cos \theta \sin 270° \overset{?}{=} -\cos \theta$$
$$\sin \theta(0) + \cos \theta(-1) \overset{?}{=} -\cos \theta$$
$$-\cos \theta = -\cos \theta$$

Study Guide

Double-Angle and Half-Angle Formulas

Sometimes you want to find the cosine or sine of double an angle or half an angle. To do this you can use the following formulas.

Double-Angle Formulas
$\sin 2\theta = 2 \sin \theta \cos \theta$
$\cos 2\theta = \cos^2 \theta - \sin^2 \theta$
$\cos 2\theta = 1 - 2 \sin^2 \theta$
$\cos 2\theta = 2 \cos^2 \theta - 1$

Half-Angle Formulas
$\cos \dfrac{a}{2} = \pm\sqrt{\dfrac{1 + \cos a}{2}}$
$\sin \dfrac{a}{2} = \pm\sqrt{\dfrac{1 - \cos a}{2}}$

Example: Suppose x is between $90°$ and $180°$ and $\cos x = -\dfrac{3}{5}$.

Find $\cos \dfrac{x}{2}$.

Since x is in the second quadrant, $\dfrac{x}{2}$ is in the first quadrant and $\cos \dfrac{x}{2} > 0$.

$$\cos \frac{x}{2} = \sqrt{\frac{1 + \cos x}{2}}$$

$$= \sqrt{\frac{1 + \left(-\frac{3}{5}\right)}{2}}$$

$$= \sqrt{\frac{1}{5}} \text{ or } \frac{\sqrt{5}}{5}$$

Find the exact values of sin 2x, cos 2x, sin $\dfrac{x}{2}$, and cos $\dfrac{x}{2}$ for each of the following.

1. $\sin x = \dfrac{1}{4}$, x is in the first quadrant.

2. $\sin x = -\dfrac{1}{8}$, x is in the fourth quadrant.

3. $\cos x = -\dfrac{3}{5}$, x is in the third quadrant.

4. $\cos x = -\dfrac{4}{5}$, x is in the second quadrant.

5. $\sin x = -\dfrac{3}{5}$, x is in the fourth quadrant.

6. $\cos x = -\dfrac{2}{3}$, x is in the second quadrant.

Algebra 2

Double-Angle and Half-Angle Formulas

Sometimes you want to find the cosine or sine of double an angle
or half an angle. To do this you can use the following formulas.

Double-Angle Formulas
$\sin 2\theta = 2 \sin \theta \cos \theta$
$\cos 2\theta = \cos^2 \theta - \sin^2 \theta$
$\cos 2\theta = 1 - 2 \sin^2 \theta$
$\cos 2\theta = 2 \cos^2 \theta - 1$

Half-Angle Formulas
$\cos \dfrac{a}{2} = \pm\sqrt{\dfrac{1 + \cos a}{2}}$
$\sin \dfrac{a}{2} = \pm\sqrt{\dfrac{1 - \cos a}{2}}$

Example: Suppose x is between $90°$ and $180°$
and $\cos x = -\dfrac{3}{5}$.
Find $\cos \dfrac{x}{2}$.

Since x is in the second quadrant, $\dfrac{x}{2}$ is in
the first quadrant and $\cos \dfrac{x}{2} > 0$.

$$\cos \frac{x}{2} = \sqrt{\frac{1 + \cos x}{2}}$$

$$= \sqrt{\frac{1 + \left(-\frac{3}{5}\right)}{2}}$$

$$= \sqrt{\frac{1}{5}} \text{ or } \frac{\sqrt{5}}{5}$$

Find the exact values of $\sin 2x$, $\cos 2x$, $\sin \dfrac{x}{2}$, and $\cos \dfrac{x}{2}$ for each of the following.

1. $\sin x = \dfrac{1}{4}$, x is in the first quadrant.

$\sin 2x = \dfrac{\sqrt{15}}{8}$, $\cos 2x = \dfrac{7}{8}$

$\sin \dfrac{x}{2} = \dfrac{\sqrt{8 - 2\sqrt{15}}}{4}$,

$\cos \dfrac{x}{2} = \dfrac{\sqrt{8 + 2\sqrt{15}}}{4}$

2. $\sin x = -\dfrac{1}{8}$, x is in the fourth quadrant.

$\sin 2x = -\dfrac{\sqrt{63}}{32}$, $\cos 2x = \dfrac{31}{32}$,

$\sin \dfrac{x}{2} = \dfrac{1}{4}\sqrt{8 - \sqrt{63}}$,

$\cos \dfrac{x}{2} = \dfrac{1}{4}\sqrt{8 + \sqrt{63}}$

3. $\cos x = -\dfrac{3}{5}$, x is in the third quadrant.

$\sin 2x = \dfrac{24}{25}$, $\cos 2x = -\dfrac{7}{25}$,

$\sin \dfrac{x}{2} = \dfrac{2}{5}\sqrt{5}$, $\cos \dfrac{x}{2} = -\dfrac{\sqrt{5}}{5}$

4. $\cos x = -\dfrac{4}{5}$, x is in the second quadrant.

$\sin 2x = -\dfrac{24}{25}$, $\cos 2x = \dfrac{7}{25}$,

$\sin \dfrac{x}{2} = \dfrac{3\sqrt{90}}{10}$, $\cos \dfrac{x}{2} = \dfrac{\sqrt{10}}{10}$

5. $\sin x = -\dfrac{3}{5}$, x is in the fourth quadrant.

$\sin 2x = -\dfrac{24}{25}$, $\cos 2x = \dfrac{7}{25}$,

$\sin \dfrac{x}{2} = \dfrac{\sqrt{10}}{10}$, $\cos \dfrac{x}{2} = -\dfrac{3\sqrt{10}}{10}$

6. $\cos x = -\dfrac{2}{3}$, x is in the second quadrant.

$\sin 2x = -\dfrac{4\sqrt{5}}{9}$, $\cos 2x = -\dfrac{1}{9}$,

$\sin \dfrac{x}{2} = \dfrac{\sqrt{30}}{6}$, $\cos \dfrac{x}{2} = \dfrac{\sqrt{6}}{6}$

Study Guide

Solving Trigonometric Equations

Trigonometric identities are true for *all* values of the variable for which both sides are defined. Most trigonometric equations are true for *some* but *not all* values of the variable. Usually trigonometric equations are solved for values of the variable between 0° and 360° or 0 radians and 2π radians.

Some trigonometric equations have *no solutions*. It is important to check your solutions because some algebraic operations may introduce answers that are *not* solutions to the original equation.

Example: Solve $\cos x = 1 - \sin x$ if $0° \le x < 360°$.

$$\cos^2 x = (1 - \sin x)^2$$
$$1 - \sin^2 x = 1 - 2 \sin x + \sin^2 x$$
$$0 = -2 \sin x + 2 \sin^2 x$$
$$0 = 2 \sin x(\sin x - 1)$$
$$0 = 2 \sin x(-1 + \sin x)$$

$2 \sin x = 0$ $-1 + \sin x = 0$

$\sin x = 0$ $\sin x = 1$

$x = 0°, 180°$ $x = 90°$

The solutions appear to be 0°, 90° and 180°. However, 180° does not satisfy the original equation. Thus, the solutions are 0° and 90°.

Find all solutions if 0° ≤ x < 360°.

1. $\cot^2 x = 1$

2. $2 \sin x - 1 = 0$

3. $3 \sin^2 x - \cos^2 x = 0$

4. $2 \cos^2 x + \cos x = 1$

5. $\sin^2 x \cos^2 x = 0$

6. $\cos 2x = \dfrac{\sqrt{3}}{2}$

7. $\sin \dfrac{x}{2} = 1$

8. $2 \sin x - \sqrt{3} = 0$

9. $\tan x \sin x = \tan x$

10. $4 \sin^2 x - 1 = 0$

Study Guide

Solving Trigonometric Equations

Trigonometric identities are true for *all* values of the variable for which both sides are defined. Most trigonometric equations are true for *some* but *not all* values of the variable. Usually trigonometric equations are solved for values of the variable between $0°$ and $360°$ or 0 radians and 2π radians.

Some trigonometric equations have *no solutions*. It is important to check your solutions because some algebraic operations may introduce answers that are *not* solutions to the original equation.

Example: Solve $\cos x = 1 - \sin x$ if $0° \le x < 360°$.

$$\cos^2 x = (1 - \sin x)^2$$
$$1 - \sin^2 x = 1 - 2\sin x + \sin^2 x$$
$$0 = -2\sin x + 2\sin^2 x$$
$$0 = 2\sin x(\sin x - 1)$$
$$0 = 2\sin x(-1 + \sin x)$$

$$2\sin x = 0 \qquad\qquad\qquad -1 + \sin x = 0$$
$$\sin x = 0 \qquad\qquad\qquad\quad \sin x = 1$$
$$x = 0°, 180° \qquad\qquad\qquad\quad x = 90°$$

The solutions appear to be $0°$, $90°$ and $180°$. However, $180°$ does not satisfy the original equation. Thus, the solutions are $0°$ and $90°$.

Find all solutions if $0° \le x < 360°$.

1. $\cot^2 x = 1$
45°, 135°, 225°, 315°

2. $2\sin x - 1 = 0$
30°, 150°

3. $3\sin^2 x - \cos^2 x = 0$
30°, 150°, 210°, 330°

4. $2\cos^2 x + \cos x = 1$
60°, 180°, 300°

5. $\sin^2 x \cos^2 x = 0$
0°, 90°, 180°, 270°

6. $\cos 2x = \dfrac{\sqrt{3}}{2}$
15°, 165°, 195°, 345°

7. $\sin \dfrac{x}{2} = 1$
180°

8. $2\sin x - \sqrt{3} = 0$
60°, 120°

9. $\tan x \sin x = \tan x$
0°, 90°, 180°

10. $4\sin^2 x - 1 = 0$
30°, 150°, 210°, 330°